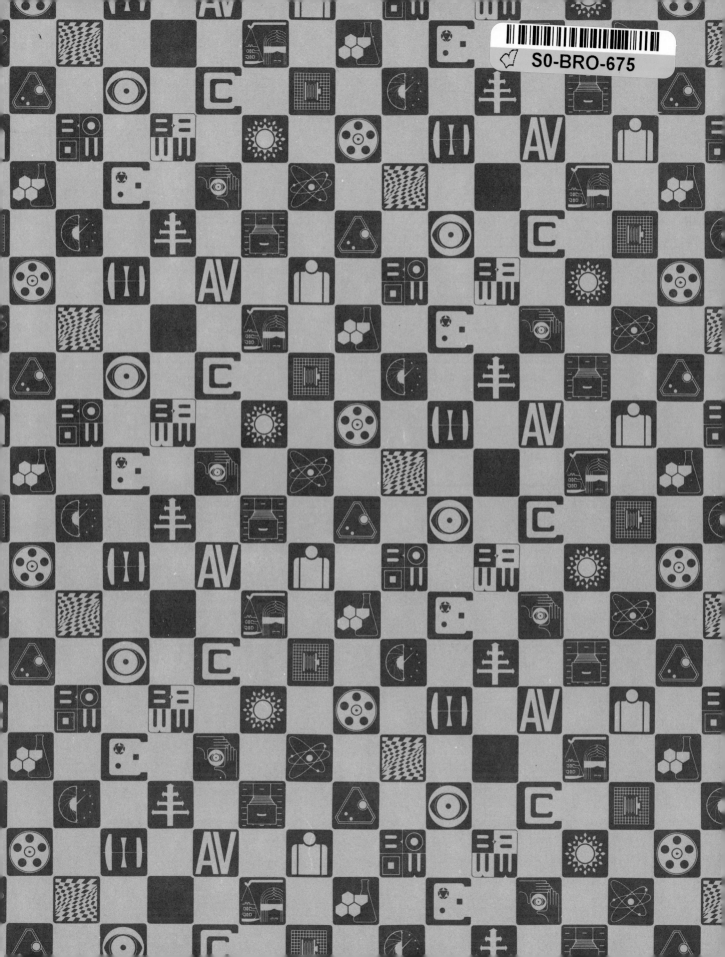

Encyclopedia
of **Practical**
Photography

Volume **9**
L-Mi

Edited by and published for
EASTMAN KODAK COMPANY

AMPHOTO
American Photographic Book Publishing Company
Garden City, New York

Note on Photography

The cover photos and the photos of letters that appear elsewhere in this encyclopedia were taken by Chris Maggio.

Library of Congress Cataloging in Publication Data

Amphoto, New York.
   Encyclopedia of practical photography.

   Includes bibliographical references and index.
   1. Photography—Dictionaries. I. Eastman
Kodak Company. II. Title.
TR9.A46   770'.3   77–22562

ISBN 0–8174–3050–4 Trade Edition—Whole Set
ISBN 0–8174–3200–0 Library Edition—Whole Set
ISBN 0–8174–3059–8 Trade Edition—Volume 9
ISBN 0–8174–3209–4 Library Edition—Volume 9

Editorial Board

The *Encyclopedia of Practical Photography* was compiled and edited jointly by Eastman Kodak Company and American Photographic Book Publishing Co., Inc. (Amphoto). The comprehensive archives, vast resources, and technical staffs of both companies, as well as the published works of Kodak, were used as the basis for most of the information contained in this encyclopedia.

Project Directors

Seymour D. Uslan
President, American Photographic
Book Publishing Co., Inc. (Amphoto)

Kenneth T. Lassiter
Director, Publications, Professional
and Finishing Markets, Eastman
Kodak Company

Technical Directors

John S. Carroll
Senior Director

William L. Broecker
Associate Director

Project Editors

Herb Taylor
Editor-in-Chief, American Photographic
Book Publishing Co., Inc. (Amphoto)

Robert E. White, Jr.
Copy Coordinator, Professional and
Finishing Markets, Eastman Kodak
Company

Associate Editors

Amphoto
Cora Sibal-Marquez
Managing Editor
Nadine Dumser
Editor

Kodak
W. Arthur Young
Consulting Technical Editor
Elizabeth M. Eggleton
Editorial Coordinator and
Consultant

**Graphic and Production Editors
(Amphoto)**

Richard Liu
Graphic Art Director

Susan Fineman
Coordinating Artist

Contributing Editors—Volume 9

Gene Balsley
William L. Broecker
John E. Brown
John S. Carroll
George Chernoff
George Dowbenko
William R. Hawken
Rudolf Kingslake
Frank N. McLaughlin
John T. Phelps

William Price
Rosa Russell
Hubert Scheffy
Harvey Shaman
Gerald J. Skerrett
Robert H. Stetzenmeyer
Herb Taylor
W. George Temlitz
David Vestal
W. Arthur Young

Symbol Identification

 Audiovisual

 Color Processing and Printing

 Picture-Making Techniques

 Biography

 Equipment and Facilities

 Scientific Photography

 Black-and-White Materials

 Exposure

 Special Effects and Techniques

 Black-and-White Processing and Printing

 History

Special Interests

 Business and Legal Aspects

 Lighting

 Storage and Care

 Chemicals

 Motion Picture

 Theory of Photography

 Color Materials

 Optics

 Vision

Guide for the Reader

Use this encyclopedia as you would any good encyclopedia or dictionary. Look for the subject desired as it first occurs to you—most often you will locate it immediately. The shorter articles begin with a dictionary-style definition, and the longer articles begin with a short paragraph that summarizes the article that follows. Either of these should tell you if the information you need is in the article. The longer articles are then broken down by series of headings and sub-headings to aid further in locating specific information.

Cross References

If you do not find the specific information you are seeking in the article first consulted, use the cross references (within the article and at the end of it) to lead you to more information. The cross references can lead you from a general article to the more detailed articles into which the subject is divided. Cross references are printed in capital letters so that you can easily recognize them.
Example: *See also:* ZONE SYSTEM.

Index

If the initial article you turn to does not supply you with the information you seek, and the cross references do not lead you to it, use the index in the last volume. The index contains thousands of entries to help you identify and locate any subject you seek.

Symbols

To further aid you in locating information, the articles throughout have been organized into major photographic categories. Each category is represented by a symbol displayed on the opposite page. By using only the symbols, you can scan each volume and locate all the information under any of the general categories. Thus, if you wish to read all about lighting, simply locate the lighting symbols and read the articles under them.

Reading Lists

Most of the longer articles are followed by reading lists citing useful sources for further information. Should you require additional sources, check the cross-referenced articles for additional reading lists.

Metric Measurement

Both the U.S. Customary System of measurement and the International System (SI) are used throughout this encyclopedia. In most cases, the metric measurement is given first with the U.S. customary equivalent following in parenthesis. When equivalent measurements are given, they will be rounded off to the nearest whole unit or a tenth of a unit, unless precise measurement is important. When a measurement is considered a "standard," equivalents will not be given. For example: 35 mm film, 200 mm lens, 4" × 5" negative, and 8" × 10" prints will not be given with their customary or metric equivalents.

How Articles are Alphabetized

Article titles are alphabetized by letter sequence, with word breaks and hyphens not considered. Example:

> Archer, Frederick Scott
> Architectural Photography
> Archival Processing
> Arc Lamps

Abbreviations are alphabetized according to the letters of the abbreviations, not by the words the letters stand for. Example:

> Artificial Light
> ASA Speed

Contents
Volume 9

Lacquers

There are various types of lacquer available for applying protective coatings to color transparencies, color negatives, and color prints. The purposes are mainly to protect the film or paper from moisture, fingerprinting, and other damage, but there are additional reasons for lacquering, as well.

Film Lacquers

Kodak processing laboratories ceased to lacquer color negatives and transparencies in 1970. If, however, you feel that your negatives or transparencies need the added protection of a lacquer coat, Kodak film lacquer is available in a number of container sizes; it is applied according to directions on the label. The usual method is by dipping the film in the lacquer, allowing the surplus to drain off, and hanging the film to dry by one corner.

Lacquer does not, to any large extent, prevent dye fading or color changes due to exposure to light or other causes. It does help to protect the surface of the film from fungus attack and from minor physical damage. That is, light abrasions resulting from handling of the film, slipping it in and out of envelopes, and such will affect the lacquer layer. If the lacquer is removed, most of the abrasions will come off with it, and the film may then be relacquered. Fingerprints may usually be wiped off a lacquered surface without need of removing the coating.

Uses of Print Lacquers

Many professional photographers coat all their color prints with a lacquer. This is done for protection against damage in handling, but lacquering serves other purposes. When a print is to be framed under glass, without a mat, it is well to lacquer the surface of the print to avoid its sticking to the glass, thereby preventing surface damage to the print. Lacquering serves as an aid to protect retouching and spotting, and also as a means of covering up such handwork. Good print work shows mostly as a change in the surface characteristics of the area worked on. The lacquer eliminates this difference.

Beyond merely providing protection or concealing evidence of retouching, lacquering can enhance a print in several ways.

When a beam of oblique, incident light strikes a print surface, most of the light bounces off at the same angle. But a small part of the beam is reflected

Lacquering helps protect a print from abrasions and can also control the degree of surface gloss. In addition, it may be used to enhance the print in a variety of ways.

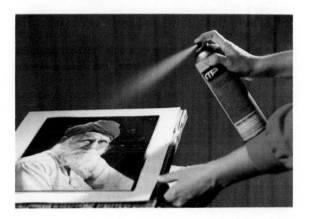

up toward the observer's eye by the tiny surface irregularities—that is, the "texture" of the print. These irregularities, while they may seem small, are nevertheless huge when compared with the wavelength of light. From this, it can easily be seen that the rougher the surface, the more the light beam will be deflected or scattered into the observer's eye. Light-tone print areas do not suffer very much by being diluted with this stray light, but shadow areas, which should be quite dark, are "grayed down" considerably by it. Thus, the surface sheen of a print has a direct influence on print quality.

The way to keep shadow areas dark is to provide them with a smooth surface from which the oblique, viewing light beam can bounce off easily without interference from the paper texture; and a smooth surface is exactly what lacquer finishes supply. The smoother the print surface, the greater the range of densities in the print. And the greater maximum density available, the higher the quality of the print. In fact, mask off a diagonal half of a low-key print, and lacquer the other half with a high-gloss lacquer. Pull away the mask and compare the treated and the untreated portions. You will find:

1. The blacks have become blacker, extending the tonal range (density scale) of the print.
2. Shadow details are more evident because the separation between them has been increased.
3. The color of a toned print has been considerably improved because of increased color saturation. Similarly, the colors of a color print are definitely more saturated—reds are redder, blues are bluer, and so on.

If you are going to lacquer a print, you will not need to compensate in exposure for the annoying tendency of a matte-surface black-and-white print to "dry down," because the surface reflectivity of a print coated with a high-gloss lacquer is about what it was when the print was wet during processing. In fact, you can use any print surface and still make a "glossy" print.

Of course, it is no more advisable to put a high-gloss finish on every subject than it is to print all subjects on glossy paper. Portrait customers usually do not want glossy prints, and neither do a good many other people. But, aside from a consideration of personal likes and dislikes, there is no "photographic" advantage to adding a high-surface gloss to high-key prints or to those of atmospheric fog scenes, both of which have a relatively short tonal range.

Types of Print Lacquers

A variety of print lacquers are available from various manufacturers; most of these are intended for application with a spray gun, but some are available in spray cans as well, and a few must be applied with a brush or other applicator.

McDonald makes a number of lacquers. One dries to a suede-matte finish and is intended mainly as a preliminary coating before retouching. Prints coated with this lacquer can be retouched or spotted with ordinary colored pencils. After all handwork has been done, the print is given another coat of lacquer, and any one of several types may be used, depending upon the final finish required. Other lacquers supplied by McDonald include: a clear lacquer which dries to a very high gloss, a "lustre" lacquer which has a more subdued gloss, a "matte-special" lacquer which is semi-matte with a slight sheen, and a "matte" lacquer which dries completely flat.

Special-effects lacquers available from McDonald include Protecta-Cote Florentine, Pro-Texture, and Pro-Texture Plus. Protecta-Cote Florentine cracks and reticulates as it dries, giving the effect of an old oil painting with many coats of varnish. The drying may be controlled to give small or large cracks, depending upon the size of the print and the effect desired. Pro-Texture lacquer is a heavy-body high-viscosity coating that can be sprayed on the print surface to produce a wide variety of textured surfaces. Pro-Texture Plus is a water-based high-viscosity lacquer that can be textured to create brush-stroke effects; it dries clear and flexible. More will be said about these special-effects lacquers later in this article.

Sprays are also available to produce certain surface effects. Century Clear Spray and Century Dull Spray produce glossy and matte finishes, respectively; they are supplied in 20-ounce aerosol cans. They are claimed to contain an ultraviolet absorbing filter dye, which is said to retard fading of lacquered prints.

A variety of similar products is available from other manufacturers; all work in much the same way. It is wise to use only lacquers made specifically for photographic use. The solvents in some lacquers made for other purposes can adversely affect the print dyes.

Spraying Lacquers. Any spray outfit must be equipped with an air filter in the hose to the spray gun. Cellulose-base lacquers are very intolerant of water in the air supply, and moist air will cause white spots in the lacquer coating. The air filter removes moisture from the air before it reaches the spray gun; it should be watched, and emptied frequently.

For the same reason, it is well not to attempt to spray prints in very damp weather; sometimes the coating will turn white if the humidity is very high.

Air Pressure. Because print lacquers are viscous liquids, effective spraying requires an air pressure not lower than 50 pounds per square inch. Spraying at substantially lower pressures requires a thinner mixture of lacquer; as a result, more coats are needed to cover the print surface properly. Also, low pressure sprays tend to give a less uniform coating.

Compressed air is used for a number of purposes in large photographic departments, and you may be able to connect the spray gun to a branch line from a centrally located compressor. Otherwise, you will need a separate compressor unit. This compressor should be a heavy-duty unit equipped with a compressed-air tank to maintain a constant pressure. As a rule, the less expensive compressor units that employ a vibrating diaphragm to pump air are not powerful enough to spray viscous liquids properly.

Spray Guns. Use a good quality, professional-type spray gun. Generally, low-priced spray guns are not designed for use with high pressure nor are they fitted with the necessary external-mix nozzle.

Spray Booth. A concentration of lacquer vapor in a room represents both a fire and health hazard as well as being unpleasant. If regular spraying is to be done, use an approved (Underwriters' Laboratories) booth. For less frequent spraying, a homemade booth can be used. This is essentially a large box, about 6 feet high by 3 feet wide and 3 feet deep, equipped with an exhaust fan and an air duct to outdoors. This box should be constructed of a non-combustible material, preferably metal. The exhaust duct must not be connected to any general ventilating duct.

Lighting in such a booth should be furnished with enclosed lights placed entirely outside the booth. Glass windows can be provided for the lights to shine through. All light switches, in fact, any electrical equipment, must also be on the outside of the booth. Switches must be of the enclosed type and if the exhaust fan is mounted in the air duct, the fan motor should also be Underwriters' approved for spray-booth use. Another possibility is to use a belt-driven fan and mount the motor outside the air duct. Wiring may be of any type approved for Class I, Div. II locations (rigid conduit, electrical metallic tubing, or Type MI wiring). Any competent electrician should be familiar with the rules for such installations; they are fully outlined in the National Electrical Code, Article 500. Copies of this code are available from the National Fire Protection Association.

Spray booths must be kept clean. It is good practice to coat the inside of the booth with a grease that can be wiped off, along with lacquer deposits that may have accumulated.

A no-smoking sign should be placed on the booth and this rule rigidly enforced. Most lacquers are volatile and combustible and should be applied only with adequate ventilation and away from sparks or flame.

Spraying Technique. Shake the container of matte lacquer well before use. The matting agent in this lacquer settles after standing for a time. As a result, the sprayed surfaces may not be uniform.

The distance from the spray nozzle to the print is important. The best distance for use with the air pressure and equipment mentioned earlier is 10 to 12 inches. If the spray nozzle is too far away, the lacquer will dry before it reaches the print, and the sprayed surface will have a white, powdery appearance. If the spray nozzle is too close, the lacquer may run.

To avoid uneven spraying, keep the gun moving all the time the print is being sprayed. Use a steady sweeping motion that covers, with overlapping, the entire surface of the print, and maintain the correct spraying distance throughout the operation. The technique of spraying requires some practice; it is a good idea, therefore, to spray a number of waste prints before working on more valuable material. As a rule, one or two coats of print lacquer are enough for good coverage. Allow a minute or so for the first coat to dry before applying the second one.

When several different mixtures of lacquer are to be used within a short time, you can avoid frequent emptying and cleaning the spray-gun cup by using disposable containers that can be attached to the gun instead of the metal cup that is normally used. Plastic-coated cardboard containers of suitable size and shape are excellent for this purpose. Mixtures of lacquer can be kept in these containers for a few hours if they are covered with the lids provided.

When spraying quick-drying lacquers, you must clean the spray gun immediately after; otherwise, the spray orifices in the nozzle and the needle valve in the gun soon become clogged with dried lacquer. To clean the spray gun, follow this procedure:

1. Empty any remaining lacquer from the spray-gun cup.
2. Rinse the cup with print lacquer thinner.
3. Pour some thinner into the cup, and return it to the gun.
4. Spray the thinner in short bursts for about 10 seconds, or until you judge the gun to be free from lacquer.

To avoid too frequent cleaning of the spray-gun cup, you can clear the gun by spraying thinner directly from one of the disposable containers described above.

Special-Effects Lacquers. These lacquers allow you to create effects such as stipple and brush surfaces, and checked patterns (to make prints look like old oil paintings).

Texturizing Lacquer. By varying the type of lacquer, its dilution, and the method of application, you can achieve a variety of surfaces including stipple and brush effects. For example, McDonald Pro-Texture is a high-viscosity lacquer that is used to create a brush-stroke texture when applied with a brush, or several interesting texture effects when applied with a spray gun. The surface effect is controlled by three variables:

1. The *size* of the texture particles is determined by the spray gun's fluid adjustment. To produce a round spray stream, use masking tape to close the side outlet holes in the "horns" of the spray-gun air cap.
2. The angle of application determines the *shape* of the texture pattern. A low angle (10 degrees) produces an elongated weave-type pattern. A higher angle (60 degrees) produces a leather-like finish. Apply the lacquer from two sides of the print to achieve good uniformity of the pattern. However, apply it sparingly enough to leave a small space between the lacquer particles, or else they will tend to run together and produce a smooth coat.
3. The particle *height* is determined by the distance the spray gun is held from the print. Applied close to the print, the lacquer is wetter and tends to "lie down." Used farther from the print, it arrives at the surface in a drier condition and tends to "stand up." For example, use a spraying distance of about 16 inches if you want a coarser, rougher texture. You can repeat any particular effect if you keep records of all the variables that produced it.

To produce brush marks, apply an even coat of Pro-Texture directly from the container. Wait for about 4 minutes until the lacquer has partially dried, and it will retain brush strokes. Lay the print flat. Using one-half of a scrub brush held at a 10-degree angle to the surface of the print, strike the print sharply with a twisting, stippling motion. This causes the individual tufts of bristles to create separate random brush strokes. Be sure not to leave an area until the bristle marks are retained. The brush should be stored in ¾ inch of lacquer thinner kept in a sealable container. Before use simply shake the excess lacquer thinner from the brush and proceed.

Brushes can be used to produce a deep texture effect with the following procedure: Pour some Pro-Texture into three wide-mouth, clean containers. Leave the top off the first for one day, the second for two days, and the third for three days. (Of course, this schedule can be modified for unusual temperature and humidity conditions.) This will give three stock solutions of varying viscosity to be used as follows: Use the three-day material on backgrounds

Painter-like brush strokes can be added to either black-and-white or color prints. The strokes are made on a partially dried coat of Pro-Texture lacquer, or with lacquer that has been thickened before it is applied.

and obviously rough-textured subject areas. Use the two-day material on clothing, hair, and the like. Use the one-day material on flesh, smooth fabrics, and areas where minimum texture is desired. Apply the Pro-Texture of the desired viscosity to one area, about 5″ × 7″, at a time and keep working it until it *retains* the individual brush strokes. The brush strokes should look crisp, not "gobby." Be sure to *follow* subject contours with brush strokes—*do not cross them.* If you do not like the effect, you can remove the coating with lacquer thinner without harming the print.

Reticulating Lacquer. McDonald Florentine is a reticulating lacquer that will "check" coats of Clear Lacquer, or Pro-Texture and Clear Lacquer, previously applied to a print. This creates the effect of a very old oil painting. You can control Florentine to create either large or small checks.

The most artistic effect is obtained by first applying Pro-Texture Lacquer to the print with a brush to produce a brush-stroke pattern, following the subject contours, and then applying a coat of Clear Lacquer. When these coats are thoroughly dry, apply the Florentine as an even wet coat from side to side and bottom to top. Interestingly, the *amount* of Florentine applied determines the size of the reticulated segments:

1. A heavy, wet coat produces approximately ½-inch segments.
2. A medium, wet coat produces approximately ¼-inch segments.
3. A light, wet coat produces approximately ⅛-inch segments.

If you are intrigued with the pictorial possibilities of this "old masters" print surface, you may want to further the effect by applying an antiquing coat to emphasize and darken the checked pattern. The glaze is made up as follows:

Parts	Material
2	burnt umber
1	lamp black
1	boiled linseed oil
2	turpentine

Brush the print evenly with this mixture, let it dry for 5 to 10 minutes and then wipe it with a clean paper towel folded into a pad (to prevent cleaning up "valleys" of texture) to remove the excess. Wipe from the direction of the subject lighting, changing the towel when necessary, until you achieve the desired effect. Be sure the glaze is uniform over the entire print surface. If it is not, drag a dry 2-inch brush across the print, first horizontally and then

Lacquers

1485

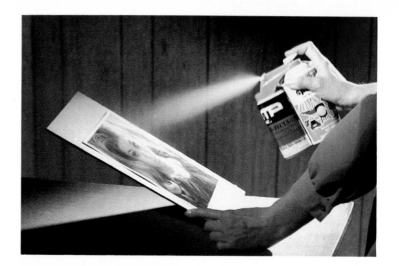

To create the effect of an old, cracked oil painting, first spray with clear lacquer, or with a combination of clear lacquer and Pro-Texture. Then apply McDonald Florentine, a reticulating lacquer that will check the previous coat.

The reticulating pattern can be controlled to yield either fine or coarse checking, depending upon the amount of Florentine applied.

vertically. With a cotton-tipped skewer, remove all the glaze from the eyes, remove most of it from flesh tones, and enough of it from important highlights so that they will retain their sparkle.

Without waiting, when all the work is complete, add a finishing top coating of Pro-Tecta-Coat Clear Lacquer.

Removing Lacquer from Films

A lacquered surface is more readily cleaned, and in cases of minor damage, it is possible to restore the surface by removing the old lacquer and applying new. Most lacquers can be removed by either of the following methods. (If there is fungus growth on the film, use the ammonia-alcohol solution method.)

Removing Lacquer with Sodium Bicarbonate. Dissolve a level tablespoon of sodium bicarbonate (baking soda) in 240 millilitres (about 8 fluidounces) of room-temperature water. (If Kodachrome transparencies are used, add 15 millilitres [½ fluidounce] of formaldehyde, 37 percent solution.) Agitate a transparency for 1 minute, or a color negative for 4 minutes. Rinse for 1 minute in room-temperature water. Bathe the film for about 30 seconds in Kodak Photo-Flo solution (diluted as stated on the bottle), or equivalent, and hang it up to dry in a dust-free place. When the film is completely dry it can be relacquered. Apply Kodak film lacquer as directed on the label.

Removing Lacquer with Ammonia-Alcohol. Add 15 millilitres (about a tablespoon) of nondetergent household ammonia to 240 millilitres (about 8 fluidounces) of denatured alcohol. Use shellac-thinning alcohol. Agitate the film in the solution for no longer than 2 minutes at room temperature. Longer times may change the color in areas of minimum density. Hang the film up to dry.

• *See also:* PRINT FINISHING.

Lambert's Law

When illumination from a point source strikes a surface along the normal—that is, from a direction perpendicular to the surface—the luminance of the surface varies according to its distance from the source. If, at any distance, the surface is inclined to the direction of the light, its luminance will be decreased because the same amount of light will be spread over a greater area (see the accompanying diagram). The difference is in proportion to the cosine of the angle of incidence. The luminance at the inclined surface equals the luminance at the perpen-

dicular surface multiplied by the cosine of the angle of incidence at the inclined surface, or:

$$E_2 = E_1 \cos \theta$$

The law is strictly true only for a perfectly diffuse surface. It was formulated by Johann Heinrich Lambert (1728–1777), a German-French philosopher and scientist, as an expansion of the inverse-square law, which he also formulated. Lambert's law accounts for one of the cosine factors that makes up the cosine-fourth law, which governs the relative illumination across a film plane.

• *See also:* INVERSE-SQUARE LAW; LIGHT.

Laminating

Laminating is the process of permanently sealing a photograph or document between sheets of plastic. It is accomplished by the use of heat, which fuses the plastic together at the edges and to the back and front surfaces of the enclosed material. Lamination protects against soiling, handling damage, and atmospheric effects.

Photographers find laminating an excellent way to extend the life of prints in sample books and portfolios. It is especially valuable in preserving tear sheets of work published in magazines and newspapers. The laminating material not only protects the relatively fragile paper, but it prevents or greatly

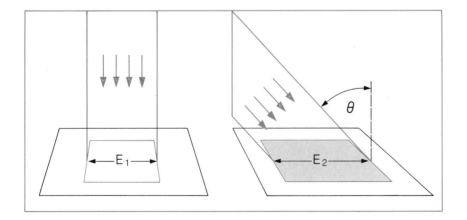

Lambert's Law

E_1 = Luminance of surface perpendicular to direction of light

E_2 = Luminance of larger area covered by same amount of light striking from an angle

θ = Angle of incidence.

retards fading of the ink image and yellowing of the paper. Plastic lamination is also widely used to protect ID cards from tampering and wear, and to preserve wallet-size photographs.

The information in this article is a general guide; for more specific information, consult the manufacturers of lamination materials to learn the conditions and materials specifically recommended for a particular laminator.

General Considerations

Prints on conventional photo papers may be laminated with ease. Greater care must be used with prints on resin-coated papers, especially color prints: Excessive heat can damage the paper base as well as the emulsion. It is important to follow the instructions provided by the manufacturer of the laminating material in order to achieve the best results.

Laminating Color Photographs

The successful lamination of a color photograph in particular requires strict adherence to recommended procedures. Changes should not be made in the procedures unless extensive experimentation proves that such changes will have no adverse effect on the photographic material. Failure to investigate a new procedure thoroughly may result in poor lamination or loss of color in a print. Either of these faults could reduce the security value of an ID card and spoil its appearance. The following are of particular importance to successful lamination:

1. Laminate at the lowest temperature possible.
2. Laminate for the shortest time possible.
3. If written or rubber-stamped information is to be placed on the back of the print, be sure to use inks that will not be affected by the lamination and will not bleed through the paper base of the print.

Experiments may be required to determine the correct laminating procedures. When correctly laminated, the plastic adheres to both sides and all edges of the print. Also, proper lamination causes no change in the color of the print.

The application of heat for a certain length of time is required to make the plastic flow for lamination. Excesses in this combination of heat and time can cause a change in the color of the print. Therefore, control of the laminating time and temperature is critical.

When experimenting (using discarded color prints) to find the most suitable temperature and time, start with low temperatures and short laminating times. Either or both should be increased gradually until acceptable results are obtained. At this point, further experiments should be made to determine just how much the temperature and time can be increased before print color is affected.

Laminating without Special Equipment

Occasional laminating jobs can be done without special equipment, if a heat-developing office copier (such as the 3M Dual Spectrum copier) or a thermographic copier (such as the 3M Thermofax) is available. Two types of laminating film are available for use with these copiers; it is merely necessary to place a sheet of laminating film on the print to be laminated, and run the sandwich through the Thermofax copier, or through the processing section of the Dual Spectrum copier.

One type of laminating film for these machines is glossy and is used where only protection is required; it can, however, be marked with china-marker crayons, and the marks later rubbed off. The second type of laminating film has a matte surface and can be written on with pencil and erased, or permanently marked with Magic Markers or felt-tip pens.

At least one manufacturer offers laminating material that may be applied in a photographic dry-mounting press, or even by a household hand iron.

Identification Cards

The Estar thick base of Kodak Ektacolor Duratrans print material 4023 is suitable for laminating identification cards at temperatures up to 138 C (280 F) for a short period of time. For best results, laminate at times, temperatures, and pressures just sufficient to allow the laminating material to flow and bond properly. When correctly laminated, the plastic laminant adheres to both sides and all edges of the print film, and any attempt to separate the components will destroy the photographic image. Also, proper lamination causes no change in the color of the print.

Proper lamination causes no change in the color of the print, and will adhere to the entire card in such a way that any attempt to remove the laminant will destroy the photographic image. Photo by John Menihan.

Self-writing credit cards, containing positive photographic identification, can be made by laminating identification cards on Kodak Ektacolor Duratrans print material 4023 between two 10-mil sheets of clear vinyl, and embossing the resulting sandwich with the necessary informational characters. The 9-mil thickness of the print material, plus the two 10-mil clear vinyl overlaminants, make up the 29-mil thickness usually suggested for a self-writing credit card.

• *See also:* PRINT FINISHING.

Land, Edwin Herbert

(Born 1909)
American inventor and scientist

Edwin Land's contributions to science and photography have been many and varied. He was the first to devise polarizing materials in sheet form, and the first to design and market cameras for making instantaneous photographs, that is, photographs processed in the camera and finished in a matter of seconds or minutes. He has done intensive theoretical research in color vision and advanced the proposal that traditional concepts of how the eye sees color are not valid in terms of ratios of visible energy at various wavelengths.

The Polarizer

While still a freshman at Harvard University, Land became interested in the phenomenon of polarization in light. This had been known for over 100 years, but the existing equipment for its utilization was inadequate. The first really effective polarizer was invented by William Nicol in 1828, but this device—known as the Nicol prism—was limited in its use because the length of the device in proportion to its aperture gave it a very limited angle of view. More important, the single crystal of a mineral from which the Nicol prism was made was extremely rare and available only in small pieces when found in the desired quality.

Land decided that there was no theoretical reason why a polarizer of any desired size could not be made in sheet form; his approach was to substitute for the single crystal an array of submicroscopic polarizing elements suspended in clear glass or plastic. In time, his researches led to not one but a variety of polarizing sheet materials, which in turn found use in such widely varied products as glare-free auto headlights, three-dimensional color moving pictures, camera filters, sunglasses, and gun sights.

Land organized Polaroid Corporation to manufacture and market polarizing materials, with himself as President, Chairman of the Board, and Director of Research; from the beginning, the company was so organized that he could spend most of his time doing research.

Instant Materials

In 1947, Edwin Land demonstrated the first "instant" camera and print process to the Optical Society of America, and it was marketed commercially by the end of 1948. In the following years it was extensively improved—processing that previously took one minute was reduced to 10 seconds at the same time as high-speed (ASA 3000) film was introduced. Other forms of instant materials that he introduced include high-contrast films for line copying; transparency films for lantern slides; an ultrafast (ASA 10,000) film for oscillography; 10-second x-ray packets; color-print materials (available as large as 8″ × 10″, but an experimental camera is in use for full-size copying of much larger full-color originals); and currently, the SX-70 instant-color camera with a film that develops outside the camera and has no paper or negative to discard.

Theoretical Science

In theoretical science, Land has done considerable work questioning existing theories of color vision, and attempting to show that they are inconsistent with the facts, insofar as they propose that measured amounts of red, green, and blue light will produce a given color sensation on the eye.

He has proposed the existence of three independent image-forming mechanisms in the eye that he called "retinexes"; he also has postulated that the sensation of a given color is due to the comparison at each image point of the sensations produced in each receptor. To demonstrate the meaning of this point, Land has shown projected color images that were apparently seen in full color by some viewers, yet were produced by either two-color projection or, in some cases, by projection with only red light and white light. However, the color materials produced by Polaroid are based on the traditional three-color additive and subtractive color theories.

Current Endeavors

Edwin Land has been a Visiting Professor at Massachusetts Institute of Technology, and was for many years a member of the President's Science Advisory Commission. In addition to receiving the Presidential Medal of Freedom in 1963, he is a Fellow of the National Academy of Sciences and of the National Academy of Engineering. He also holds at least 14 honorary doctorate degrees from the leading universities and colleges.

Land's latest contribution to the art of photography is an instant-color motion-picture process that utilizes a line mosaic of additive color filters and a black-and-white diffusion-transfer-type emulsion and process. After exposure, the film is placed in a special projector for immediate self-processing and viewing.

Landscape Photography

The essential subject matter of a *landscape* is a natural scene. It is usually a large view of a scene. Although it may show fairly close subjects as well as the usual middle- and far-distant subjects typical of landscapes, natural close-ups in themselves are not considered landscapes. Landscape pictures may contain small traces of the human touch, such as fences and farm buildings, or even people, but the overall emphasis is on the land and its covering of plants rather than on the human aspects.

Some definitions of landscapes limit the subject matter to inland rural scenes, while others are broadened to include cityscapes and shore scenes. The latter is still considered a landscape as long as the emphasis is on the shore elements and not the sea.

Landscapes have traditionally been almost as popular a subject as people for photographers; they were favorite subjects of painters before the advent of photography, so photographers had a tradition of landscape pictures to follow—or to change. Part of the fascination of photography has been its ability to record a scene with utmost accuracy of detail in a fraction of a second. Today, millions of amateurs record, in black-and-white and color snapshots, such spectacular subjects as the Grand Canyon, Niagara Falls, and the Alps, as well as other attractive but less spectacular scenes they encounter in their travels. More serious workers may choose similar subjects, but they work with skill and proficiency somewhat above that of the snapshooter, and capture the visual essence of the landscape.

In reaction to the soft, fuzzy style of landscape photography popular in the late 1880's, the photographers of the "f/64" school used large-format cameras and very small apertures to produce photographs of extremely sharp focus and great depth of field. Photo by Ansel Adams.

Photographic Treatment and Style

While modern automated equipment gives the snapshooting amateur a high percentage of successful exposures, he or she is fortunate to get an occasional picture that is more than a mere record of the scenes photographed. Most of these pictures are a disappointment even to the amateur; the sense of splendor that was experienced in viewing the scene is somehow lost in the photographic translation.

In contrast, the serious worker, whether advanced amateur or professional, has learned that photographs must make a statement or convey a feeling about the landscape subject, as well as repro-

duce the visual aspects of the subject, if the landscape picture is to be more than a snapshot.

The sum total of choices the photographer makes in putting on film and paper a feeling and/or a statement about a scenic subject is called *treatment*. Treatment includes the choice of equipment and materials, camera position and aim, type of light and direction, as well as exposure and processing choices, and any normal or special darkroom techniques.

As a serious photographer makes numbers of landscape photographs using relatively consistent choices of treatment, the resulting pictures show these consistencies. The recognizable effects of the consistent selection of subject types and treatment combine to form a *photographic style*. If a photographer's work becomes well known, he or she will be recognized by a particular style.

Schools of Photography. When photography was in its early stages, the choices of treatment were limited. Because painters had established a landscape style that was essentially realistic, and because photography, even in those early days, could reproduce detail so easily and so well, the first photographers used a realistic, straight photographic approach to treatment and style.

With the invention of photography in the years following this event, many artists abandoned the straight approach in their painting, and impressionism was born. Impressionism is a style of painting that emphasizes the effects of light in a landscape as the painter sees them, rather than the landscape subject itself. Partly because of the effects of this school of painting, and partly because photographers tired of the straight style, a soft focus or fuzzy style of landscape photographic pictorialism started in the late 1800's.

The "*f*/64 school" was a reaction to this soft-focus style. The member photographers believed that photography was best when it was super sharp, so they used large-format cameras and small apertures to make photographs that were full of sharp detail and great depth of field. Today's variety of photographic treatments such as tone-line, posterization, and Sabattier effect derivation, as well as collage, multiple printing, and mosaic, are all evidence of efforts to treat photographic subjects in ways other than the straight photographic style.

Photographic Materials. Early photographic materials were sensitive only to blue light and ultraviolet radiation. This gave a particularly unreal tone-reproduction treatment of colors. With today's black-and-white panchromatic films and filters, landscapes can be reproduced in a gray-tone rendering of colors that approximates their visual brightnesses. In addition, panchromatic film permits the use of contrast filters that allow the photographer to distort the gray-tone rendering to provide a treatment that will enhance the essence or mood of a scene. The choice of a special film, such as one with infrared sensitivity, provides further choice.

The earliest cameras were simple structures with small aperture lenses and the sensitized materials were exceedingly slow so that all exposures were, of necessity, very long time exposures. This limited

Choice of lens focal length and format determines how the photographer will treat space and perspective. Here, two treatments of the same scene produce vastly different results. Photos by Robert Holland.

the photographer to bright sunlight conditions, windless days, and relatively unmoving objects. Today, fast lenses and films, and a wide variety of camera types permit picture-taking under almost all light and wind conditions, as well as the photographing of fast-moving subjects. Of prime importance to the landscape photographer, these advances in materials and equipment make possible the photography of landscapes under photogenic low-sun conditions, stormy conditions, backlit, dusk, and even moonlit conditions. These factors have widely broadened the possible subjects and treatments available to the landscape photographer.

The ready availability of a wide variety of camera focal lengths, from extreme wide-angle to very long telephoto, has also broadened the photographer's ability to treat space and perspective in landscape pictures. With wide-angle lenses, space can be expanded and perspective can be treated so that it emphasizes close and mid-distant subjects while subordinating the visual importance of distant objects. With telephoto lenses, space can be compressed and emphasis can be given to distant objects. With faster films, the depth of field can be expanded, while with large-aperture lenses, the depth of field can be reduced and the subject emphasized by selective focus. Slow films, with their increased sharpness and fine-grain characteristics, permit the use of smaller-format cameras while maintaining adequate definition and grainless tones in enlarged prints.

View cameras with swings and tilts permit the photographer to adjust perspective by the repositioning of vanishing points. A multiplicity of special optical devices such as diffusion filters, star filters, sky filters, and prismatic lens attachments can give a variety of in-camera photographic effects. The development of a variety of darkroom techniques has opened up new choices in photographic treatments for the photographer who wishes to avoid the straight approach. Derivation methods, texture screens, and a number of the older processes such as the paper negative, the platinum process, and the carbro process are currently available.

Much of the flexibility in treatment applies to both black-and-white as well as color film. Some treatments, such as contrast filters, are limited to black-and-white. Others, such as the control of color saturation with polarizing screens, are available in color only. Many of the treatments and controls are equally applicable to both mediums, while the choice of color or black-and-white film is in itself a choice of treatment.

Dramatic clouded skies make excellent subjects for landscape photography. Here, they appear in overwhelming contrast to the tranquil, gently rolling terrain. Photo by Fred Ragsdale.

Subject Selection

The landscape subjects that a photographer chooses are based primarily on three factors: (1) what is available to photograph, (2) what he or she likes to photograph, and (3) style.

There are usually landscape subjects in most areas where photographers live and work, and choosing subjects that are easily available is natural. The photographer may grow to like these subjects because of their familiarity; thus a style may evolve and a way of seeing may develop from the photographer's experiences with the near-at-hand subjects.

On the other hand, a photographer's style and preference may lead to a type of terrain that is far from home. Business can sometimes be combined with pleasure by arranging business trips to the general area he or she prefers, or vacations can be taken in the region of the photographer's choice. Working close to home has the advantage of convenience. Repeated visits to a photogenic spot at different times of the year, different times of the day, or when lighting conditions are best, can lead to improved pictures. New places, however, can act as a stimulus to vision, and the excitement of different landscape scenes often results in good pictures.

Over time, the three factors that influence the selection of landscape subjects work together. What a photographer likes and what is available to photograph, along with the photographer's own way of seeing, in large part lead to the development of style. Once that style has developed, it is likely to lead the photographer to other areas that have similar characteristics, but different landscape scenes.

Following are some subjects that photographers have selected for landscape photography over the years:

Hill country
"Soft" mountains—broken down with time and with trees and grass
"Raw" mountains—newer mountains with bare slopes
Forests

Snow—any of the above subjects but with the special effect of snow
Desert—either raw dunes or softer dunes with cactus-type vegetation; also with buttes, as in Monument Valley
Sky—any terrain but with emphasis on dramatic clouded skies
Tropics—palm country such as the Everglades, or tropical islands or forests
Shoreline—beaches, tidal pools, rocky cliffs
Canyons—rocky walls, or walls with trees, streams, or rivers.

Photographing the Subject

Viewing Frames. When the photographer is in the field actively looking for landscape pictures, some of the choices become limited. However, location becomes partly determined by choice of landscape terrain. The subject distance choice depends on the particular scenes the photographer finds and on general distance preferences (style), and in part on where the camera can be located.

For distant landscape pictures it is necessary to place the camera a long way off from the scene, and this can mean a lot of walking around. Once the general location has been chosen, other treatment selections must be made. A decision must be made as to the most important visual elements in the scene, and how to treat them. Important factors are the control of perspective and space, field coverage, and exact camera position. If a lightweight camera is being used with a single lens—perhaps a zoom—these selections can all be made with the camera finder at the photographer's eye. If, however, there is a choice of lenses, a tripod being used, and/or a view camera, a viewing frame will help in making the choices more quickly and easily.

To make a simple viewing frame, take a piece of dark cardboard about 8½″ × 11″ to 10″ × 12″ in size and cut a rectangular opening in the center of it. This opening must have the same aspect ratio as

Rock canyons, broken and sheared off by the forces of the earth's movement, have always ▶ fascinated landscape photographers. Choice of the most important visual elements may be difficult with a subject such as this; use of a viewing frame will assist considerably in making the decision. Photo by Robert Walch.

Sometimes the best view of an area is from the air; this is particularly true of shorelines, where there may be literally nowhere else to position a camera. The magnificent sweep of Waikiki Beach looking toward Diamond Head could not have been photographed except from an airplane. Photo by Ralph Amdursky.

the negative. Following are some suggested common frame sizes:

Camera	Format
35 mm	4″ × 6″
2¼″ × 2¼″	5″ × 5″
2¼″ × 2¾″	
4″ × 5″	4″ × 5″
8″ × 10″	

Mark on the card the distance from the eye the card should be held to determine the field coverage for each focal length lens. To find this, first determine the magnification factor of the opening compared to the film format. For example, the 4″ × 6″ opening is four times the size of the 35 mm format. Multiply the focal length of the lens by this factor. The normal lens for this format is 50 mm or 2 inches; 4 × 50 mm is 200 mm, while 4″ × 2″ is 8 inches.

Following are the distances from the eye for some of the common lenses used with the 35 mm format.

Focal Length	Distance from the Eye
20 mm	80 mm or 3⅛″
24 mm	96 mm or 3¾″
28 mm	112 mm or 4½″
35 mm	140 mm or 5½″
90 mm	360 mm or 14″
100 mm	400 mm or 16″
135 mm	540 mm or 21″
200 mm	800 mm or 31″

It is obvious that a second card with a smaller hole is required for use with the longer telephoto lenses.

Two refinements are possible with a viewing card. A sheet of transparent plastic can be taped over the opening, and lines can be put on the plastic to outline the coverage of each lens when the card is held at a constant convenient distance from the eye. The opening is cut for the widest-angle lens that is available. The illustration on the next page shows such a viewing screen for 35 mm cameras, where the shortest lens available is 28 mm and the convenient eye distance is 8 inches. Solvent-type (waterproof) felt-tip markers can be used to make the lines on the sheet plastic.

The second refinement applies to the viewing frame used at different distances (single opening). The marks are put on a sheet of transparent plastic, but they are used as an aid in composition.

Control of space and depth of field for such vast subjects as the great falls of Yosemite is best achieved with a view camera. Photo by Chuck Abbott.

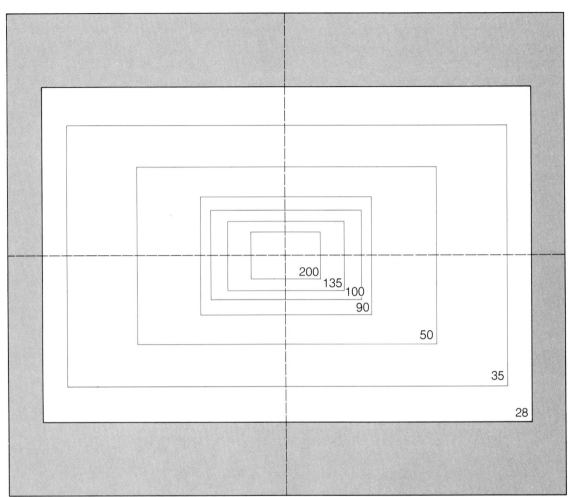

Eye distance: 8″   10″x12″ card

The card opening is 7″ × 10½″. Find the viewing distance for the 28 mm lens as follows:

Opening magnification: 7 inches ÷ 1 inch = 7×
Viewing distance: 28 mm × 7 = 196 mm = 8 inches (rounded off)

Find the ratio of each lens to the 28 mm lens:

$$28 \div 34 = .80 \qquad 28 \div 50 = .56$$
$$28 \div 90 = .31 \qquad 28 \div 100 = .28$$
$$28 \div 135 = .21 \qquad 28 \div 200 = .14$$

Then multiply each of the dimensions of the opening by the ratios:

Lens			
35 mm	7″ × .80 = 5½″	10½″ × .80 = 9½″	5½″ × 9½″
50 mm	7″ × .56 = 3¾″	10½″ × .56 = 6½″	3¾″ × 6½″
90 mm	7″ × .31 = 2⅛″	10½″ × .31 = 3⅝″	2⅛″ × 3⅝″
100 mm	7″ × .28 = 1⅞″	10½″ × .28 = 3¼″	1⅞″ × 3¼″
135 mm	7″ × .21 = 1½″	10½″ × .21 = 2½″	1½″ × 2½″
200 mm	7″ × .14 = 1″	10½″ × .14 = 1½″	1″ × 1½″

8″ x 10″ opening

10″ x 12″ card

Composition Viewing Frame

The lines on the transparent plastic sheet on this frame are designed as an aid to composition. The vertical and horizontal lines divide the opening area into thirds each way. Different "rules of composition" suggest placing the center of interest at: (1) the intersection of the lines, (2) the golden section, and (3) the intersection of a diagonal with a perpendicular drawn to the other corners. Since each of these methods locates four points that are away from the center of the format and away from the edges of the format, the kidney-shaped areas can be used as locating areas for the primary and secondary centers of interest. Most photographers look upon these as rules of thumb to be generally used, but to be broken when the subject itself, or the mood to be established, makes it seem desirable. The same type of rules suggest the lines as good places to locate the horizon.

This frame is placed at an eye distance equal to the lens focal length when used with an $8'' \times 10''$ camera, at twice the lens focal length when used with a $4'' \times 5''$ camera, and at $3\frac{1}{2}$ times the focal length when used with a $2\frac{1}{4}'' \times 2\frac{3}{4}''$ format.

The landscape is viewed with one eye through the viewing frame. This eliminates parallax problems, and takes the first step towards distinguishing between the true stereo vision of depth in the scene and the single-eyed depth the camera lens sees and will create in the picture. The frame is used to survey the interesting aspects of the landscape, and to locate the potential pictures. As the picture is narrowed down, the key elements are identified as an aid to composition. If the viewing frame is used carefully at the correct distance from the eye, it will help locate the best camera position, and the view on the ground glass will closely match the image as seen through the frame once the camera is set up. If conditions are not right, if the sun angle is wrong, or if the scene would be better at another time of year, this can be determined before the camera is set up, and the equipment can be brought back at another time.

Composition. Basically, composition is the arrangement of the subject matter to best communicate the visual essence of the landscape—as the photographer sees it—to the viewers of the final picture. In landscapes, the subject cannot be moved around and physically arranged as props in a studio can; therefore, the photograph must be composed by selection. The photographer selects the scene, the camera position, the field of view, the camera aim, and the emphasis and subordination of the visual elements.

Whether using a viewing frame or a ground glass, the photographer tries to leave in the picture all the visual elements that contribute to a concept of the visual essence of the scene, and to emphasize the most important elements. Emphasis is accomplished with tone, contrast, color, size, and location. All those elements that do not contribute to the visual message being created are eliminated, as far as possible, by camera cropping and subordinating those elements that cannot be cropped.

Usually the photographer is able to take the landscape as it is, but it is sometimes possible to add a single element, such as a figure, to complete the composition. Or an object such as a branch can be added in the near foreground to provide a frame for the scene, and to add to the illusion of depth. Another use of the added element is to block a distracting or inappropriate detail, such as a car, from the camera's view. Care must be taken so that the added element does not become dominant, otherwise it can become the theme of the picture and the landscape itself is relegated to the role of background.

Depth in Landscape Pictures

The illusion of depth is obtained in two-dimensional photographs by the use of visual-depth clues provided by the various forms of perspective.

Types of Perspective (Depth Clues). The illusion of depth is so important to the success of nearly all landscape pictures that a brief review of the various types of perspective are included here, along with some practical approaches to the reproduction of the depth clues. (These are discussed in detail in the article PERSPECTIVE.)

Geometric Perspective. Geometric perspective is the drawing of a photograph by the camera lens. Geometric principles explain how the size and location of subjects are imaged by the lens. The location is determined solely by the camera position, while the sizes of the various subjects are determined by the lens focal length.

In photography, linear perspective is a part of geometric perspective that relates to straight lines from objects to the camera lens, which represent light rays. When considered all together, these lines show how objects are imaged by the camera.

Many subjects have parallel lines, often representing the boundaries of planes that form solids. In the images of such objects, extensions of the parallel lines meet at intersections called vanishing points. The positions of the vanishing points help to show the rate of depth change and the angle the planes make to the line of sight of the camera. This is called vanishing-point perspective.

The photographer need not always seek out magnificent views for landscape photographs; color, rather than form or content, may also be the most important visual element. Photo by Robert Walch.

While it is common experience that the ground is level, the ground in a picture (as represented by a plane) rises to the horizon. Location of objects on the ground plane gives a good indication of their relative distances. This is known as ground-plane perspective.

The farther away objects are from the camera position, the smaller they are imaged, following optical geometric rules. This is known as diminishing-size perspective.

Objects farther from the camera position may be partially obscured by nearer objects that are in similar lines of sight. This is called line-of-sight obstruction.

Light and Shade Perspective. When the lighting gives good subject modeling by highlights and shadows, the form of the subject is made more apparent, adding to the three-dimensional illusion.

Shadows of objects falling on the ground plane help show their solidity, and the images of the shadows on the ground plane rise along with the plane, making the relative distances clearer. This is known as shadow perspective.

Aerial Perspective. Far objects are viewed through masses of air. When there is any moisture, smoke, or dust in the air, the appearance of far objects is altered. Their overall tone is lightened, their local contrast lowered, their color saturation reduced, and their image sharpness reduced. The degree of these effects increases with distance, giving good visual clues to the relative distances.

Nearly all landscape pictures contain subjects in the far distance. The effects of haze that provide aerial perspective are quite useful when the distant objects are primarily background, and the haze effects can be emphasized to provide aerial perspective. In black-and-white pictures, blue filters will exaggerate the appearance of the haze. In color work, exposing with no filter at all provides the maximum haze effect. A detailed discussion of this subject is given in a later section of this article on the use of filters.

Importance of Depth Clues. In addition to aerial perspective, the other perspective-depth clues are important to the success of landscape photography. Light and shade perspective are controlled largely by the choice of light and its direction. Subjects that are softly illuminated by overcast skies, and subjects that are frontlit have little of this type of perspective. Forty-five-degree illuminated subjects do show considerable form, and their shadows on the ground show the distances between near and far objects as they rise on the ground plane. With sidelighting, the perspective effect of these two factors is increased.

By outlining various features of the landscape, backlighting increases the separation between near and far objects. When the near object obscures part of a farther object, when there are receding planes, and when the diminishing size of objects is acting as a depth clue, backlighting enhances the effect.

While linear perspective and vanishing points are much easier to demonstrate with the parallel lines and planes of architectural subjects, landscape subjects with unevenly shaped objects follow the same perspective principles. Fences or roads often make this type of perspective clear, while rows of trees, and various objects rising on the ground plane give all the clues the eyes need to interpret the third dimension.

One good way to demonstrate the principle of geometric perspective is to take three pictures of the same subject with three lenses of different focal lengths. Move the camera between each picture so that the same foreground area is covered in each picture.

In the picture taken with the lens of the shortest focal length—a wide-angle lens—the background objects will be much smaller than the same objects in the other two pictures. In the picture taken with a telephoto lens, the background objects will be largest. If there are a number of planes in the pictures, the wide-angle picture will show a great separation between the closer planes, while distant planes will be squeezed together. In the telephoto picture, the planes will be more evenly spaced throughout the distance but will appear squeezed together. The normal-lens picture will show an intermediate effect.

If there is a row of trees at an angle to the lens axis, vanishing-point lines can be drawn through the average position of the tops and bases of the trees, showing that this type of perspective is at work even though there are no straight lines to make it clearly evident where the vanishing points are.

For complete control of geometric perspective in landscape photography, a view camera is essential. By keeping the film plane vertical, subjects such as trees will be imaged vertically on the film so that the vertical vanishing points will be at infinity. By using the rising front, or by using both front and back tilts as the camera aim is raised or lowered, the position of the horizon can be placed at the best location, compositionally, while retaining the verticality of the perspective. By raising the horizon, the land area is emphasized; by lowering it, the sky area receives the emphasis.

With rigid cameras, this effect must be obtained by tilting the camera to raise or lower its aim, which makes the verticals converge or diverge, affecting the perspective. If there are few verticals, especially if they are near the center of the format, this may not be of too much consequence. Where the entire picture is in the far distance, the slight change in vertical perspective will probably be unnoticed.

The use of dark areas in the foregrounds of landscape pictures adds to the sense of depth. Where appropriate, framing with almost black branches is effective. Darkening the ground plane in the immediate foreground, either by selecting a place where there is a natural shadow or by printing it in during enlargement, adds to the depth effect. For transparency work, the use of a gelatin neutral-density filter placed in front of the camera lens, but covering only the lower portion of the lens, accomplishes the same results. Neutral-density values of 0.10 or 0.20 are usually enough. Viewing the effect in the ground glass before the exposure at the final shooting aperture will indicate exact placement of the filter.

Equipment for Landscape Photography

Nearly any type of camera can be used for landscape photography; however, the best type for a particular use varies with a number of factors. For example, if slides are needed for projection, a 35 mm camera may be best. A single-lens reflex camera with interchangeable lenses is useful for controlling the effect of space and some kinds of perspective. There are a few lenses that are equipped with a sliding mechanism called perspective control that acts in the same way as the rising and falling front on a view camera for keeping verticals parallel when raising or lowering the horizon. These are usually moderate wide-angle lenses with wide-field coverage so that they still give good illumination and sharpness when moved the maximum amount.

Lenses. The landscape photographer will find a variety of focal-length lenses a big advantage. A normal 50 mm lens, a wide-angle lens—perhaps 24 or 28 mm—and a moderate telephoto lens—perhaps 100 or 135 mm—give a good working minimum for most needs. Adding a long telephoto lens, such as a 200 mm lens, and an extreme wide-angle lens with a focal length of about 20 mm, widens the control of perspective available.

Having a normal lens and two zoom lenses—one in the wide-angle range and one in the telephoto range—offers a good alternative. The big advantage of zoom lenses is that they permit the photographer to locate at the best viewpoint and then frame exactly as desired. This is especially useful with slides where cropping is the rare exception. A disadvantage of zooms is that they tend to have a high flare level compared to single-focal-length lenses. With high-contrast subjects this can be an advantage because flare tends to reduce contrast. However, with distant subjects, the contrast level is lowered by the haze, and further lowering by the lens can be disastrous to an image.

Cameras. For black-and-white landscape photography, 35 mm cameras can be used if the final enlargement is not to be a mural. The same care that is given to a view camera to avoid camera movement, combined with the use of a very fine-grain film, permits prints of moderate size without the effects of grain and loss of sharpness that often accompany enlargements of great magnification. A film like Kodak Panatomic-X is fine for most uses.

Medium-format cameras have essentially the same advantages and disadvantages as 35 mm cameras in controlling space and perspective. However, medium-speed films can be used in them and quite large prints can be made.

The best control of geometric perspective is achieved with adjustable view cameras, and the 4″ × 5″ and 8″ × 10″ format negatives permit large prints with most negative materials. They are equally suitable for color-negative landscape photography, and are unsurpassed for transparency photography when the landscape pictures are to be used for halftone reproduction.

The precision-type metal view cameras are very accurately made, and the adjustments are usually well-calibrated for easy use. However, they are somewhat heavy to carry, and their odd structure makes them bulky. There has been increasing use of lightweight field view cameras that weigh from 2½ pounds to about 4 pounds and fold up into a compact form for easy carrying. These 4″ × 5″ cameras have double-extension bellows, limiting their use to a maximum of 300 mm, or 12-inch-focal-length lenses, unless a special extension tube is made, or true telephoto lenses are used that have a relatively short back focus.

Tripod. A sturdy tripod is necessary for all types of cameras used for landscape photography. When a moderate-speed film is used with the lens stopped down for depth of field, and a filter is put on for tone and aerial perspective, the shutter speed is likely to be relatively long. Only a camera mounted firmly on a tripod will assure the photographer that there is no camera movement. And, of course, with view cameras, a tripod is essential for viewing and focusing.

Lens Hood. Lens hoods are a requirement to minimize flare, especially when the scene is backlit. The usual round hoods are adequate for 35 mm and medium-format camera lenses, but the adjustable bellows-type lens hood is the best choice for a view camera. These lens hoods are adjustable for different focal-length lenses, and have the greatest light-shielding capabilities possible with each lens.

Changing Bag. A changing bag is very useful for loading film holders for view cameras in the field. Fewer holders have to be carried, and being able to change film away from a darkroom often means that the best pictures are not missed.

Exposure Meter. A good exposure meter is almost a necessity in achieving quality negatives. Built-in meters in 35 mm cameras and some medium-format cameras are usually adequate, but if the zone system or contrast-index method of controlling contrast is used, a hand meter that permits measuring the luminance range of the subject is a necessity. Reflection-averaging meters can be used, but it is difficult to measure a diffuse highlight or a textured shadow area if it is at a distance. Spot meters are the best meters for luminance range metering, for measuring highlights for transparency exposures, and for those areas where tone is to be reproduced just lighter than black when shooting with negative materials.

Miscellaneous Items. Other items such as cable releases, carrying cases, writing materials for record keeping, focusing cloths, magnifying lenses for view-camera work, and so on, are as necessary for landscape photography as for other location work.

The Use of Filters

When distant objects form the entire picture, it is usually necessary to lighten the haze effect with filters in order to obtain maximum detail and subject contrast. On the other hand, when distant objects are primarily background, it may be useful to emphasize the haze in order to show the aerial perspective. Other uses of filters are to lighten foliage, darken blue skies, or otherwise control the black-and-white rendering of colors.

Filters for Color Film. The following filters are often used with color film in landscape photography. The No. 1A skylight filter reduces bluishness and slightly reduces haze. The No. 2B and No. 2E UV absorbing filters are the same as the skylight filter, except somewhat more effective. The polarizing screen deepens the color of blue skies and is useful with the No. 1A, No. 2B, and No. 2E filters to strengthen the effect, increase color saturation, and reduce or remove reflected glare from the surface of water.

Filters for Black-and-White Film. The following filters are often used with black-and-white panchromatic film in landscape photography.

No. 8 and No. 15 Yellow Filters. These filters reduce haze somewhat and moderately darken a blue sky. The No. 8 filter gives a gray-tone rendering of colors that approximates their visual brightnesses.

No. 11 and No. 13 Yellow-Green Filters. These filters reduce haze and darken blue skies less than the yellow filters, but they lighten green foliage.

No. 8 + 11 and No. 15 + 13 Filters. These combinations reduce haze and darken blue skies more than the No. 11 and No. 13 filters alone, but they lighten green foliage.

No. 58 Deep Green Filter. This filter darkens blue skies and moderately reduces haze, but gives maximum lightening of foliage. It also darkens reds considerably.

No. 23A Light Red Filter. This filter reduces haze and darkens blue skies considerably. It also darkens green foliage.

No. 25 Deep Red Filter. This filter darkens deep blue skies to almost black, gives maximum reduction of haze with pan films, lightens reds to almost white, and darkens green foliage to almost black.

No. 25 Deep Red Filter with Infrared Film. This filter blackens blue skies, lightens foliage to almost white, and gives maximum haze reduction. It reproduces most other colors unpredictably, but natural grays photograph near their visual levels.

No. 25 Deep Red Filter + Polarizing Screen. This combination darkens blue skies to black on pan film, while reducing haze and reproducing other colors the same as the No. 25 filter alone.

No. 80A and No. 80B Light Blue Filters. These filters increase haze and darken greens and reds slightly. They also lighten blue skies.

No. 47 and No. 47B Dark Blue Filters. These filters increase haze the maximum amount, and darken greens and reds considerably.

Filter Factors. When filters are used, the exposure must be increased by filter factors. (*See:* FILTERS.) Overexposure must be avoided or some of the filter effect can be lost in the photograph. The factors for the combinations of filters with most panchromatic films are as follows:

Filter Combinations	Filter Factor
No. 8 + No. 11	6×
No. 15 + No. 11	8×
No. 25 + polarizer	20×

Filter Effects. When filters are used in landscape photography, they can achieve the following:

1. Give a gray-tone rendering of colors, which matches their visual brightnesses.
2. Help to control the degree of depth effect by reducing or increasing the aerial perspective.
3. Increase the dramatic effect by darkening the sky.
4. Control local contrast by separating colors, such as darkening skies and lightening foliage.
5. Reduce glare on water in both black-and-white and color photography (polarizing screens).
6. Increase color saturation in color photography (polarizing screens).
7. Create dramatic effects by making foliage nearly white (red filter with infrared film).

Films

There are many choices of black-and-white films in the 35 mm and roll-film sizes for landscape photography. Color negative and transparency films offer a more limited choice.

Black-and-White Film. Because the type of light that produces shadows is quite useful in

A wide-angle lens, stopped down for maximum depth of field, was used to obtain the sharp focus in both foreground and very distant background. Photo by Robert Walch.

strengthening many of the depth clues, a film that produces good separation in the dark tones is a good choice for landscape photography. Such films have characteristic curves with short toes. (The toe is the crescent-shaped lower part of the characteristic curve.) In addition to curve shape, other criteria are film speed, graininess, and sharpness as indicated by resolving-power listings and modulation-transfer-function curves. While the choices are not as wide in sheet films, the same factors have to be considered. When the film size is larger, film speed may take some precedence over graininess.

Kodak technical pan film (Estar - AH base) SO-115 is a useful 35 mm film for landscape photography. Although not ordinarily listed in the usual sources of information, it is available in 4″ × 5″ sheet sizes. Despite its relatively slow speed (EI 25) when processed for landscape negatives, it has extremely fine grain and high resolving power (320 lines/mm). It also has the short-toed characteristic curve so useful in this type of photography. (See the special processing instructions in the section on creative darkroom work in this entry.) Kodak technical pan film is coated on a roll-film thickness base, and

Gentle, rolling hills and valleys present a scene of pastoral tranquility reminiscent of an eighteenth-century landscape painting. Photo by Esther Henderson.

Landscape Photography

Deeply cut gorges, half shrouded in haze, seem to go on forever. The frame of dark trees in the foreground adds to the sense of depth. Photo by Robert Walch.

some users expose and process sheets to a D-max black to use as spacer sheets under the film in sheet-film holders. This brings the emulsion up to the normal level of a sheet film on a thick base, and prevents slippage in the holder grooves.

Color Film. The daylight types of color film are normally used for outdoor photography, but if exposure times are longer than 1 second, the type L films are recommended. Exposing type L films with a No. 85B filter (in daylight) provides negatives that will print easily. Usually normal-speed films are used because of their fine grain, but when small apertures are needed for depth of field and when the subject has movement, as trees in wind, a high-speed color-negative film will be useful. This type of film is not available in sheets, but a roll-film adapter can be used on a view camera with the 120 roll-film size, and the 35 mm size can be used with a camera of that format.

There may be slight differences in color rendition and in contrast between different color-negative films. For example, Kodacolor films may record colors with slightly greater saturation and with slightly higher contrast than Vericolor type S film; and Vericolor type L films may have characteristics somewhere between the two. Because these subtle differences may change as various minor manufacturing changes are made, it is a good idea to run tests comparing the films using a standard subject to find the most suitable color rendition and contrast.

Position of the sun and the shadows it casts create light and shade perspective. Subjects illuminated at forty-five degrees, such as this one, show considerable form, and their shadows on the ground show the distances between near and far objects as they rise on the ground plane. Photo by Ray Atkeson.

The same type of situation exists with color-transparency films. The choice is limited in sheet films, but in 35 mm films there is a wide choice. The color rendition and contrast of all the color-transparency films is similar, so the selection will be based on film speed and end use.

Although high-quality halftone reproductions can be made from color prints, photoengravers prefer transparencies, especially large-sized ones. The chances of a landscape photographer's work being accepted for reproduction are better if the sheet-film transparency medium is used. Roll-size transparencies are next preferred, while 35 mm landscape transparencies are accepted by few publications.

One method of using the smaller transparencies is to enlarge them on color-duplicating film. This requires extra darkroom work, but in the field the load is lightened. Photoengravers accept enlarged duplicate color transparencies if they are well made.

Exposure

As in any type of photography, correct exposure is necessary to obtain the best results.

Color Transparencies. Exposure is critical in color-transparency work. If color transparencies are being made for projection, they should receive slightly more exposure than if they are being made for halftone reproduction. Slightly thin slides are necessary for projection in large auditoriums, while normal slides will project well under home-projection conditions.

The photoengraver has a difficult job reproducing a transparency in which the highlights are thin. In full-scale subjects it is sometimes impossible to get detailed, tone-separated highlights and full shadow detail with transparency film. A slight loss in shadow detail is usually less serious from a reproduction standpoint than a loss in highlight detail. This is why the highlight method of computing exposures is preferred when using transparency films.

Color Negatives. With color-negative materials, the shadow method of measuring the subject for finding exposure is recommended. With almost any landscape scene, if the shadows are properly exposed, the highlights will still be well separated in the negative. If the scene has an extended luminance range, the highlight areas may have to be burned-in when making the enlargement, but the detail is there in the negative to be brought out by the burning-in. On the other hand, if there is a lack of detail in the shadow areas as a result of underexposure, there is no way of putting it in.

With very short-range subjects, using the midtone or averaging method of calculating exposure is best. The shadow method will put the lower tones on the toe of the characteristic curve, and much needed contrast will be lost. Using the highlight method will result in overexposure, giving unneeded density to the negative. The midtone method places the exposure up off the toe so that all of the contrast is available, yet overexposure is avoided.

Black-and-White Negatives. For best overall black-and-white print quality, a method of film development should be used to obtain negatives with consistent density ranges that are appropriate for the enlarger, the paper to be used, and the contrast taste of the photographer. This means using a system of finding developing times that takes into consideration all of the contrast-controlling factors in the photographic system. Once the other factors are determined, the developing times are changed to compensate for the changes in subject luminance range. The zone system is one such method, and another is the contrast-index method given in the article CONTRAST. When development times are changed, the speed of the film also changes. This must be taken into account when making exposure calculations.

With black-and-white film, as with color-negative film, the shadow method of measuring the subject for calculating exposure is best for normal and long-luminance-range subjects, while the midtone or averaging method is best for short-luminance-range subjects.

Exposure Meters. While both incident and averaging reflection exposure meters are used successfully by competent photographers to calculate exposures, it is much simpler to use a spot meter when measuring exposure by the shadow and highlight methods. The article EXPOSURE TECHNIQUES gives details about the use of meters with different types of subjects and lighting.

Although most photographic equipment is made to high standards, there are small variations in almost all of the equipment that relate to exposure. It is always a good policy to test the equipment that will be used to take landscape pictures before going out into the field. It may be found that using a film speed somewhat different from the rated ASA will result in better pictures.

• *See also:* AERIAL PERSPECTIVE; ATMOSPHERIC HAZE; BACKLIGHT; BAD-WEATHER PHOTOGRAPHY; COMPOSITION; DEPTH OF FIELD; FILTERS; FLARE; INFRARED PHOTOGRAPHY; MOONLIGHT PICTURES; NATURAL LIGHT; PANORAMIC PHOTOGRAPHY; PERSPECTIVE; PICTORIAL PHOTOGRAPHY; SKY FILTER; SUNRISE AND SUNSET PICTURES; TELEPHOTOGRAPHY; VIEW CAMERA; WIDE-ANGLE PHOTOGRAPHY; WINTER PHOTOGRAPHY; ZONE SYSTEM.

Further Reading: Brown, Dean. *Photographs of the American Wilderness.* Garden City, NY: Amphoto, 1976; Kane, Art. *The Persuasive Image.* New York, NY: T.Y. Crowell, Inc., 1975; Naef, Weston J. *Era of Exploration: the Rise of Landscape Photography in America.* New York, NY: New York Graphics Society, 1975; Wall, Alfred H. *Artistic Landscape Photography.* New York, NY: Arno, 1977; Wright, Cedric. *Words of the Earth.* San Francisco, CA: Sierra Club Books, Inc., 1960.

Large Color Prints and Transparencies

Large color prints and transparencies make dramatic displays for commercial and artistic purposes. They are used widely for advertising and promotion, interior decoration, and both as backgrounds and as principal subjects in museum and gallery exhibits.

Materials

Because color materials such as Kodak Vericolor papers and film are available in large sheet and roll sizes, they are especially suited for making display-size color images. Very large displays are made by mounting or splicing several sheets or strips of processed material side by side. For example, the Kodak Colorama in New York City's Grand Central Station—the world's largest color transparency at 18' × 60'—is made up of 40 strips of 18-inch-wide print film spliced together. (*See:* COLORAMA.)

Handling Materials. Materials for large color images are used in much the same way as in making smaller-size prints and transparencies. The primary differences in technique are in achieving balanced exposures and in the handling of the materials during processing. In some cases, the quantity or concentration of a solution may have to be adjusted according to the amount of emulsion area being processed. The finishing and mounting procedures must be adapted to the large image size, of course.

A box of large sheets or a long roll contains much more material than will be used in a single printing session. The bulk material should be kept sealed and refrigerated at 10 C (50 F) or lower to prevent changes in emulsion response. Adequate warm-up time must be allowed before the package is unsealed, as specified in film or paper instruction sheets. A lighttight wooden or metal container facilitates moving, storing, and dispensing film or paper in rolls.

Color materials have some sensitivity to all wavelengths of light; therefore, safelight recommendations must be followed *exactly* to avoid unwanted exposure and fogged images. Because the handling of large-size materials is more difficult, procedures are much slower than with those of smaller sizes. It is important to keep track of the *accumulated* safelight exposure of each piece of material—not just the length of the maximum individual exposure.

(Above) Large color prints may be used dramatically for decorative purposes. Here, a basement recreation room is brightened by a large print of a sunlit Southwestern landscape; the theme is carried out in the rest of the room's furnishings. (Right) An office reception area is decorated by a large color print relating to the company's business. Photo courtesy Canadian Pacific.

Large Color Prints and Transparencies

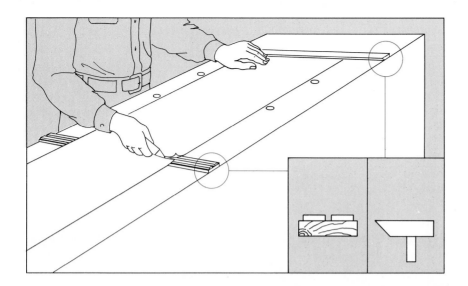

A simple device for measuring and cutting roll paper or film uses a movable stop (at right) and a grooved cutting marker.

Cutting Unexposed Material. When large rolls of film or paper are used instead of sheets, a bench on which to measure and cut the desired length from the roll is required. The bench should be about 8 inches wider than the material, and long enough to accommodate the greatest length to be processed. A simple device for measuring and cutting paper from large rolls is shown in the accompanying illustration.

The paper or film is unrolled with its emulsion side down. Care must be taken to avoid scratching or damaging the emulsion. The leading edge is tucked into the beveled edge of the wood measuring stop. If the wood stop is equipped with pegs, and the bench with holes at measured distances, material of commonly used lengths can be measured quickly. At the cutting position on the bench, attach a piece of hard maple with two strips of metal, spaced slightly apart, mounted on it. In the dark or under the necessary safelight conditions, a single-edged razor blade or knife, such as a linoleum knife or a rolling-blade cutter, can be easily guided to cut the paper or film in the area between the metal spacers. The sheet of material should allow an ample border, up to several inches, around the print image.

To prepare mural-size images, several sheets of exposed and processed film or paper can be joined to form the complete picture. Adjacent sheets of the eventual mural should be cut from adjacent sections of the roll. In addition, the sheet edges to be matched

in the mural should be either those edges that were along one side of the roll or those edges adjacent at the cut. Whether the matched edges are from one side of the roll or adjacent at the cut will depend on the general picture format desired. Aligning and matching the edges will prevent any slight differences in thickness across the width of the material from causing noticeable edge mismatch on the finished mural. In preparing murals, the exposures should be overlapped enough so that the prints can be trimmed and matched easily.

Equipment

Liquid Negative Carrier. A high degree of magnification is generally encountered in making large transparencies. Cinch marks, oily fingerprints, and even minute surface scratches on negatives become important considerations.

Some of these defects can be eliminated immediately by using a "liquid negative carrier" in the enlarger. This type of carrier is constructed so that the negative is exposed while it is immersed in a fluid that has the same refractive index as the film base. One fluid that has been found to work well with acetate-base film is Decalin® (decahydronaphthalene). Beware of liquids that will affect the film base or emulsion—including water.

This immersion method will render fine scratches and defects on the film base and emulsion side of the negative almost invisible in the print, particularly when a diffusion-type enlarger is used. However, any scrapes that destroy the emulsion layers will still print and will have to be retouched on the finished print or transparency.

Enlarger. Making large color prints requires a rigidly mounted enlarger that provides sufficient illumination. Tungsten and tungsten-halogen enlarger lamps are suitable sources of illumination if the negative is protected by proper placement of heat-absorbing glass. Enlargers equipped with ordinary fluorescent lamps are not recommended. Fluorescent lamps that are deficient in red require heavy filtering; with such lamps, exposure times at large magnifications may be impracticably long. Variations in exposure time will affect both the color balance and the contrast. Exposure times should be kept uniform wherever possible; density changes should be made by adjusting the lens aperture.

Greater magnification can be obtained with most vertical enlargers by rotating the head to a horizontal position and projecting the image onto a wall. An alternative is to turn the enlarger head so that the image is projected onto the floor. A lens of shorter focal length will also give greater magnification; however, too short a focal length results in unsharp edges and uneven illumination.

When enlarging to high magnifications, optical deficiencies, mechanical irregularities, and uneven illumination are greatly accentuated; therefore, it is wise to check for these defects before starting work. Be particularly sure that the enlarger is properly centered in relation to the easel, so that the projected image will be in equal focus from edge to edge.

Mural-size images are usually made from larger negatives that are often projected in sections to obtain a larger print. Work of this kind requires a specially built enlarger. Information about this type of equipment is available from various manufacturers and distributors.

Lens. An enlarging lens should be of sufficient focal length to cover the negative sharply to the edges. As a general rule, a suitable focal length is equal to the length of the diagonal of the negative (the distance between diagonally opposite corners). A lens of longer focal length can be used, but this will increase the lens-to-paper distance.

A good-quality enlarger lens is indispensable for making big color enlargements. Specially designed lenses, having a long throw with optimum sharpness at 50 or more diameters of enlargement, are available for making murals and extremely large prints. Color-corrected lenses will produce prints with better definition and greater freedom from color fringing than some older lenses intended only for black-and-white work. Whatever lens is used, it must be clean and free from dust; a good enlargement cannot be made with a dirty lens.

Easel. It is desirable to have an easel large enough to accommodate the full size of the eventual image, so that the negative does not have to be moved to make successive sectional exposures. If a sufficiently large vacuum board is not available to hold that much print material during the exposure, the next best provision is for a vacuum board that can be moved across the field, so that the negative can be exposed in sections. Lacking vacuum equipment, tack the film or paper to a flat surface or, for smaller transparencies, roll it onto a smooth surface that has been treated with a stick-and-release medium ("Sticky Back"), from graphic arts suppliers.

Because a transparency will be displayed with its emulsion side toward the viewer for improved dye stability, the negative and film should be oriented so that the emulsion side of the negative in the enlarger faces the emulsion side of the print film on the easel. That is the same orientation normally used to make prints on paper.

Making Exposures

Focusing. Focusing is often more difficult at high magnifications. Lack of field flatness may make it impossible to obtain critical sharpness over the whole area of the image. The solution is to focus at a point about one third of the distance in from the edge of the picture. Furthermore, with some lenses the focus tends to shift as the aperture is reduced. To overcome this difficulty, focus with the lens stopped down to the aperture to be used for the exposure.

Exposing. The negative edges must be masked in the negative carrier so that no light surrounds the projected image; such light is reflected by adjacent surfaces and will degrade the enlargement by adding fog to the highlights. That effect is more serious with a dense negative, which requires a long exposure.

If the enlarger has sufficient light intensity, reduce the lens aperture. Do not, however, use the full aperture of the lens; enlarger illumination is rarely even with the lens wide open.

Make a test exposure on a strip of paper or film that includes the edges of the picture. If extra exposure is needed to compensate for uneven negative density, time it carefully so that it can be repeated exactly in the final print, or in the succeeding sections if the enlargement is to be made in more than one part. Make as many test exposures as necessary to get correct exposure; good print quality depends largely on this.

It is not possible to expose all the sections of a mural simultaneously because an overlap of image is necessary for splicing. Mark the negative where splices are expected, and locate the paper or film on the easel so that the marks and 38 mm (1½ inches) of extra image are included. That method allows for enough overlap to make splices, and to permit trimming of rough edges and pin marks.

Special precautions must be taken so that successive strips will match in density and color balance. One such precaution involves the time lapse between exposure and processing, which should be approximately the same for each strip.

Reciprocity Effect. All photographic emulsions are subject to reciprocity effect. Enlargements of very great magnification nearly always require long exposure times. The reciprocity effect can then be seen as underexposure, a change of contrast, a change in color, or all three. For example, suppose the printing time for a negative at a magnification of $4\times$ is 10 seconds at $f/8$. If the magnification is raised to $16\times$, the calculated exposure becomes 160 seconds at $f/8$; but a print exposed for this length of time would be underexposed because of the reciprocity effect. If the exposure time is increased to compensate, the relative densities of the color images in the dye layers will be changed and the color balance will be affected again. More tests, probably with increased exposure and a change in filter pack, will be necessary.

Since the low-intensity reciprocity effect is compounded by every increase in exposure time, always increase the exposure by opening the lens aperture or by increasing the level of illumination, whenever these alternatives are possible.

Latent-Image Keeping. For the most consistent results, the time interval between exposure and processing should be kept as nearly uniform as possible. If a large number of prints are to be made from the same negative, hold the test print, and later the production prints, at room temperature for the same length of time (such as 4 hours) after exposure. At the end of the period, process the paper or store it in a cold, dry place (preferably at 2 C [35 F] or lower) until it can be processed. The maximum cold storage time is 3 days, whereas the maximum storage time at room temperature is 24 hours. Uniform latent-image keeping time is particularly important in printing sections of a negative onto strips of paper for a color mural. Differences in keeping time may result in color and density shifts; thus, the sections will not match.

Processing

Processing may be carried out in tanks, trays, drums, or tubes of sufficient size. Automatic-processing machines provide the best uniformity for mural-length strips.

With experience and care, up to eight 16″ × 20″ sheets, or four 30″ × 40″ sheets, can be processed simultaneously in a tray. In that case, a developer tray of extra depth is required to provide enough solution for the amount of emulsion being processed. The technique is to clip one corner of the first sheet for identification, and to immerse the sheets in the developer at about 15-second intervals, making sure that they do not stick together. When the last sheet has been immersed, the stack is continually agitated by moving the bottom sheet to the topmost position. A good deal of practice is necessary to avoid damaging the softened emulsion by contact with the edges or corners of the stack. With very large sheets, it is helpful to have two people handling the materials. At the end of the developing time, the sheets are removed and drained in order, beginning with the clipped-corner sheet, and placed in the next solution. It is essential to wear rubber or plastic gloves to protect the skin from chemicals in color-processing solutions.

Color papers and print films should be processed according to the manufacturers' recommendations. Where specific recommendations for processing large sizes of paper or film are not given in the instructions, ask your dealer or write to the manufacturer for details.

Subsequent steps include drying, finishing, and displaying the images. The procedures differ for prints and transparencies, and are discussed separately in the following sections.

Finishing Prints

Drying Prints. Depending upon the base material, large color prints can be machine-dried in air-impingement dryers or, with the emulsion side out, on double-belt dryers equipped with special liners to prevent sticking of the emulsion to the belts.

Prints processed in a tank system can be dried vertically by hanging them on racks still attached to the stainless steel rods with weighted clips in place.

To dry water-resistant papers, plastic screening stretched and tacked to both sides of a wooden frame can be used to hold 16″ × 20″ prints and smaller-size prints emulsion side up. By attaching small wooden spacers to these screened frames, many frames holding prints can be stacked. Because the screening stretches around the entire frame, prints cannot curl more than the distance provided by the spacers.

Prints should never be placed with the emulsion surface in contact with a blotter roll or between blotters because the soft, wet emulsion will adhere to the blotter surface.

Squeegeeing the prints will minimize the drying time, but care should be taken to avoid abrasion of the emulsion side.

Mounting Prints. Certain materials require specific methods of mounting. Among these methods are the following.

Dry Mounting Prints. Big enlargements up to 48″ × 96″ can be readily dry-mounted on suitable ¼-inch cardboard, Masonite panelwood, Fom-Cor mounting board, or plywood with dry-mounting tissue if a large mounting press is available.

Adhesives for Mounting Water-Resistant Paper Prints. Prints made on water-resistant, resin-coated papers can be mounted on mounting board. Masonite, or plywood with adhesives that has good adhesion properties, has no deleterious effect on image stability, and has resistance to blistering and wrinkling. Brands that have given satisfactory results include:

1. Special No. 67 GV Padding Compound, made by Harad Chemical Company.
2. Cascorez GRC-7 and Elmer's Glue-All, both made by Borden Chemical Company. Elmer's rubber cement is also satisfactory but does not provide as

strong a bond as the other adhesives mentioned. That type of adhesive may be preferred in applications where easy removal of prints may be required.

3. Lamin-All, made by McDonald Photo Products, Inc.
4. Glue-Fast, made by Glue-Fast Equipment Company, Inc.
5. Kodak rapid mounting cement, made by Eastman Kodak Company.
6. Scotch Spra-ment, made by 3-M Company. Scotch Spra-ment is quite satisfactory except for butt splices, which may separate during humidity changes.

In the case of each of these products, it is advisable to make tests and evaluate the adhesive according to a particular application.

Mounting on Nonporous Surfaces. Special considerations must be made when prints are mounted on nonporous surfaces. Adhesives that depend on solvent evaporation do not work well, since the solvent cannot escape from between the mount and the print. In this case it is necessary to use double-faced adhesive tape or a contact adhesive. An alternate approach is the use of a thermosetting adhesive, such as Lamin-All, which depends upon heat to set the final bond.

Splicing Murals. If a big color picture is made in more than one section, the pieces must be spliced together on the mount. Splices should be so contrived that they are hardly visible. A joint is less obvious if it coincides with a natural line in the picture, such as the horizon or the side of a building. The recommended method is butt-mounting.

Retouching Prints. When possible, it is a good rule to do all the necessary retouching on the color negative before making the final prints. However, when the negative size is small, retouching and corrections are more easily done on the enlarged print. Any minus-density areas in the color negative such as pinholes or scratches, which would result in unwanted plus-density areas on the print, should be opaqued in the negative. It is easier to add density to the print than to remove it. Etching, the physical removal of dye layers, is not recommended.

Information on retouching techniques can be found in Kodak publication No. E-70, *Retouching EKTACOLOR Prints* and in the article RETOUCHING.

Making a Large Color Transparency

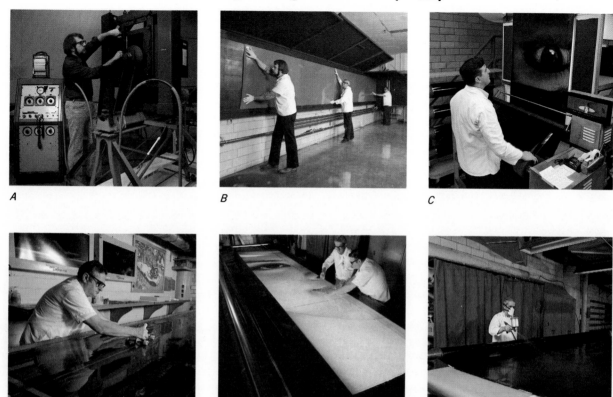

A   B   C

D   E   F

(A) The negative is placed in an enlarger which will expose portions of it onto 20 strips of a thick-based Estar film. Individual strips are 3 feet wide and 18 feet long. (B) Each strip of film is positioned into an exposing easel and exposed for approximately 6 minutes. (This operation is done in total darkness.) (C) Exposed film is processed and inspected. Processing the 20 strips takes nearly 5 hours. (D) Processed film is now ready for assembly. First, the 2 inch overlap and the registration edge of each strip are slit; excess film is removed for salvage. (E) To assure proper image registration, adjacent strips are temporarily joined. Later, permanent splices are made using acetate splicing tape and print film cement. (F) Matte spraying of the viewing surface provides an antireflective finish, reducing glare by 65 percent. Print is now ready for final inspection before mounting.

Lacquering. To enhance and protect the appearance of prints, coat them with one of a number of lacquers available from photo dealers. These lacquers are made especially for photographic use. Varying the type of lacquer, dilution, and method of application will result in any of a variety of surfaces ranging from glossy to matte and including stipple and brush effects. Lacquering helps protect the surface from abrasions, fingerprints, atmospheric con-

taminants, humidity, and dirt. A lacquered print can be cleaned with a damp cloth.

Displaying Prints

Lighting. The importance of proper display lighting for the finished print cannot be overemphasized. The number and placement of lamps should produce an even lighting over the entire surface of the print. Either incandescent (tungsten) or fluorescent lighting can be used. However, the Color Rendering Index (CRI) of the lamps chosen should preferably be 90 or higher. Some "daylight" type fluorescent lamps have a severe deficiency in red output. They have a low CRI and are not suitable for illuminating color prints.

Test prints should always be evaluated under illumination of the same color quality and intensity (at least 50 footcandles) as the illumination under which the final print will be viewed.

Balance. In many cases display lighting conditions will vary. For example, a print might be displayed in an area in which there is considerable sunlight during the day, but incandescent light at night. Such a situation presents almost impossible extremes, yet the print must somehow be balanced to accommodate both the daylight and the incandescent light and look good in either situation. Under the circumstances, a compromise must be made. Some intermediate color temperature must be chosen, say 3900 K, and the print balanced accordingly.

If incandescent lamps are used, the wattage rating of the bulbs should be high enough to illuminate the print at least to the level of light in the room. The lamps can be reflector floods or ordinary lamps mounted in reflector housings. Because of their inherently warm character, incandescent lamps are often preferred over fluorescent lamps. However, the ultimate selection must remain a matter of choice and convenience.

Finishing Large Transparencies

Drying Display Transparencies. Large transparencies can be dried on racks by hanging them with film clips or spring clothespins. If necessary, attach small weights to the bottom of each transparency to minimize curling during drying.

Transparencies on print film should be dried at low temperatures. Applying excessive heat or forced air will cause the transparencies to become brittle, and the emulsion surface to become glossy. Drying at temperatures below 49 C (120 F) with gentle air circulation leaves the transparencies desirably pliable and the emulsion surface less glossy.

Assembling Large Transparencies. Assembling large transparencies from multiple strips is largely a commercial operation requiring elaborate equipment and technique. The details of one method are given in Kodak publication No. E-58, *Preparing*

Large Transparencies on KODAK EKTACOLOR *Print Film.*

Displaying Large Transparencies. The successful display of large-size transparencies depends to a great degree on the manner in which they are mounted and lighted. The size of the transparency will govern the manner in which the mounting and lighting should be accomplished. Generally speaking, transparencies up to 30″ × 40″ can be sandwiched between glass or plastic and illuminated with comparatively few fluorescent tubes. Larger transparencies may require a suspension system that involves hooks, springs, and extensive fluorescent or cold-cathode tubing.

Diffusion Materials. Transparencies displayed in light boxes need a suitable diffusion material between the film and the light source. For the display of transparencies up to 30″ × 40″, try translucent Plexiglas sheeting, ⅛″ thick, specification W-2447. Plexiglas sheeting is available in large pieces, but a local supplier can cut a small piece to meet specific requirements. The transparency is sandwiched be-

A Colorama transparency measuring 18′ × 60′ is unrolled from left to right across the face of the illuminator (which is not normally lighted during installation).

tween the Plexiglas sheeting (on the lamp side) and ordinary glass or clear Plexiglas sheeting.

The transparency can also be mounted in contact with the translucent Plexiglas sheeting without a covering sheet if the sheeting is rigidly supported in the illuminator. When a transparency is displayed in this manner, a spray coating of matte print lacquer will both protect the film surface and reduce reflections.

The Light Box. Large transparency illuminators can be constructed from either wood or metal and should include air vents on at least two sides, but preferably on all four sides. If space can be provided between the illuminator and any wall near which it may be positioned, air vents should also be placed in the back surface.

Since the dissipation of heat from the lamps is one of the important considerations in planning a light box, a large illuminator incorporating ordinary incandescent light is difficult and expensive to construct. For the same quantity of light, fluorescent lamps develop far less heat than incandescent lamps.

This transparency is backlighted by 277 metal arc lamps, of 175 watts each. Fluorescent lamps may also be used for illumination.

Also, a more even illumination over the entire transparency can be obtained from fluorescent lamps.*

The interior of the illuminator should be painted with a truly white paint that will not yellow with age. Most high-quality, pure white enamels are suitable. One widely used paint for illuminator interiors is Sherwin-Williams Kem SaveLite EgShel White, which can be obtained in a minimum quantity of one gallon from Sherwin-Williams branch stores in most cities. When ordering this paint, refer to Code No. B47W7, and state the intended use for the paint so that instructions for applying both the undercoat and the finish coat will be furnished.

Transparency Illumination. Fluorescent lamps are available in a variety of standard lengths. In planning the size of the light box and transparency, it is wise to build around a standard lamp size. Utilizing standard lamp sizes also simplifies the purchase and stocking of replacement lamps.

The color balance of a display transparency can be adjusted to allow for the type of illumination by which the transparency will be viewed. Therefore, illuminators used for color balance evaluation of test transparencies should utilize the same type of light source as that used in the display illuminator.

A number of fluorescent lamps that have color temperatures ranging from 3800 to 5000 K can be used. The proper choice depends upon the color temperature of the light in the area surrounding the display illuminator. The CRI of lamps chosen, however, should be 90 or higher.

The number of fluorescent lamps mounted in the illuminator must be determined on the basis of the viewing conditions (room illumination) under which the illuminator will be used. The amount of illumination may vary from a minimum of 350 to a maximum of 900 footlamberts: that is, from 110 to 285 candles per square foot. The lamps should be placed about 3 inches from the diffusion sheeting.

Transparency Display Life. Any transparency will fade after being exposed to light for an extended period. Fading is also influenced by other factors such as heat, humidity, improper film processing, and atmospheric contamination.

---

*All electrical wiring devices and equipment used for lighting of the illuminators should carry the stamp of the Underwriters' Laboratories, and should be installed in accordance with the National Electrical Code and any local codes.

A definite advantage in retarding fading is gained by placing the base side of the transparency toward the light source. The right-to-left orientation can be arranged at the printing stage to be correct for the final positioning. Adequate ventilation of the light box is important. Either laminating the transparency with ultraviolet-absorbing plastic sheeting, or sandwiching it in glass helps retard fading. A transparency on print film can be reprinted from a properly stored negative when necessary.

• *See also:* COLORAMA; COLOR FILM PROCESSING; COLOR PRINTING FROM NEGATIVES; MURALS; PANORAMIC PHOTOGRAPHY; PRINTS, MOUNTING; RETOUCHING; SCALING PRINT SIZES; SLIDES AND TRANSPARENCIES, MOUNTING.

Further Reading: Bomback, Edward S. *Manual of Color Photography.* Garden City, NY: Amphoto, 1964; Elisofon, Eliot. *Color Photography.* New York, NY: Viking Press, Inc., 1961; Feininger, Andreas. *Successful Color Photography,* 4th ed. Englewood Cliffs, NJ: Prentice-Hall, Inc., 1967; Hornby, George and the Editors of Eastman Kodak Co. *Photographing America.* New York, NY: Crown Publishers, Inc. 1976; Insert, G. *The Art of Colour Photography,* New York, NY: Van Nostrand Reinhold Co., 1972.

Lasers

The beam from a laser is a form of radiation that has unique properties when compared with light from conventional sources. Although the photographic application of lasers is often associated with making holograms (*See:* HOLOGRAPHY), the potentialities and applications of lasers have not yet been fully explored.

The laser's capabilities and its potential for making widespread changes in existing technologies relate as much to the future as to the recent past; and some of these changes will most likely engage the attention of the photographer as well as photographic scientists and engineers. Holography is an immensely promising field, but the advent of lasers also promises quantum leaps in both the pure sciences and the technologies that are the practical application of abstract science.

The Origin of Lasers

In 1917, Albert Einstein proved that in theory an atom in an excited state—an atom containing stored energy—would eventually decay to a lower state of energy and, in the process, emit a photon of energy. Einstein then showed that the emission could be caused to occur sooner if the excited atom were struck by an outside photon of a particular level of energy; *two* photons would leave the original atom—the original photon *and* the stimulated one. He also showed that the two photons would leave together and travel in the same direction in phase with each other.

Einstein was describing the stimulated emission of radiation; however, his theoretical understanding of stimulated emission of radiation found no practical application for nearly 40 years because the chances of controlling the process seemed very unlikely. (It often occurs in less than 1/100,000,000 of a second.)

In 1954, three American scientists, James P. Gordon, Charles H. Townes, and H. J. Zieger, applied Einstein's discovery to microwaves by amplifying them through stimulating transitions between the energy levels of molecules in the same way that light could be produced by stimulating atoms in an excited state. The new device was called the maser—an acronym for "microwave amplification by stimulated emission of radiation."

In 1958, Townes and his colleague Arthur Schawlow theorized that stimulated emissions—since they could amplify microwaves—could indeed be used for amplifying light waves. Two years later, Theodore Maiman constructed the "optical maser," which was, in fact, the first laser. This laser was built around a ruby crystal, and its name was an acronym for "light amplification by stimulated emission of radiation."

The Properties of Laser Light

The radiation emitted by a laser differs from that emitted by conventional sources (a light bulb, for example) in four respects: its intensity, directivity, coherence, and narrowness of band width.

Intensity. In a light bulb, the emitted radiation is produced by individual atoms more or less at random. A tungsten atom is excited by heating a tungsten filament with household electrical current. The atom decays spontaneously and then requires another excitation. The many tungsten atoms produce a random and irregular stream of photons. A laser, however, emits a very intense beam of radiation. Depending on the type of laser, emission is at wavelengths in the ultraviolet, visible, or infrared regions of the spectrum. (*See:* SPECTRUM.)

Directivity. Laser beams such as those used in ophthalmic surgery can be focused to spots only $\frac{1}{10}$ mm in diameter, and the direction of the beams can be controlled with great accuracy. Even at considerable distances, laser beams spread only slightly.

Coherence. Coherence means that the separate light waves in the laser beam are in phase—they are exactly in step with one another. The difference between coherent laser beams and incoherent light is shown in the accompanying diagram. The quality of coherence is what makes holography possible; and it also allows the observation of interference effects (fringes) that occur when wave trains overlap and intersect.

Band Width. Laser radiation is emitted at discrete wavelengths that are usually expressed in nanometres (nm) or angstroms (Å). This means that the frequency distribution of a stated wavelength is extremely narrow. In sharp contrast, tungsten lamps emit radiation over a wide range of wavelengths—mostly in the visible region of the spectrum, between 400 and 700 nm.

Applications

Among the major uses of lasers are range-finding and altimetry. A low-flying aircraft, for example, can be equipped with an altimeter and a terrain-mapping system that makes a profile of the terrain below at as much as 1000 measurements per second. "Smart" bombs and other military equipment would not exist without laser technology.

Another application of lasers has been in the precise alignment of large structures, airframes, pipelines, and large machinery. Laser communication systems are well along in the experimental stage. And lasers are used in medicine and the biological sciences for treating retinal detachments, skin disorders, and skin cancer. Lasers are also finding such applications in industry as metallurgy, welding, drilling metals, machining, photographic platemaking, and even as cutting devices in the garment industry.

How a Laser Works

From the original ruby laser, the device proliferated into many designs and utilized many lasing materials. (See HOLOGRAPHY for a partial listing of types of lasers emitting in the visible spectrum.)

The Helium-Neon Gas Laser. This is the laser most commonly used in holography and can stand as a model for the mechanics and physics of laser systems in general. In order to understand how it works, consider the practical aspects of Einstein's theoretical discovery—the various exchanges of energy that can occur within an atom.

Ordinarily, an atom (consisting of a nucleus and electrons rotating in orbits around that nucleus) remains at an energy level that requires the least amount of energy to remain stable. This ordinary energy level is called the ground state, or level.

When a certain amount of energy—either light energy or electrical energy—is applied to an atom, the energy level can be raised through absorption of energy. During this absorption of energy, an atom enters what is called an unstable, excited level. An electron actually changes its orbit to an orbit closer to the nucleus of the atom—using the solar-system

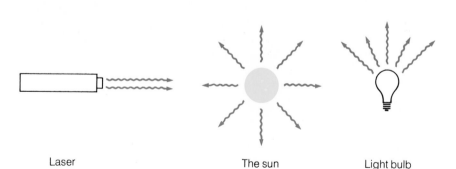

Laser   The sun   Light bulb

Light waves of the same frequency moving together in phase are known as coherent light. Incoherent light is light waves of different frequencies moving in different directions.

Helium-Neon Laser

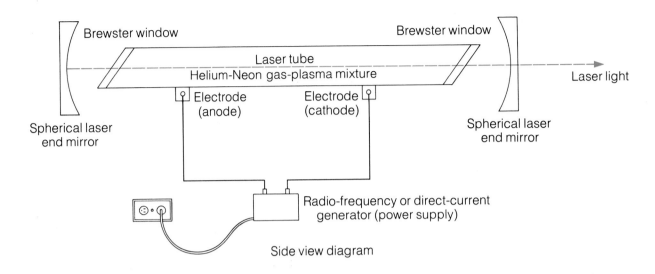

Brewster window

Brewster window

Laser tube
Helium-Neon gas-plasma mixture

Laser light

Electrode
(anode)

Electrode
(cathode)

Spherical laser
end mirror

Spherical laser
end mirror

Radio-frequency or direct-current
generator (power supply)

Side view diagram

(Above) The laser most commonly used in holography is the helium-neon gas laser. The laser tube, which contains the lasing medium, is required for amplification of the light energy and also provides the direction for the travel of the light energy. The mirrors at either end of the laser tube reflect the light energy back and forth through the tube, magnifying and amplifying it as it travels. (Left) The laser is a source of coherent, monochromatic light. This helium-neon laser emits at a red-orange wavelength.

analogy, Venus changes its orbit to the orbit of Mercury. An atom, however, can remain in this excited state for only a very short time. Sooner or later it will return to its ordinary state, releasing an increment of light energy in the process. This change in energy levels with its corresponding emission of light is called spontaneous emission.

When an excited atom is further stimulated by energy, stimulated emission occurs. In other words, the atom returns to the original level or to another energy level, releasing light waves of identical frequency. Light energy released by the excited atom triggers another excited atom into releasing its energy, and so on. This chain reaction of sorts eventually produces coherent light (laser light). However, this process does not occur naturally, simply because there are not enough excited atoms in any given space and time. When enough atoms are raised to a higher energy level, lasing action becomes possible, and laser light is produced.

Another reason why stimulated emission of light energy does not mean that laser light will necessarily be produced is that an enclosed space is required for the continued amplification of the light energy. This enclosed space is the laser tube itself, usually a glass, ceramic, or aluminum tube with closed-off ends. The laser tube not only physically contains the lasing medium (for example, a mixture of helium and neon gases) but also provides direction for the light energy to travel.

In the case of a helium-neon (He-Ne) gas laser (a commonly used laser in making holograms), the lasing medium itself is a helium and neon gas plasma —a mixture of about 90 percent helium and 10 percent neon gases. These gases are contained in a sealed tube, the laser tube. At each end of the laser tube, there are highly reflective mirrors that reflect the light energy produced by stimulated emission, magnifying and amplifying this energy back and forth throughout the length of the tube.

In a He-Ne laser, the excitation of the gas plasma is initiated by an electrical discharge in the

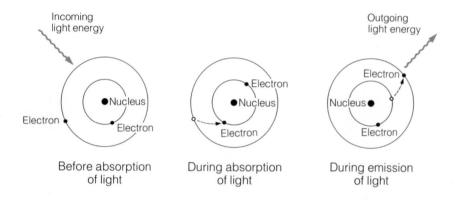

Before absorption of light

During absorption of light

During emission of light

Absorption and Emission of Light Energy

Light enters the atom, exciting one of the electrons that orbits around the nucleus. The excited electron is raised to a higher energy level by changing its orbit. Light energy is absorbed by the atom, and when the atom changes back to its original energy level, energy in the form of light is released or emitted.

Helium-Neon Laser Energy-Level Diagram

In the metastable state, the excited helium atoms transfer a certain amount of energy to the unexcited neon atoms. When a certain number of neon atoms remain at the excited energy level, there are more excited than unexcited neon atoms. Then, the excited neon atoms release their energy and make a transition to another level. At this point, the radiation emitted is a coherent red light beam with a 632.8 nm wavelength. Most wavelengths produced by the laser are in the infrared region (3391.2 nm wavelength) of the energy spectrum. But because of the laser mirror placement and the mirror reflectivity, the He-Ne laser also produces visible red laser light (632.8 nm wavelength).

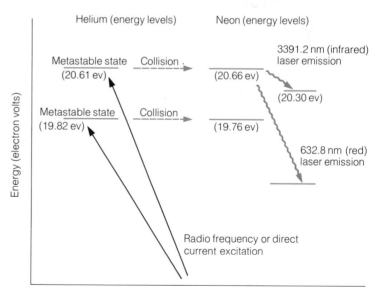

form of direct current or radio-frequency stimulation. This energy introduced into the gas plasma raises the energy of the helium atoms to the so-called metastable state. Metastable, in this sense, means that the energy level is higher than the ordinary stable level, so that the excited atoms tend to remain in this state longer than at another excited level.

In the metastable state, the excited atoms of helium transfer a certain increment of energy to the unexcited neon atoms. This transfer of energy takes place during electron collisions within the system. When a certain number of neon atoms are energized and remain at that excited energy level, there will be more excited neon atoms than unexcited ones. At that time, the excited neon atoms release their energy and thereby make a transition to still another level. During this transition, the emitted radiation is a beam of coherent red light at a wavelength of 632.8 nm. This occurs when the light energy passes back and forth from mirror to mirror enough times to produce continuous emission. The He-Ne laser, therefore, is called a continuous wave laser. A ruby laser usually operates in a pulsed mode, emitting pulses of light that last only nanoseconds (billionths of a second).

It should be noted that there are many different energy levels to which the excited atoms can return and as many different and separate frequencies of light that can be produced. Most of the wavelengths produced by a He-Ne laser actually are in the infrared (invisible) region of the energy spectrum. However, because of the placement of the laser mirrors, as well as their specific reflecting quality, the He-Ne laser has been optimized to produce visible red laser light.

Other Lasers. Besides the helium-neon and ruby lasers, there are other lasers that can be described according to the lasing medium—gas lasers, metal-vapor lasers, and solid-state lasers.

Gas Lasers. Many gas lasers utilize the noble gases, usually in a mixture: helium, neon, argon, krypton, xenon, and their ions. The ion lasers use argon gas, krypton gas, or a mixture of the two gases depending on the desired wavelengths of light. A krypton-gas ion laser, for example, produces laser light at wavelengths ranging from red (647.1 nm), yellow (568.2 nm), green (520.8 nm), to a blue-violet (476.2 nm). The gas in an ion laser is excited to its ionic state by a direct-current electrical discharge.

First, the gas is ionized, and then the whole system is raised to an excited energy level from which lasing action is possible.

Unlike the helium-neon laser, the krypton-ion laser is massive and bulky and requires an elaborate power supply. This in turn requires a water-cooling system because of the heat generated during lasing.

The argon-ion laser produces laser light mostly in the green and blue end of the visible spectrum: green (514.5 nm), blue (488.0 nm), and violet (457.9 nm). The argon laser is not as bulky as the krypton laser, and does not require water cooling if the total power output of the laser is less than one watt. However, the cost of an argon laser is several times greater than that of a helium-neon laser.

Metal-Vapor Lasers. Besides the gas-ion lasers, there are also metal-vapor lasers, which include the helium-cadmium (He-Cd) laser and the helium-selenium (He-Se) laser. Both of these produce laser radiation in the deep blue (441.6 nm) and the ultraviolet (325.0 nm) end of the electromagnetic energy spectrum.

The laser tube of the He-Cd laser is filled with a mixture of helium gas and cadmium vapor (produced by heating solid cadmium to its vaporized state). This plasma is also excited with direct current, which produces certain energy transitions resulting in laser light at those particular frequencies.

Solid-State Lasers. Lasers that utilize a solid or crystalline material for the lasing medium itself are called solid-state lasers.

The ruby laser, for example, has a rod of aluminum oxide (Al_2O_3), which is also called synthetic sapphire. This rod contains a small amount of chromium oxide (Cr_2O_3), which gives the rod its characteristic red color. A flash lamp is usually coiled around the cylindrical ruby rod, providing the light energy necessary to raise the chromium atoms to an excited energy level. When a certain state is reached, stimulated emission occurs in the red (693.4 nm). When further amplification occurs, the ruby laser emits light in an intense pulse that lasts only several microseconds.

Due to their strobe-like capability—which effectively stops motion—pulsed ruby lasers have been used to make holograms of moving objects: insects, aerosol particles, animal subjects, and humans. However, holograms of human subjects made with pulsed ruby lasers have a tendency to appear waxy

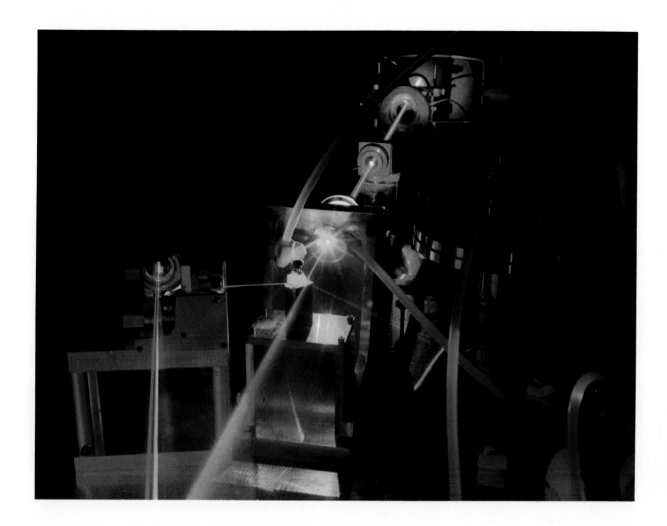

This experimental, tunable gas laser can provide multiple wavelengths of coherent light.

and lifeless due to the special nature of high-intensity red light. The cost of ruby lasers puts them at the level of the institutional or industrial research organization.

Future Technology

Lasers are leading to new knowledge about both atomic and molecular structures as well as the nature of light itself. These powerful tools offer new solutions to production and measurement problems. Laser technology is a commercial fact in some industries and a likely adjunct in other fields in the foreseeable future.

The cost of a laser is largely a function of its power and its type—pulsed or continuous. Simple continuous lasers (about $100) are now found in many school science laboratories. More powerful lasers are still within reach of the individual at $500 or $600. Most laser manufacturers will assist interested persons in developing new applications and will help in selecting the most suitable laser and related equipment for the individual's needs. Applications of laser technology now on the horizon will very probably effect considerable changes in life as we know it today.

• *See also:* HOLOGRAPHY; SPECTRUM.

Latensification

There are two basic methods of increasing the effective speed of an emulsion before the image is developed: (1) hypersensitization, which is carried out before the image-forming exposure, and (2) latensification, which is carried out after the image exposure. Latensification is generally easier to do. Either method can be accomplished by special exposure to light, or by treating the emulsion in a chemical bath or in chemical vapors. No specific procedures can be given, because results will vary according to subject, image exposure, emulsion, and subsequent processing. Only experimentation can determine the effect of either method under a particular set of conditions.

Latensification by Exposure

Latensification means *latent-image intensification;* its effect is to increase the size of the latent-image specks formed during the image exposure without appreciably raising the fog level. It may be effective in overcoming reciprocity failure resulting from very brief high-intensity exposure such as that sometimes encountered with high-speed electronic flash.

Black-and-White Film. A common method of latensification of black-and-white moderate-contrast film by exposure is to place the film (in a darkroom) about 1.5 metres (5 feet) from a safelight equipped with a 7½-watt bulb and a Kodak No. 3 (dark green) filter. The latensifying exposure is from about 4 seconds (fast film) to 1 minute (slow film). Exposure time can be found by making a test; it should be just enough to produce a slight fog when the film is developed. Such an exposure increases the film speed by one-half to one stop. The film speed can be increased slightly more in one of three ways:

1. By increasing the fogging exposure time up to about an hour;
2. By decreasing the intensity of the fogging light;
3. By increasing the distance.

Light from a Neutral Surface. A kind of latensifying effect is produced by "flash" and "bump" exposures in graphic arts photography, or by a flash-ing exposure of a color-transparency film to reduce contrast and bring out shadow-area detail. The additional exposure is given by light from a neutral surface, such as a white or gray card thrown out of focus, to provide diffusion of the light. An exposure of from $\frac{1}{50}$ to $\frac{1}{200}$ of the original image-forming exposure is usually required. If the card is put in the subject position, neutral-density filtration makes it possible to achieve the reduced exposure precisely without disturbing the camera settings. The use of a Kodak neutral test card and an ND2 filter at the same exposure given the subjects provides a latensification exposure $\frac{1}{100}$ of that of the image-forming exposure. (*See:* FLASHING; GRAPHIC ARTS PHOTOGRAPHY.)

Prolonged Exposure. A kind of unwanted latensification is produced by prolonged exposure of printing materials to safelight illumination, or even relatively short exposure to the wrong safelight exposure. Faded safelight filters can also cause unwanted latensification exposure. The result is visible as extra density in highlights of the image long before it can be detected as fogging of border areas. (*See:* SAFELIGHTS.)

Latensification by Chemicals

Latensification by treatment in a chemical bath takes only a few minutes, and the film can be processed immediately after treatment. Two latensifying baths are as follows:

Latensifying Solution No. 1

Water	400 ml
Sodium bisulfite or	
potassium metabisulfite	2.5 g
Sodium sulfite	2.5 g
Water to make	500 ml

Latensifying Solution No. 2

Ammonia-silver nitrate	
solution*	15 ml
Alcohol	121 ml
Water	364 ml

*To prepare, make a 1 percent silver-nitrate solution by dissolving 1 g silver nitrate in distilled water to make 100 ml. Add a few millilitres of 0.88 ammonia (0.88 refers to the specific gravity of the ammonia—washing ammonia available in grocery stores is close to this strength). A precipitate will form. Continue adding ammonia in small amounts, stirring continuously, until the precipitate dissolves.

Latensification

In complete darkness, immerse the exposed film in either of these solutions for 3–5 minutes at 20 C (68 F) and agitate gently. After treatment, drain the film and wash it for about 5 minutes in running water to flush out the latensifying solution before transferring to the developer. Allowing the film to dry before development may produce an even greater speed increase. It is advisable to add an antifoggant to the developer when Solution No. 2 is used.

A third latensifying bath can be made with a very dilute (1–2 percent) solution of hydrogen peroxide in water. This can also have an intensifying effect; it is used as described for Solutions 1 and 2.

These three chemical baths are old formulas that worked with early emulsions. As no recent tests are known to have been made with emulsions that are currently available, these baths must be regarded as experimental.

Chemical vapor latensification is an old process that is no longer recommended because of the hazards involved. It was accomplished by placing the exposed film in a sealed container along with an open container holding a small amount of mercury or sulfurous acid (H_2SO_3). The mercury fumes, or sulfur dioxide fumes from the acid, would slowly penetrate the emulsion and intensify the latent image. Mercury fumes were used to develop the latent image on daguerreotypes by intensifying it to a visible state.

Vapor treatment may take up to 24 hours to have a significant effect. It is no longer used because there is no practical way to be sure that the fumes will penetrate an emulsion evenly, and because of the hazards involved. Sulfur dioxide fumes have a pungent, choking odor, while mercury fumes in sufficient concentration are extremely poisonous. When around photographic materials, any sulfur gases can shorten the life of negatives and prints, while mercury fumes can fog those materials that are unexposed.

Hypersensitization

Hypersensitization of an emulsion before exposure is seldom used for most ordinary applications of photography. There is a problem in handling films without marking or damaging the emulsions, and the speed enhancement quickly dies away, so exposure must be made as soon as possible after treatment. However, hypersensitization is used for special motion-picture applications and for scientific and technical purposes that involve very long exposures with dim light, such as those required in astronomical photography.

The effect of hypersensitizing an emulsion is to create uniformly distributed latent-image specks that are too small to be developable themselves, but upon which the image-forming exposure can build. The ultimate image specks formed in this way are larger than those that would be produced by the image exposure alone. Therefore, an image of greater density (but less contrast) will be produced upon development, with little or no increase in fog level. Hypersensitization can be said to be a fogging exposure that overcomes the inertia of the film to the image-forming exposure.

Hypersensitization by pre-exposure is achieved by giving the emulsion an exposure to diffused, neutral light that is about $\frac{1}{100}$ to $\frac{1}{200}$ of that which normally would produce a minimum printable density (that is, about 0.1 above film-base-plus-fog density). See the instructions given previously for achieving this type of exposure using an ND2 filter and a Kodak neutral test card. One advantage to giving this type of exposure in the camera as compared to the darkroom method is that it can be given to individual frames on a roll rather than to the entire roll.

Chemical-bath hypersensitization can be as simple as washing the emulsion in distilled water to remove some excess soluble silver bromide. In the past, film was treated in the same solutions mentioned for latensification, but before image exposure. One problem with this approach is that the film must be dried quickly to retain maximum effect, and in complete darkness it is difficult to insure that surface moisture has been removed sufficiently for spot-free drying.

Mercury or sulfur dioxide vapors were once used as they were in latensification, but the same disadvantages of time, uneven effect, and hazardous fumes prevailed.

• *See also:* ANTIFOGGANT; CHEMISTRY OF PHOTOGRAPHY; DENSITOMETRY; DEVELOPMENT; FLASHING; GRAPHIC ARTS PHOTOGRAPHY; INTENSIFICATION; LATENT IMAGE; RECIPROCITY EFFECT; SAFELIGHTS.

Latent Image

Upon exposure to suitable energy, a photographic emulsion forms an invisible, or latent, image (Latin *latens* = hidden). The image can be made visible by prolonged exposure (printing out) or, as is the conventional procedure, by the chemical action of development. In general terms, the latent image is produced as follows.

Latent-Image Formation

A photographic emulsion consists of silver halide crystals held in suspension throughout one or more layers of gelatin. Each crystal is composed of a lattice structure of silver ions and halogen ions; in film emulsions the halogen is almost entirely bromine. Each crystal also has traces of silver sulfide in discrete specks on the surface and within the lattice structure; these are known as sensitivity specks.

When photons of light strike an emulsion crystal, one or more electrons is released, some of which are attracted to a sensitivity speck and trapped by the speck. A negative charge results from the trapped electron. This change attracts a positively charged silver ion to the speck, where it combines with the electron to neutralize the charge and form a silver atom. As a given sensitivity speck attracts more electrons and ions in sequence, more atoms form and a speck of metallic silver is formed which grows in size and stability. When stable enough to not decompose before processing, and of sufficient size to be developable, it is said to be a latent-image speck. It is believed that from three to twenty silver atoms are sufficient to form a developable latent-image speck, depending on the type of emulsion.

If exposure is continued long enough with a suitable emulsion, silver will continue to be produced by the exposure action alone, with the result that the image becomes visible. This mechanism of printing out the image requires such long exposures that it is not practical for camera use and is inconvenient for most printing. In addition, the contrast range and image color of printing-out emulsions are quite limited by modern standards.

The conventional photographic process depends on the fact that a very brief exposure produces a latent image strong enough to be stable in the crystals for a long period of time and capable of being developed into a visible image by chemical action. Each sensitivity speck that has collected enough silver atoms to become a latent-image speck acts as a catalytic point, or development center, at which the chemical reaction begins. Developers are sources of electrons that take the place of the exposure electrons in converting silver ions to silver atoms. Development continues the process of changing exposed halide crystals to atoms of metallic silver that form the grains that make up the visible image, while at the same time leaving the unexposed crystals undeveloped.

With ordinary emulsions, the latent image is formed primarily at surface sensitivity specks that are readily accessible to the developer diffusing through the emulsion. Kodak instant print films have a unique emulsion that traps the latent image at sensitivity specks within the affected crystals, not at the surface. Development then reduces the unexposed rather than the exposed crystals, producing a positive instead of a negative image. (*See:* DIFFUSION TRANSFER PROCESS.)

Factors Affecting the Latent Image

The strength or development potential of the latent image is affected significantly by emulsion sensitivity, exposure intensity, and the interval between exposure and development.

Silver halide crystals are inherently sensitive to ultraviolet and blue wavelengths. Sensitizing dyes added during manufacture extend the sensitivity to the green, red, and infrared wavelengths. Thus a small amount of multiple-wavelength energy such as white light can produce as strong a latent image as a much greater amount of a single band of wavelengths. Crystal size, controlled during the ripening process in emulsion manufacture, affects overall sensitivity. The larger a crystal is, the more responsive it will be to even small amounts of whatever wavelengths it is sensitive to. Chemical sensitizers, such as gold salts, can be added to increase the sensitivity still further.

The number and size of latent-image specks formed depends upon the total exposure, but equal exposures can produce different results. A brief exposure to high-intensity light will produce many small latent-image specks, while an equivalent long exposure to a much less intense light will produce a few large specks. The first stages of exposure are critical; very slight exposure can produce a stable speck condition that is nevertheless undevelopable. This is largely the cause of underexposure known as the reciprocity effect—although one exposure is mathematically equivalent to another, not enough crystals are raised to a developable level so that equivalent densities will be produced by processing.

When silver ions form silver atoms in the latent image, their associated halogen ions are released. The gelatin of the emulsion absorbs the halogen, but its capacity is limited. Unabsorbed halogen will tend to recombine with silver ions, especially those that are weakly held in minimally exposed crystals. This action can destroy a significant number of latent-image specks. Printing-out emulsions have added halogen collectors to overcome this problem, but developing-out emulsions do not. Therefore, it is advisable to process an exposed emulsion as soon as possible after exposure, before free halogen has an opportunity to degrade the latent image. The effect is negligible with black-and-white emulsions that have received full exposure to normal light intensities, but it may be significant for exposures made under minimal conditions.

Color emulsions are much more likely to show effects of latent image change resulting from delayed processing. This is because there are three distinct latent images—one in each color-sensitive emulsion layer—that do not have equal stability. Even a very small change in one latent image will cause noticeable color shifts in the processed image. Storing an exposed emulsion under refrigeration or freezing it will minimize or virtually halt latent-image deterioration if processing must be delayed. The emulsion must be sealed against moisture loss and must be properly thawed or warmed to avoid condensation effects before it can be processed.

Technical Explanation

Film and paper emulsions form latent images in the same way. A more technical explanation of the process than that given in the preceding discussion is as follows.

The first step in the formation of latent image is the absorption of a photon (quantum) of radiant energy. The effect of this absorption is to raise an electron, or photoelectron, from the valence band of the microcrystal to the conduction band. Assuming the silver halide grain was electrically neutral before absorption of a photon, elevation of an electron to the conduction band must simultaneously produce a corresponding positively charged entity—a positive hole. Both the photoelectron and the positive hole have mobility. The positive hole, in effect, moves from place to place within the crystal lattice as an electron associated with one released halide ion drops into a neighboring hole, simultaneously creating the positive hole at a new lattice location. If the mobile electron and the hole encounter each other, they may recombine with the release of energy. Where recombination occurs, no lasting photo effect takes place. The result is the same as though the incident photon had never been absorbed.

The probability is high that recombination will occur unless alternate routes for consuming the mobile species are provided. A photoelectron may be localized by traps—traces of chemical impurities or structural defects at the surface of a crystal or within its crystal lattice. Once such an electron has been immobilized at a trap, or sensitivity center, a mobile interstitial silver ion may diffuse to the photoelectron and neutralize it with the accompanying formation of a single, quasi-stable silver atom. Such a silver atom constitutes an area of high chemical activity, and additional photoelectrons find their way to the sensitivity center. Subsequent migrations of mobile silver ions gradually form a silver speck of increasing size and stability.

The mobility of positive holes must also be considered at the same time. A hole can migrate to an internal trap or to the grain surface where it may either unite with another positive hole to form a halide molecule or, more likely, react with the surrounding gelatin. The positive hole must be consumed because it is an oxidizing agent that is capable of destroying the photo-produced silver specks.

From this brief overview of the primary photographic process, it is clear that a sequence of events must take place before a silver halide grain is rendered developable. Mobilities of the component parts differ. Photoelectrons have the greatest mobility, followed by positive holes, and then interstitial silver ions. These differences in mobility contribute to the probabilistic nature of latent-image formation. By exercising some control over mobility rates and other variables, the manufacturer is able to design emulsions to perform optimally under certain conditions of exposure and development. Many constraints are imposed, however, in order to produce products that remain stable under conditions of normal storage and use. Certain post-manufacturing methods for altering speed characteristics work because they provide a more favorable, though temporary, environment in which the complex mechanisms of latent-image formation can proceed.

• *See also:* CHEMISTRY OF PHOTOGRAPHY; COLOR FILMS; DEVELOPMENT; DIFFUSION TRANSFER PROCESS; EMULSIONS; EXPOSURE; RECIPROCITY EFFECT.

Latitude

Exposure Latitude

Exposure latitude is generally thought of as the ability of a film to be either underexposed or overexposed and still produce usable negatives. In the early days of photography, when it was difficult to estimate exposures exactly (there were no meters to measure light), and when the characteristic curves of film and plate emulsions shouldered off fairly quickly, latitude was a critically important factor.

Today, with exposure meters that permit the photographer to accurately measure the subject luminance, with film speeds measured by the manufacturer, and with the very wide latitude of most continuous-tone black-and-white films, latitude does not present a serious problem to the photographer.

However, there are a number of factors that influence negative quality—density contrast, graininess, definition, tone-reproduction characteristics, and so on—and exposure has an effect on them all.

Color-negative films have about the same latitude as black-and white films. Color reversal film has a latitude of about plus or minus half an *f*-stop.

(Above right) This subject has a fairly short brightness range. It can be given more than the normal exposure without making the highlights too dense. There is considerable exposure latitude with normal-contrast film. (Right) Because of the long brightness range of this subject, the negative requires careful development to avoid losing highlight detail. There is limited latitude for exposure.

Most films have very little latitude on the underexposure side, about one stop maximum. However, *from the tone reproduction standpoint only,* there are many stops of overexposure latitude built into Kodak films made for general-purpose photography. When developed to an 0.40–0.56 contrast-index range, which covers common practice, these films have as many as 10 stops beyond the diffuse highlight region where the straight-line portion of the curve continues without forming a shoulder.

However, since the density increases in proportion to the amount of overexposure, the practical disadvantages of long printing exposure times and the quality losses of definition and increase in graininess become factors. The photographer is wise not to use any more of the overexposure latitude than necessary to obtain adequate shadow detail. Three stops is considered a practical limit.

When the subject luminance ratio is less than that of a full-scale subject, as happens on overcast days, for example, the exposure latitude increases. On the other hand, with high-luminance-ratio subjects, the exposure latitude decreases. With long-scale subjects, exposure should be calculated by the shadow-reading method to obtain adequate shadow detail. If the contrast-control method described in the article CONTRAST is used in processing, the density range will be held to near that of a normal negative, and the quality losses previously described will be kept to a minimum.

The practicing photographer who exposes color-transparency materials necessarily learns to control exposures to a fraction of a stop for maximum quality. This same care applied to black-and-white work will also result in negatives that will print with maximum quality.

Development Latitude

Black-and-white photographic papers that do not change appreciably in contrast and image tone with reasonable variations in development are said to have good development latitude. However, for best quality, the developing time should be as near as possible to that recommended for the paper.

Black-and-white films, on the other hand, have a moderate developing latitude. The amount of development is used as a control of density range. If a film receives somewhat more or less development than intended, the negatives can usually be printed using papers of lower or higher contrast grade.
• *See also:* CONTRAST; CONTRAST INDEX; EXPOSURE.

Lea, Matthew Carey

(1823–1897)
American chemist and photographic researcher

Lea was a pioneer in latent-image research, and also of development theory. He is said to have originated the dye-mordant process of color toning of photographic images (circa 1865). Lea was a strong believer in the sub-halide theory of the latent image, and carried out extensive researches to produce and identify such silver compounds, which he called "photohalides." He was also the discoverer of the ferrous oxalate developer; because of its freedom from stain, this developer was extensively used in researches on sensitometry by Hurter and Driffield, and later by Sheppard and Mees. Similar developers using other salts of iron, such as ferrous succinate, were considered by Lea, but did not come into practical use. Lea also worked on the theory of darkroom safelights, and showed that a green safelight would be preferable to the red ones then in use because of the higher visibility in green light, and because he claimed it tended to preserve the eyesight of the user. Although he made this suggestion before the invention of orthochromatic and panchromatic emulsions, his theory is applied today in the filter recommended for use with panchromatic films.

Another Carey Lea invention that has been invaluable in color photography is the colloidal silver filter. He discovered that colloidal silver (microscopically fine particles) suspended in gelatin acts like a filter. The size and number of particles determine the filter color. A yellow Carey Lea filter layer is coated under the blue-sensitive layer and over the green- and red-sensitive layers of color films. It filters out the blue light to which the bottom layers are also sensitive, recording only the green and red images. Being silver, the filter particles are removed in the bleach and fix steps of the color process, leaving clear gelatin, which does not interfere with the color image.

Legal Aspects of Photography

Presented here is a brief summary of laws relating to photography for both the professional and the amateur photographer. This section is a necessarily brief treatment of a complex subject. It is not a substitute for legal advice, which must come from a lawyer. For a more definitive treatise, see *Photography and the Law* (5th ed., 1977), Chernoff and Sarbin.

Introduction

Except where a statute contravenes the United States Constitution, each state has the right to decide for itself what its laws will be. As a result, what is legal in one jurisdiction may be illegal in another. Therefore, no article that attempts to inform the photographer as to the law covering his or her profession or hobby can possibly be comprehensive; this can only be done if separate articles are written for each state.

The following information is primarily a statement of general principles. When faced with a photo-legal problem of importance, you would do well to consult an attorney within your own state borders to establish exactly what the rulings in such jurisdiction have been in the past.

In this summary, special emphasis has been placed upon the laws of the State of New York, which appear to be followed by a majority of the other states.

It must also be borne in mind by the reader that the photographer is an individual, subject to the same laws that govern persons in other professions or in other hobbies. All laws apply equally to the photographer. This article deals primarily with those statutes and legal decisions that have particular interest or direct relevancy to photography, even where the law involved is of general application.

The Photographer—Definition

It is generally accepted that the photographer is an artist, not a mechanic. The problem arose in two states in entirely different ways.

In Louisiana, a certain tax was imposed, but the State Constitution had specifically exempted all persons engaged in mechanical pursuits from the payment of such tax. The question was raised, therefore, whether or not the photographer was a mechanic who might claim exemption. The Court stated:

Certainly in both painters and photographers, the hand and the sense of sight are controlled by an unusual exertion of a superior intellect which, to direct and accomplish properly, must be distinguished and actuated by rare knowledge, ability and practice not found in or acquired by first comers. . . . It strikes common sense that the defendant is not an automaton but one who, practicing a science or a liberal art, is a scientist or an artist although of an inferior grade. (City of New Orleans v. Robira, 42 La. Ann. 1098)

Therefore, the court concluded that the photographer could not claim the mechanic's exemption.

In New York, the question came up whether or not a photographic studio need comply with factory regulations. The court stated:

We are of the opinion that ordinary photography, as here described, may not be said to be manufacturing. We may take judicial notice that it is merely the production, by the chemical action of light, of objects upon film, imposed upon glass, metal, celluloid or other suitable material, and the reproduction of such objects by further light action by means of the negative placed between the light and paper, or other substance, also sensitized to the chemical action of light. Such process is in no way the making or manufacturing. . . . (People v. Cross and Brown Co., 232 A.D. 587)

Licenses

The license problem is one of particular interest to all photographers, especially to the amateur who finds his or her activity somewhat curtailed because of local ordinances or state regulations that may apply to the infrequent sale of a print. On the whole, it may be safely said that licensing provisions apply to the professional photographer and do not cover one who finds an occasional opportunity to sell a picture.

Where the Photograph Is Taken

The Studio. Generally speaking, the photographic studio is a place of business and subject to the same regulations that affect other industries, despite the fact that the photographer per se is not considered a manufacturer (People v. Cross and Brown Co., see above).

Negligence in the Studio. It is not surprising, therefore, that the general rules of negligence should apply to photographic studios, which must be maintained just as safely as any other business establishment. By no stretch of the imagination can the photographer be exempt from providing reasonably safe quarters for business invitees.

When, for instance, an eight-month-old infant fell from the table on which he was being photographed and was severely burned by coming into contact with exposed steampipes immediately adjacent to the table, the court ruled that such injuries should be compensated for. The decision stated:

> The owner and tenant co-operated in creating a condition that any prudent person must have known could cause injury. (R.K.O. Midwest Corp. v. Berling, 51 Ohio App. 85)

The Street. The photographer has the right, generally, to take any pictures on the byways and highways of the city or country as long as he or she does not commit a nuisance in so doing. The photographer must beware of possible local ordinances that may have been passed by a particular town, village, or city, limiting this right in certain cases. It is impossible to cover here the innumerable communities that may have passed such local regulations.

One of the problems with street pictures occurs when the person whose picture is being taken objects and creates a scene, or attempts to assault the photographer.

As far back as 1939, New York State enacted a statute designed to protect the apparatus and equipment of the news photographer. This law declares that one who willfully injures such apparatus is guilty of criminal assault. This is separate from bodily assault on the photographer, which comes under the general category of assault and has always been a crime.

Theaters, Museums, or Other Public Places. These types of places are free to set up their own rules and generally do so. Some museums permit photographic equipment, yet ban tripods and flash. Most theaters, music halls, opera houses, and concert halls prohibit the taking of pictures during a performance. Zoos generally prohibit the use of flash because of its tendency to scare the animals. Always find out in advance what the restrictions are if you have any intentions of taking pictures.

The Courtroom. The new Canon 3, a rule promulgated by the American Bar Association, has somewhat relaxed the former rule forbidding absolutely the taking of photographs in the courtroom. A judge may now permit the taking of photographs under the following conditions:

1. The means of taking the pictures will not distract participants in a case or impair the dignity of the proceedings.
2. The parties have consented.
3. The pictures will not be shown until the case is concluded and all appeals are exhausted.
4. The reproduction will be exhibited only for instructional purposes in educational institutions.

Aside from the possibility of an occasional local ordinance, the photographer's right to take pictures on public streets is clear so long as he does not interfere with traffic or create a nuisance. Photo by B. Sastre.

What May Be Photographed

Generally, anything may be photographed, except when specifically prohibited by law. For example, there are restrictions against photographing money, or other obligations of the United States, and postage stamps. The law provides that black-and-white photos may be taken "for philatelic, numismatic, educational, historical, or newsworthy purposes." However, the use of such pictures for advertising (except by legitimate advertising of qualified numismatic or philatelic dealers) is prohibited. Photographing a portion of an obligation or security of the United States is subject to the same restrictions as photographing the whole. The federal law places the same restrictions on pictures of postage stamps as on money.

The federal government forbids the photographing of military and naval installations, and this power may be extended in time of war to cover anything deemed to contain vital information, the secrecy of which must be safeguarded in the interest of national defense. Certificates of citizenship may not be photographed. Bills of lading are subject to restrictions since they could easily be offered as genuine documents. Photographing a bill of lading with intent to defraud is a crime.

Right of Privacy

Essentially, the law of privacy prohibits the use of a photograph of any living person for advertising or trade purposes without that person's written consent. The New York statute, which is the model for similar statutes in several other states, provides that violation of this law is a criminal offense. Virtually everywhere, the wrongdoer can be sued for damages and the use of the photograph enjoined. However, the development of the right of privacy in this country has largely been by rule of court rather than by statute. At present the right of privacy has been held by the courts to exist in the following states:

Alabama	Kentucky
Arizona	Louisiana
Arkansas	Michigan
California	Missouri
Colorado	Montana
Connecticut	New Jersey
Delaware	New York
District of Columbia	North Carolina
Florida	Ohio
Georgia	Oregon
Idaho	Pennsylvania
Illinois	South Carolina
Indiana	South Dakota
Iowa	West Virginia
Kansas	

Still other states have followed the lead of New York in enacting statutes protecting the right of privacy. Such legislation has been enacted in Utah, Virginia, Wisconsin, Oklahoma, and Nebraska, although the prohibition of the Wisconsin statute applies to the publication (except as may be necessary in the institution or prosecution of a criminal proceeding) of the name of a woman who may have been raped or subjected to criminal assault. The Utah and Virginia statutes essentially follow the New York statute.

When photographing money, securities, and postage stamps, there are certain restrictions that should be studied carefully. In general, the idea is to avoid any possibility of producing what might be considered a true facsimile of the original. Photo by B. Sastre.

Legal Aspects of Photography

Ownership of Photographs

One of the earliest principles established by a court in the field of photography was that the relationship between a photographer and his (paying) customer is that of employer and employee. In 1913, a New York court ruled:

> It is settled law that the ordinary contract between a photographer and his customer is a contract of employment. The conception as well as the production of the photograph is work done for the customers, and they, not their employee, are the exclusive owners of all proprietary rights.

It is the law today that in the absence of an agreement to the contrary, in the usual customer-photographer relationship, ownership of the picture is vested in the customer. Nevertheless, the photographer has the right to retain the negatives in the absence of an agreement to the contrary. But he or she has no right to use them without the customer's permission. However, when pictures are taken on the photographer's own initiative (without his or her being hired to do so), all rights in the photographs belong to the photographer.

Loss or Damage to Film

Most camera stores and film processors give the photographer a receipt for the film when it is delivered for developing. These receipts invariably contain a legend limiting the processor's liability to the cost of replacing the film. Normally, a person who signs a contract is bound by its terms in the absence of fraud. While a receipt is not a contract in the sense that the photographer has signed anything, the limitation is generally binding unless the photographer can convince a court that he was unaware of the limitation, which is an extremely difficult burden. When the limitation is printed on the package in which the film is sold and the price includes processing, the photographer will probably be bound by the limitation as long as it is clearly written (Willard Van Dyke Productions, Inc. v. Eastman Kodak Company, 12 N.Y. 2d 301).

Obscenity

The laws and postal regulations that render "obscene" pictures unmailable still exist. To say to the photographer that "anything goes" is far from accurate; and photographers must be warned that in spite of the vast liberalization of the law regarding obscene pictures, hard-core pornography is still not tolerated.

Libel by Photograph

A libel, as defined by the law dictionaries, is that which is written or printed, and published, which injures the reputation of another by bringing him into contempt, ridicule, or hatred. Applying the basic principles of libel to photography, the courts have currently stated that a person may be held up as an object of ridicule, contempt, or hatred by means of a picture, just as by means of words.

In the definition of the word "libel," publication is required. This does not mean that only pictures appearing in magazines or newspapers can be libelous. The term "publication" is far broader than this and includes all types of display. Thus, if a photographer places a picture in a showcase in front of his or her studio, or shows the picture to people other than the subject, that photographer has "published" that print for the purposes of the law of libel. Mere possession of a print is not publication. The distinction is important.

Photographs as Evidence

There are three principal ways of using photographs as evidence:

1. As a means of identifying an individual through a photograph made at some previous time;
2. As a method of discovering, recording, or preserving evidence relating to an accident or crime;
3. In the courtroom, as a means of presenting to the jurors a visual impression of the pertinent elements of a crime.

In general, photographs, when shown to be a correct resemblance of the person or thing represented, are competent as evidence, and will be so accepted.

• *See also:* AGENCIES, PICTURE; BUSINESS METHODS IN PHOTOGRAPHY; COPYRIGHT: CRIME PHOTOGRAPHY; EVIDENCE PHOTOGRAPHY; MODEL RELEASE; RIGHTS.

Lens Converters

A camera lens (the "prime" lens) may be converted to a different focal length by adding certain kinds of lenses in front of it or behind it. There are three kinds of such lens attachments or converters: (1) supplementary lenses, (2) afocal attachments, and (3) lens extenders. Attachments or converters are often used to avoid the expense of additional complete lenses; however, they almost invariably reduce image quality, often to a considerable extent, and they may restrict the focusing range and change the *f*-stop values of the prime lens.

Supplementary Lenses

A supplementary lens is a single element—or, for better correction, a cemented pair of elements—that is usually placed in front of, and as close as possible to, the prime lens. A positive (converging) supplementary lens shortens the effective focal length of the prime lens. On a bellows camera, the addition of a positive supplementary lens can be used to obtain a wider angle of view if the bellows can be compressed enough to shorten the lens-to-film distance to the new focal length; infinity focusing will then be achieved if the field coverage of the original lens is greater than that required for the format. On rigid-body and other cameras in which the lens-to-film distance cannot be changed, infinity focusing is not possible, but closer-than-normal focusing is possible (this same capability is also available with a bellows-type camera). Since closer focusing produces larger images, positive supplementary lenses are used as close-up attachments.

When a supplementary lens is used to shorten the focal length of a view-camera lens, the *f*-number markings are no longer accurate when photographing distant subjects. When used to focus at close distances, provided that the original lens is in the infinity position, the *f*-numbers are valid. The increase in relative aperture resulting from the supplementary lens equals the exposure correction necessary for close focusing. (*See:* CLOSE-UP PHOTOGRAPHY.)

A negative (diverging) supplementary lens lengthens the effective focal length of the prime lens, giving a long-focus or telephoto effect. It must be possible to extend the lens-to-film distance to the new focal length in order to achieve infinity focusing; an even farther extension is necessary to focus on close objects. An accessory bellows unit permits this adjustment with many rigid-body cameras. Because the focal length is longer, the marked *f*-numbers are no longer accurate. While both positive and negative supplementary lenses are used on the *front* of the camera lens, there are some cases when placing the supplemental lens on the *back* of the lens provides less image deterioration, a flatter field, or wider field coverage.

(Top) Close-up lenses such as these are designed for attachment to regular lenses to permit focusing at close-up distances. Lenses at center and right may be used in combination to allow work as close as 9 inches from the subject. Lens at left is for use on telephoto lenses. (Bottom) Extension tubes increase magnification of the subject by lengthening the lens-to-film distance. Shown here are 14 mm, 21 mm, and 28 mm lengths; used singly or in various combinations, they will give magnification of approximately 0.27× to 1.35× with a standard 50 mm lens. Photos courtesy Minolta Corp.

For methods of determining combined focal length, *f*-stop values, and other factors with positive and negative elements, see the article SUPPLEMENTARY LENSES.

Afocal Attachments

An afocal lens is essentially a simple telescope system focused at infinity that requires the addition of a converging lens behind its rear element or group of elements to produce a focused, real image (*afocal* means without focus). In the case of a telescope, monocular or binocular, the viewer's eye is the converging lens; in photographic applications the camera lens serves that function.

When an afocal attachment is composed of a positive element in front of a negative element, it has a telephoto effect; the opposite arrangement produces a wide-angle effect. Afocal attachments have the advantage of not requiring increased (for telephoto) or decreased (for wide-angle) lens-to-film distances. With a fundamental afocal system, the camera lens is left at its infinity focus position (shortest lens-to-film distance), and focusing is achieved by varying the distance between the front and rear afocal elements. However, such simple systems introduce significant aberrations and typically require apertures of *f*/11 or *f*/16 to obtain images of acceptable quality (not of the quality produced by the prime lens alone).

Aberrations can be greatly reduced when the afocal attachment is specifically designed for a particular prime lens. In that case the normal focusing movement of the prime lens is generally used, while the afocal attachment provides the same degree of magnification or reduction (wide-angle effect) throughout the normal focusing range. This approach has been used to create telephoto and wide-angle attachments for twin-lens reflex cameras (for example, the Mutar attachments for Rolleiflex cameras) and for simple, fixed-lens movie cameras.

Today, afocal attachments are relatively rare for still cameras except in the case of fisheye attachments, in which little or no attempt is made to correct extreme wide-angle curvilinear distortion. Almost all small-format movie cameras are now equipped with zoom lenses, which achieve the effects of both types of afocal attachments in a single lens in a much more convenient and flexible way.

Lens Extenders

A lens extender is a diverging lens system placed between the prime lens and the film plane to form a larger image without significantly changing the lens-to-subject distance. That is, the extender increases the effective focal length of the prime lens in order to achieve increased magnification. These so-called tele-extenders are almost exclusively manufactured for use with single-lens reflex 35 mm cameras, in powers that increase the prime-lens focal length by 2×, 3×, or 4×. There are theoretical limits to the increase in focal length, but the degree of correction needed increases as the magnification increases.

An extender produces better results in terms of image quality with a long-, rather than a normal-focal-length prime lens. Thus, a 2× or 3× increase quickly reaches the practical limit of handheld operation with 35 mm cameras. The effective aperture of each numbered *f*-stop grows significantly smaller as the focal length increases; this limits the number of apertures at which a shutter speed suitable for handheld operation can be used under normal illumination, and makes tripod operation essential at any speed under lower illumination.

Lens extenders will allow a larger image without significantly changing the lens-to-subject distance. This 2× converter will double the prime-lens focal length. Photo courtesy Minolta Corp.

The exposure adjustment required with a lens extender can be determined in two ways:

1. The exposure increase is equal to the square of the telephoto power of the extender—a $2\times$ extender requires $2^2 =$ 4 times more exposure; a $3\times$ extender requires 9 times more exposure; and a $4\times$ extender requires 16 times more exposure.
2. The actual value of a marked f-stop on the prime lens equals the f-number multiplied by the extender power. An $f/8$ lens setting $= f/16$ with a $2\times$ extender, $f/24$ with a $3\times$ extender, and $f/32$ with a $4\times$ extender.

Other Converters

Some lens converters do not change lens focal length, but do alter the linear proportions of the image; such attachments are used for wide-screen projection and extreme reductions. For further information on this subject, see the articles ANAMORPHIC SYSTEMS and MICROPHOTOGRAPHY.

• *See also:* BINOCULARS, PHOTOGRAPHING THROUGH; CLOSE-UP PHOTOGRAPHY; LENSES; SUPPLEMENTARY LENSES; TELEPHOTOGRAPHY; TELESCOPES, PHOTOGRAPHING THROUGH.

  Lenses

In this article, the more complex lenses that are used in various ways in photography are discussed. A simplified look is taken at how lenses are designed and manufactured, and the history of the major families of lenses is reviewed. Included is a discussion of how camera-lens performance is evaluated, and how the results of various types of evaluation can be interpreted by the photographer. Finally, other types of lenses are discussed, including enlarging lenses, condenser lenses, and projection lenses.

The article LIGHT covers what light is, how it travels, and its various forms of behavior as it encounters objects that reflect, absorb, or transmit it. In the article OPTICS, the fundamental concepts of lenses, prisms, and mirrors are discussed; basic formulas relating to image formation are given;

and inherent imperfections in images, called aberrations, are introduced. The characteristics and manufacture of optical glass are also described.

Lens Design

The design of camera lenses is basically the process of:

1. Defining the intended use of the lens.
2. Setting performance standards on the basis of its intended use.
3. Relating potential costs of the lens to the above factors.
4. Deciding which family type of lens will best meet the user's needs.
5. Designing the lens and evaluating the design.
6. Making a sample lens to verify the design.

When a photographer buys a lens, or a camera with a lens on it, he or she has certain picture-taking needs in mind. Some of the requirements can be summarized as follows:

1. Format to be covered.
2. Angular coverage of the format (telephoto, wide angle, normal).
3. Determination of the focal length based on factors 1 and 2.
4. Lens speed (maximum opening).
5. Intended subject distance (regular lens, macro lens, enlarging lens).
6. Performance capabilities versus the cost of the lens.
7. Special requirements of the lens based on the camera (long back focus for SLR cameras, mount-size requirements to fit camera limits lens diameter, interchangeable lenses, front-element focusing).
8. Requirements for special applications (low distortion for aerial mapping, high resolving power for copying printed matter, apochromatic for three-color separation work).

When a lens is designed, these same factors must be taken into consideration. In making choices a number of trade-offs must also be made. For example, to increase field coverage to make a wide-angle lens, a lower resolving power will probably have to be accepted. To increase lens speed, larger, stronger lens elements must be used. This increases most of the aberrations. To correct these aberrations, more elements are necessary; therefore, the cost of the lens goes up. In the days before lens coating, adding elements also decreased lens transmission (lowering speed) and increased flare, so there was a limit to the number of elements that could be added. Fortunately, with single-layer and multilayer coatings, many more elements can be added; and modern manufacturing techniques permit the lens designer a wide range of design latitude without costs becoming excessive.

Performance Standards and Costs

Final-definition performance standards of lenses are measured in terms of resolving power and optical-transfer functions at various apertures at different field angles. Final-illumination values are determined by f-numbers and field-illumination curves at various f-numbers. Overall image contrast is measured in terms of percent flare (or veiling glare). The degree of color correction is determined by the amount of color fringing in the image and by the comparative sizes of different color images in color reproduction. Residual distortion is often measured visually, as to whether the lens images lines near the border as straight lines.

The lens designer works with a different set of performance standards—residual aberrations. He or she knows what the acceptable level of aberrations is that must be corrected to the specific purpose of the lens design. If designing a box camera $f/11$ lens, for example, the designer knows that the user will not expect to make mural-size enlargements from the pictures; and that if the lens will produce adequately sharp snapshots, he or she has achieved the design goal. To make the lens better would raise the camera price to a level that a potential customer would be unwilling to pay.

On the other hand, if faced with designing a lens for aerial-camera mapping, the lens designer knows the lens must have a very flat field for infinite distances, that it must have nearly zero distortion so that it images the ground accurately, that the overall definition must be high enough to resolve typical ground detail, and that it must have enough speed to allow relatively high shutter speeds to avoid blurs from camera movement. The lens designer also knows that the aerial photographer expects to pay a high price for these requirements to be fulfilled.

The designer must also know about lens-manufacturing costs. If he or she designs fewer elements, the cost may go down. However, fewer elements mean stronger curves, which are costlier to manufacture. Weaker curves can be used if high-index glass with low dispersion is also used; however, this type of glass costs more. So, in addition to the basic requirements and the performance requirements, the lens must be designed with manufacturing costs in mind as well.

Families of Lenses

Five basic families of lens designs have evolved since the invention of photography. These are shown in the accompanying illustrations in chronological order.

NOTE: In all these lens diagrams, light comes from the left, which is the front of the lens. Scale is approximate and varying.

The Single-Lens Family. First came the simple, single-lens family. This started as the biconvex "magnifying" lens long before photography was invented. It was adapted to use in the camera obscura to make a brighter image than the original pinhole.

Just a few years before cameras were made to image on sensitized materials, the single lens was bent into the positive meniscus shape to improve the image definition by reducing the effects of aberrations. The effect of stopping down to further improve the quality of the image was discovered about this time.

The last major improvement came along at just the right time for photography; this was the discovery that a meniscus lens, made of a crown-glass positive lens cemented to a negative lens made of flint glass, reduced chromatic aberration. Camera lenses of this family are used today in low-price cameras in both the single meniscus lens and achromat forms. Many of these lenses are molded of plastic to further reduce their cost. This family represents the lowest cost option for the designer.

The Symmetrical-Lens Family. The next lens-design option that developed historically was the symmetrical-lens family. Daguerreotype photog-

Single-Lens Family

Antiquity. Magnifiers. Camera obscura.

1812—Wollaston rear-meniscus lens. Improved sharpness, flatter field for camera obscura. First camera lens.

Modern front-meniscus lens. Inexpensive, short back focus lens makes smaller camera. Curved field.

1829—Chevalier achromatized-meniscus lens. Color-corrected for camera obscura and early cameras. Used today in inexpensive cameras.

raphy was popular right from the start, but it had one weakness: it required hours of exposure time. One way to shorten exposure was to make faster lenses. When single lenses are made faster than about $f/11$, the aberrations become so severe that the lens is not usable for most purposes.

There was a great need to have a fast lens for making pictures of people. In 1840, Petzval designed an almost symmetrical lens that went a long way toward solving the portrait problem. His lens was an $f/3.6$ lens, which was from 12 to 20 times as fast as the single lenses then in use.

A perfectly symmetrical lens has identical front and back elements facing in opposite directions, with the diaphragm spaced evenly between them. Usually the outer surfaces of the lens are convex curves outward and concave curves inward toward the diaphragm. Petzval's lens was not quite symmetrical, but it started the trend toward perfectly symmetrical lenses and it was a very useful lens.

Several characteristics of the Petzval portrait lens should be noted. At its widest opening it had residual aberrations that reduced sharpness in the field, but it was quite well corrected near the axis. This was found to give a very acceptable rendition for close-up portraits. Because of the aberrations (severe field curvature and astigmatism), these lenses worked best when used as narrow-angle lenses, with larger-than-normal focal lengths for the size of the format. For portraits, this was found to be an advantage for two reasons. The perspective of a face appears most natural in portraits when the picture is taken from a distance of about 6 to 8 feet. A lens with a focal length about twice that of a normal lens covers the head and shoulders of a portrait subject conveniently from this distance. A normal lens covers the same area from about 3 feet, causing apparent distortion of the face. (*See:* PERSPECTIVE.)

The second important aspect of the Petzval lens was that it was *designed*. Up to that time, lenses were made by trial and error, and the principles of lenses were poorly understood. Petzval was a mathematician, and he established the first principles of lens design. He discovered the relationship of the powers of the lens elements and the refractive indices of the glass from which they are made, to the field curvature of a lens. His simple calculation is still used today by lens designers.

Many symmetrical lenses were made over the following 30 or 40 years, most of them consisting of two cemented achromats. One of these was the Rapid Rectilinear lens design, which was fairly well corrected up to $f/8$. This was a very popular lens, and was used on moderate-priced cameras well into the twentieth century. However, all such lenses suffered from uncorrectable astigmatism, which limited their speed and definition.

Abbe, in Germany, felt that lens performance could be improved if there were optical glasses available with higher indexes of refraction and lower dispersion. In 1880, he and Schott introduced new barium glasses that had these charac-

Symmetrical-Lens Family

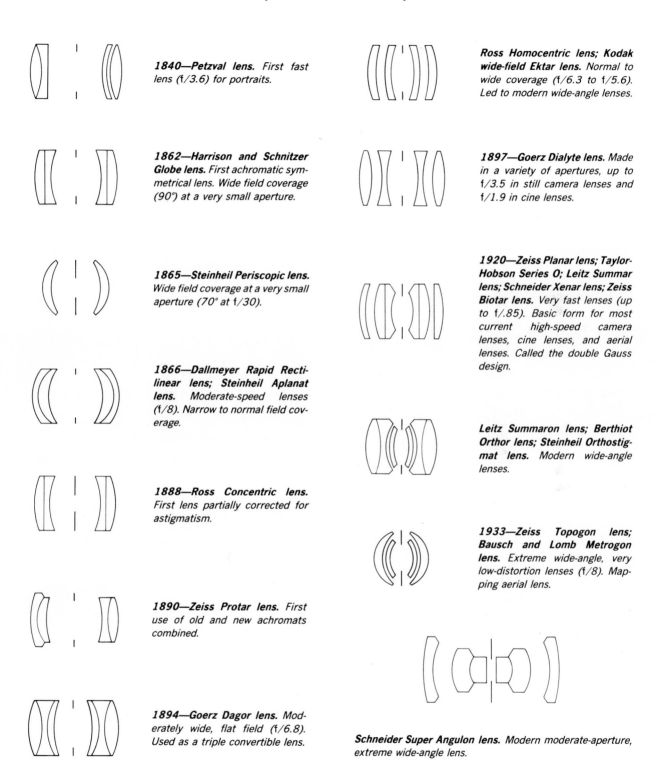

1840—Petzval lens. *First fast lens (f/3.6) for portraits.*

1862—Harrison and Schnitzer Globe lens. *First achromatic symmetrical lens. Wide field coverage (90°) at a very small aperture.*

1865—Steinheil Periscopic lens. *Wide field coverage at a very small aperture (70° at f/30).*

1866—Dallmeyer Rapid Rectilinear lens; Steinheil Aplanat lens. *Moderate-speed lenses (f/8). Narrow to normal field coverage.*

1888—Ross Concentric lens. *First lens partially corrected for astigmatism.*

1890—Zeiss Protar lens. *First use of old and new achromats combined.*

1894—Goerz Dagor lens. *Moderately wide, flat field (f/6.8). Used as a triple convertible lens.*

Ross Homocentric lens; Kodak wide-field Ektar lens. *Normal to wide coverage (f/6.3 to f/5.6). Led to modern wide-angle lenses.*

1897—Goerz Dialyte lens. *Made in a variety of apertures, up to f/3.5 in still camera lenses and f/1.9 in cine lenses.*

1920—Zeiss Planar lens; Taylor-Hobson Series 0; Leitz Summar lens; Schneider Xenar lens; Zeiss Biotar lens. *Very fast lenses (up to f/.85). Basic form for most current high-speed camera lenses, cine lenses, and aerial lenses. Called the double Gauss design.*

Leitz Summaron lens; Berthiot Orthor lens; Steinheil Orthostigmat lens. *Modern wide-angle lenses.*

1933—Zeiss Topogon lens; Bausch and Lomb Metrogon lens. *Extreme wide-angle, very low-distortion lenses (f/8). Mapping aerial lens.*

Schneider Super Angulon lens. *Modern moderate-aperture, extreme wide-angle lens.*

teristics. That same year, the Ross concentric lens was brought out, using the new glasses that had improved astigmatic correction. Two years later the Zeiss Protar lens was introduced. This design combined elements of the old-type optical glass with elements of the new barium glasses, and was well corrected for astigmatism. It had a maximum aperture of $f/7.5$.

Further improvements in image quality resulted from the use of triplet achromats paired to form symmetrical lenses, such as the Goerz Dagor. The two achromats had different focal lengths, each quite well corrected as a meniscus achromat. This lens was a convertible lens; with both achromats in the lens barrel, it had maximum aperture ($f/6.8$) and a relatively short focal length. A current (nonconvertible) lens of double triplet construction is the Schneider Angulon lens, a well-corrected, $f/6.8$ lens that covers from 80 to 105 degrees wide open at smaller apertures. By removing either of the achromats, the focal length is increased, but the maximum aperture is reduced. In this way, the convertible lens serves as three lenses, each of a different focal length.

Two adaptions of the double achromat were made in which the achromats were separated into separate lens elements. These were the Ross Homocentric and the Goerz Dialyte. The two negative elements in the Ross lens were meniscus-shaped, which led to wide-field coverage. A later adaptation was the Zeiss Topogon, which covered a 90-degree field at $f/8$, and was widely used as a mapping aerial lens because of very low distortion. The Kodak wide-field Ektar lenses in the 1940's were of this type. They had a maximum aperture of $f/6.3$, but did not cover as wide a field.

In another adaptation of the symmetrical-lens family, the negative meniscus lenses are placed concentrically on the outside, with center positive cemented lenses. The Schneider Super Angulon lenses are examples of this construction, covering 100 degrees at a maximum aperture of $f/8$ in lenses made for 35 mm, medium-, and large-format cameras. Most of the current Kodak Coloramas are taken on color-negative roll film with a Linhof camera fitted with a Super Angulon lens. The film, with a format size of $2\frac{1}{4}'' \times 6\frac{3}{4}''$, is enlarged to $18' \times 60'$, attesting to the excellent correction of aberrations in this lens. By dividing the negative

lenses into cements and adding another element to the inside rear positive cemented lens, making a triplet, Schneider has produced a very well-corrected extreme wide-angle lens for non-reflex-type 35 mm cameras. It has a maximum aperture of $f/4$. However, it does not have a long enough back focus to clear the mirror in an SLR camera.

The Dialyte design also led in another direction to a lens called the double Gauss lens. The two negative meniscus lenses were divided into cements. This type, the first example of which was the Zeiss Planar (1920), has been and is today widely used as a fast, well-corrected lens. Most high-speed normal lenses for 35 mm cameras are of this type. These types of lenses have been made to f-values below one, but typical maximum apertures run from $f/2$ to $f/1.2$, with $f/1.4$ being popular. In some of the better-corrected lenses, one or the other of the crown lenses or both are also separated into cements. In their original uncoated form, these lenses suffered badly from flare, but with the advent of coating in the 1940's, flare ceased to be a problem.

The Triplet-Lens Family. In 1893, Taylor designed the first triplet lens, which was manufactured by the Cooke Company in England. This was the first lens in which the aberrations were corrected for the lens as a whole, rather than each half being corrected, as in the previous symmetrical lenses.

Taylor took the basic achromat and corrected the field curvature by using a negative and positive lens of equal powers. He separated them to give the lens positive power. Then he divided the positive element into two lenses; one in front of and one behind the negative lens to correct distortion. By careful selection of the radii of curvature of the lenses, he corrected for spherical aberration and coma. By placing the diaphragm directly behind the negative element, he minimized astigmatism. Cooke's original lens covered 40 degrees at an aperture of $f/3$. This field was later widened to 55 degrees (normal) at an aperture of $f/4.5$

Many triplet lenses have been made because they are relatively low in cost to manufacture, but they give good images that are well corrected for aberrations. Most of the medium-priced normal camera lenses manufactured from the 1920's to the present have been of this type.

The next design change in the triplet family came in 1902 when Zeiss brought out the Tessar lens. In this lens, the back positive element was changed from a single lens to a two-element cement. This type of lens has been the most popular medium-speed lens of this century. The corrections are better than in a triplet, and the fine details are imaged with excellent contrast. With the use of high-index, rare-earth optical glass, excellent Tessar-type lenses have been made in recent years with lens openings up to $f/2.8$.

A further improvement came with the making of the front-positive element into a doublet. The Voigtländer Heliar and Dallmeyer Pentac lenses, made as early as 1907, were of this type, as was the later, excellent $f/3.5$ lens on the Kodak Medalist camera. The Zeiss Sonnar $f/2$ lens divided the negative lens into three elements: a single front lens, and a two-element rear positive lens. Zeiss further opened the aperture up to $f/1.5$ by making the back positive lens of three elements.

The Fujinon is a modern high-speed ($f/1.2$) normal-focal-length lens for 35 mm cameras designed by Fuji of Japan. The front element is a single crown, the negative lens is a three-element cement, and the rear positive lens consists of a three-element cement plus a free positive lens. In fact, this lens has certain characteristics of both symmetrical and triplet ancestry.

One of the advantages of the triplet over the years has been that it basically contains only six glass-air surfaces. This created a lower level of flare in triplets than in the symmetrical lenses with eight glass-air surfaces. This was one of the reasons for the triplet's popularity both with designers and users. With the advent of coating, this advantage became less important.

Telephoto Lenses. In order to provide a larger image size on the same camera format, a longer focal-length lens is needed. The symmetrical and triplet designs can readily be made in longer focal lengths; however, the rear nodal point of such lenses is within the lens thickness, so that the longer focal lengths require that the lenses be mounted at a considerable distance from the film. In many cases, this creates a camera-lens combination that is difficult to handle. What is needed is a lens that has a long equivalent focus with a short back focus—a lens whose rear nodal point is

Triplet-Lens Family

1893—Cooke Triplet lens. First three-element lens corrected for astigmatism. Still used extensively in moderate-priced cameras.

1902—Zeiss Tessar lens. Originally f/5.5, the aperture has been raised as high as f/2.5. High-quality lens, currently made in many forms (up to 8″ × 10″ format).

Voigtländer Heliar lens; Dallmeyer Pentac lens; Kodak Ektar lens. This type adds further correction to Tessar-type lens.

Zeiss Sonnar lens. Covers normal field at high apertures (up to f/1.5).

Front positive   Central negative   Rear positive

Modern telephoto to wide-angle zoom lens. With many of today's complex lenses, the basic type may appear to have more than one ancestor. This lens seems to be an expanded triplet. Note that the same lens is also listed in the Telephoto Afocal Converter column.

located in front of the lens itself. The true telephoto lens is just that.

In the seventeenth century, the Galilean telescope was discovered. It consisted of a front positive lens with a rear negative lens used as an eyepiece. The rear lens was placed so that the image light being emitted was essentially parallel. By placing the eye in this light, the image being formed by the long-focal-length positive element could easily be seen.

In 1891 a principle similar to that of the Galilean telescope was used in designing a telephoto lens—the Dallmeyer Aldon. It had a front positive achromat, with a rear air-spaced, triple-element negative lens. The negative lens made the light from the positive lens less convergent, and therefore, the image larger. By properly controlling the positive and negative process and the space between them, the rear nodal point was actually in front of the lens. This type of lens gave the same image size as a triplet or symmetrical lens whose nodal point was the same distance from the film; but in the telephoto lens, the entire lens structure was closer to the camera than the nodal point. This made for a compact, easy-to-handle lens-camera combination, but still gave the desired large image size.

One difficulty with this asymmetrical design is that distortion is difficult to correct. Because true telephoto lenses are narrow-angle lenses, the amount of distortion left within the field is moderate. Several designs followed the Dallmeyer Aldon, still with some degree of distortion: the Bush Bistelar in 1906, which was the forerunner of many similar wide-spaced, two-cemented element designs; and the 1914 Booth Telephoto, which was the first telephoto well corrected for astigmatism. It was not until 1925 that the Lee Distortionless Telephoto Lens solved both problems. Most modern telephoto lenses are of similar construction, although those with less than 2× magnification may be of symmetrical or triplet ancestry. Longer telephoto lenses are often made as mirror lenses. (*See:* MIRROR LENSES.)

Telephoto Afocal Converters. A converter is a multiple-lens device used with a regular camera lens to change its focal length without changing its back focus. It is especially useful with cameras whose lenses are not interchangeable. Afocal

Telephoto Lenses

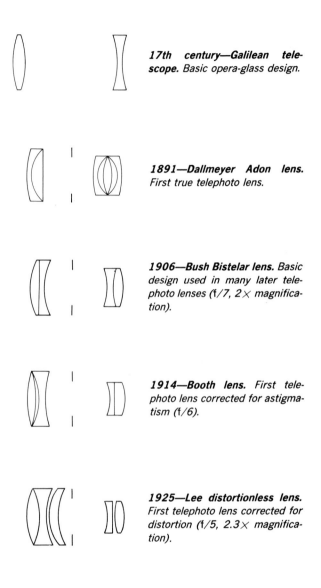

17th century—Galilean telescope. Basic opera-glass design.

1891—Dallmeyer Adon lens. First true telephoto lens.

1906—Bush Bistelar lens. Basic design used in many later telephoto lenses (f/7, 2× magnification).

1914—Booth lens. First telephoto lens corrected for astigmatism (f/6).

1925—Lee distortionless lens. First telephoto lens corrected for distortion (f/5, 2.3× magnification).

means "without forming focus," which indicates that the light rays leaving the converter and entering the camera lens are essentially parallel.

The telephoto afocal converter works just like the Galilean telescope. The positive lens converges the light to form an image; the negative lens is placed in the converging rays and has just enough power to make them parallel. The camera lens receives the parallel rays and, focused at infinity,

Telephoto Afocal Converters

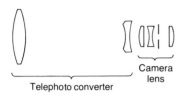

Placed in front of a camera lens focused at infinity, the converter records the image on an enlarged scale.

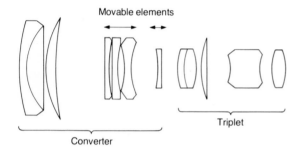

Modern telephoto-zoom lens. *Many of these lenses are based on a telephoto converter combined with a triplet or symmetrical lens, with the negative combination of the converter being movable to change focal length.*

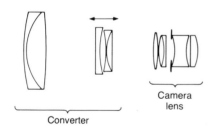

Same lens as listed in Triplet-Lens Family column. Shows how this design can be considered a converter plus a camera lens.

converges them into an image on the film. The effective focal length of the combination is longer than that of the camera lens, so that the image size is larger.

Modern afocal converters may be well-corrected in themselves and work quite well on a number of camera lenses. To provide a high level of correction, however, they must be designed to be used with a particular lens. Some converters made for high-quality twin-lens reflex cameras have had as many as five elements to provide this degree of correction. Often the converter supplied for use with the finder lens is of simpler construction.

It is usually best to stop down the lens when using a converter to minimize the effects of residual aberrations.

While regular telephoto lenses may have a magnification factor as high as 10×, converters rarely have a factor over 2×.

Wide-Angle Afocal Converters. Just as a telephoto converter is used with a normal lens to increase the image size, wide-angle afocal converters are used to decrease image size and to cover a wider field angle.

The wide-angle converter is essentially the telephoto converter reversed—the negative lens is at the front and the positive lens is at the rear. Just as in the reversed telephoto wide-angle lens, the front lens is necessarily large in size, and generally is meniscus-shaped.

Wide-angle converters can be made to work with any lens, but have the best resultant corrections when designed for use with a particular normal lens. When used on a twin-lens reflex camera, the converters are usually supplied in a pair, matched for power. The converter for the finder lens may be simpler in construction, because the same degree of aberration correction is not required.

While symmetrical wide-angle lenses and rectilinear reversed-telephoto lenses may have a magnification factor as low as 0.33×, the normal factor for converters is about 0.70×.

Reversed or Inverted Telephoto Lenses

Wide-angle lenses necessarily have a relatively short focal length. Such lenses cannot be used in single-lens reflex cameras because the lens and the mirror cannot both occupy the same space. What is needed is just the opposite of a telephoto lens. The effective focal length must be short, but the back focus must be equivalent to that of a normal-focal-length lens. The rear nodal point must be behind the rear lens. This is accomplished, optically, by reversing the telephoto lens. The inverted telephoto lens is sometimes called a retrofocus lens.

The front element of a basic reversed telephoto lens is negative. Because it must admit light from a large subject angle, it is usually negative meniscus in shape. The rear element is positive, with greater power than the negative element, and is usually quite small in diameter.

Because the inverted telephoto is so asymmetrical and covers such a wide field, it usually requires many elements to provide adequate correction, especially for barrel distortion. Retrofocus lenses can be made to form a rectilinear image (or nearly so) up to about a 100-degree field angle. They can be made to cover up to 180 degrees, but with strong distortion. Such lenses are called fisheye lenses.

Zoom Lenses

Zoom Lenses. Each lens discussed so far has a single focal length and a single magnification as manufactured. The manufacturer may use the same basic lens design in a series of lenses of different focal lengths. (The only exception is the triplet type of lens with an adjustable front air space that changes the focal length to focus the lens.)

An advanced photographer is likely to use lenses of several focal lengths—a normal-focal-length lens whose focal length approximately equals the camera-format diagonal; two wide-angle lenses: one with a magnification of about 0.50× to 0.70×, and the other, 0.30× to 0.40× for extreme wide-angle conditions. The photographer might want a moderate telephoto lens for portraits with a magnification of 1.6× to 2.0×, and longer-focal-length telephotos with magnifications from 2.7× up to as far as 10×. This makes it necessary to have, and to carry, a number of lenses.

A convenient way to limit the number of lenses required for 35 mm still cameras and motion picture cameras is to have a single lens that changes its focal length to whatever is convenient for a particular picture. Such a lens is called a

Reversed Telephoto Lenses

Reverse of the basic telephoto design; negative lens in front and positive lens in back. Because of the need to cover a wide field angle, the front lens is large and meniscus-shaped.

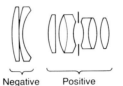

Negative   Positive

The negative part of this design is composed of two elements. The positive part is a Planar-type lens.

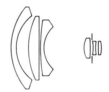

This design covers a wider field angle. Typical wide-angle lenses for 35 mm SLR cameras are 24 to 35 mm in focal length and have a maximum aperture of f/3.5 to f/2.8.

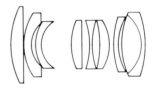

Wide-aperture, wide-angle lens (f/1.9, 75°).

Wide-angle zoom lens (f/4, 63° to 84°).

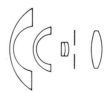

Extreme wide-angle fisheye lens (f/8, 180°).

variable-focal-length lens. If, in addition to having a variable focal length, the lens also remains in focus as the focal length is changed, it is called a zoom lens.

It would be most convenient to have the range of a zoom lens go from wide angle to telephoto. Most zooms for super 8 and 16 mm cameras do cover this type of range. A few zoom lenses for 35 mm still cameras also cover such a range—for example, 35 mm wide-angle focal length to 100 mm telephoto focal length. This is a useful, but moderate range.

The focal length of a lens can be changed in any number of ways: curves, index of refraction, number of elements, thickness of elements, and so on. But to do any of these in a single lens is impossible. The one variable that can be changed readily is the air spacing between the elements. Variable-focus and zoom lenses change focal length by changing the air spaces.

A wide-angle-to-telephoto zoom design is generally based on the triplet arrangement with the negative elements movable. The focal length is increased by increasing the air space in front of the negative elements while decreasing the air space behind them. Usually one of the air spaces in the rear-positive assembly is changed by a different amount to retain a constant focus. If the lens is just variable focus, this second air-space change is not required. Most zoom lenses focus for different subject distances by changing the front air space.

Many telephoto zoom designs are based on the combination of a telephoto converter combined with a mildly telephoto camera lens, all built into one mount. The zoom converter consists of a front positive combination of elements, followed by a negative combination that is divided into two components that move differentially. Most wide-angle zoom lenses are basically reversed-telephoto constructions in which the front and rear components move differentially to vary focal length and maintain focus.

Choosing a Lens

The first considerations in the choice of a lens are those based on whether the lens will do what is needed. Will it fit the camera? Will it cover the film format? Will it make the image size needed? Does it have the speed needed?

A new camera that is being considered for purchase may not have interchangeable lenses. Then, the choice of a lens is only part of the decision. Does the camera have the necessary features for the type of photography for which it is to be used? If there is a choice of cameras, as, for example, in 35 mm optical-finder cameras with non-interchangeable lenses, there is a wide choice of lenses of different speeds: from about $f/2.8$ up to about $f/1.7$. In such cases the choice is whether the extra lens speed will be used, and if it is worth the extra cost.

Interchangeable Lenses. Interchangeable lenses are available for view cameras, 35 mm SLR cameras and some optical-finder cameras, some medium-format reflex cameras, and for some special cameras such as copy cameras, press cameras, and process cameras.

Generally, the normal lens chosen will have a focal length about equal to the diagonal of the format, which is a coverage of 50 to 55 degrees, and a magnification of 1×. The fan-shaped diagram shows the degrees coverage and magnifications for various wide-angle and telephoto lenses. It also shows the focal lengths of lenses in each category for the common format sizes.

View-camera lenses are nearly always mounted in shutters. Shutters for larger lenses, such as those used for 8″ × 10″ cameras, are likely to have limited short shutter speeds, usually no shorter than 1/60 or 1/125 sec. Medium- and small-size shutters are likely to have speeds up to about 1/500 sec. Nearly all will have slow speeds up to 1 second, and two-position flash synchronization: one labeled "M" for medium-delay flash-bulbs; the other labeled "X" for electronic flash.

Because view cameras are so often used with swings and tilts, normal-focal-length lenses with extra field coverage (60 to 70 degrees) are desirable. One way to achieve a larger field size is with a slightly longer-than-normal focal length. For example, the diagonal of the 8″ × 10″ format is about 300 mm, but many photographers use a 350 mm lens as normal to achieve the extra field coverage. The other way is to get a wide-field lens of the normal focal length—that is to say, a moderate wide-angle lens.

Maximum apertures on view-camera lenses are limited, primarily because fast lenses for large-format cameras would be very large in size and very heavy. Typical maximum apertures range from $f/8$ on wide-angle lenses to $f/6.3$ on normal lenses in large-format cameras, $f/4.7$ to $f/4.5$ for medium-format view cameras, and up to $f/4.0$ to $f/3.5$ for small-format view-camera normal lenses.

It may be difficult to find just which lenses are available for view cameras. One approach is to find a photo-equipment directory. Two directories that list view-camera lenses are:

> *PTN Master Buying Guide and*
> *Directory*
> Photographic Trade News
> 250 Fulton Avenue
> Hempstead, New York 11550
> *Photography Directory & Buying Guide*
> (compiled by Editors of *Popular*
> *Photography)*
> Ziff-Davis Publishing Company
> One Park Avenue, New York, 10016

The manufacturer's or importer's address is given in the directory, and you can write for technical details, as well as the name of a dealer from whom the lens can be purchased.

Manufacturer's vs. Independent Maker's Lenses. For all practical purposes, when purchasing a reflex-type, medium-format camera (120 or 220 film size) you are limited to the manufacturer's lenses; independent lens manufacturers do not make lenses to fit these cameras. When choosing a camera of this format, it is wise to look into the lenses made by the manufacturer, because these will be all that is available for your camera once it has been purchased.

On the other hand, when purchasing a 35 mm SLR camera of one of the common makes, an almost endless choice of lenses is available. The directories mentioned earlier contain listings of hundreds of lenses for such cameras.

In addition to the lenses made by the camera manufacturers for their own cameras, independent lens makers manufacture many lenses with adapters to fit nearly all 35 mm SLR cameras—from 8 mm fisheye lenses to 1000 mm mirror lenses.

One Lens or More. The makers of these lenses advertise in the photography magazines, and mail-order stores run advertisements listing the particular lenses that they carry. It is quite simple to find lenses of the right focal length that will fit the common camera mounts. It is not as simple to choose between the lenses of various manufacturers, or between various lenses of the same manufacturer. For example, is it wiser to get several fixed-focal-length lenses or a zoom lens that covers the same range of focal lengths?

If your major picture-taking is for slides, zoom lenses have much to offer. Exact cropping of pictures is easy to accomplish with zoom lenses, and the slightly inferior definitions usually obtained with zoom lenses can rarely be seen when slides are projected. The slight loss in contrast because of somewhat higher flare levels typical with zoom lenses is as often an advantage with slide materials as it is a disadvantage.

The one disadvantage is loss of maximum lens speed; but one normal $f/1.4$ lens, for example, combined with a wide-angle zoom and a telephoto zoom, cover a wide focal-length range with just three lenses. An addition to these three might be a normal to moderate telephoto—a convenient range of focal lengths for a high percentage of photographs taken. If close-up pictures have a high priority, a macro lens becomes a convenience and a way of getting improved definition in pictures with magnifications up to one.

Many workers find that they can take all their pictures with just one lens. For some, this is the normal lens; for others, a moderate telephoto lens (such as 90 mm); while for others it is a moderate wide-angle lens (such as 35 mm). Other workers find that three lenses are needed for the type of pictures they take—a fast normal-focal-length lens (50 or 55 mm), a wide-angle (24 mm or 28 mm), and a telephoto (commonly 135 mm). Nature photographers will often use a macro lens for a normal lens, and will add long-focal-length telephoto lenses and mirror lenses for wildlife photography. Photographers who take many pictures of buildings will usually find the need for a variety of wide-angle lenses: 17–20 mm, 24 mm, and 28 mm focal lengths.

Three general factors are important in choosing a particular lens:

1. Basic optical factors: focal length and speed;

2. Mechanical factors: mount to fit camera; quality of "feel" in lens threads; camera-mount fit; clear, easy-to-read engraving; direction of turn and placement of controls; mechanical size and weight;
3. Image quality: definition and contrast.

Lens Speed. Speed is determined by the photographer's needs and by what is available; it is particularly balanced by two other factors: size and weight considerations. For example, it might be convenient to have an $f/1.4$, 500 mm telephoto lens, but the diameter of the front lens would have to be 700 mm (27½ inches), and you would need a truck to carry it around.

In normal and wide-angle lenses, the maximum speed is limited by the ability to correct aberrations. Normal lenses can be well corrected to apertures up to $f/1.4$; but the next half-stop step to $f/1.2$ is apparently a difficult one to make while retaining adequate corrections. Even when aspheric surfaces are used, and considerably more expensive manufacturing methods, resolving power due to residual aberrations in $f/1.2$ lenses is, in general, noticeably lower. In reverse-telephoto wide-angle lenses, the maximum speed has gradually increased in recent years from $f/2.8$ to $f/2.5$, and recently to about $f/2.0$.

Other Features. Obviously, any lens you buy should fit your camera. In some cases, usually with cameras that use 120- and 220-size roll film, this limits you to the camera manufacturer's lenses. The same limitation applies to some 35 mm cameras, but any mount—bayonet or threaded—that becomes popular soon has independent lens makers providing lenses for it.

It is certainly convenient to have all focusing rings and diaphragm controls on all your lenses turn the same way. It is inconvenient to have some lenses "left handed" and some "right handed," and this inconsistency can slow down the picture-taking operation. All actions should be smooth and easy, but not loose in feel, and switches and rings should stay where they are put. Click stops at the whole- and half-stop values should be positive but should not require much effort to change. Flutes or knurling should make rotating the rings easy but should not have a sharp feel to the fingers.

The markings showing stop and focus positions, depth of field, and zoom positions should be clear and easy to read. There has been a trend toward smaller 35 mm SLR cameras, and smaller, lighter lenses to go with them. One disadvantage of smaller lens mounts is less room for the engraving (the advantages are obvious). Look for engraving that can be read without a magnifying lens. Color coding in the numbers and lines is a help.

The two main image-quality factors are contrast and definition. Contrast is measured as percent flare (or veiling glare) and definition as resolving-power and optical-transfer function.

Some of the photography magazines test lenses and publish reports. These are good sources of information about many of the factors involved in choosing between lenses, including image-quality factors.

Lens coating has lowered flare levels in lenses considerably. The percent flare of modern, single-focal-length lenses consistently runs below 1 percent. Even zoom lenses, which formerly produced high flare levels, have been improved by mount design and coating so that lenses now being manufactured generally have moderate flare levels, and hence produce satisfactory image contrast. However, there are still a few lenses manufactured that have high flare levels, so that it makes good sense to be aware of this factor.

There is more variation in the definition produced by different lenses. Although resolving power is not the only criterion for judging definition, it is fairly simple to measure and is the main information given in the published lens tests. Generally, the number of lines resolved by a lens does give a good indication of its definition. Comparison with a magazine's criteria, as well as the resolving-power test results given on comparative lenses, provides a basis for assessing the potential definition that can be expected from a particular lens. Unfortunately, optical-transfer-function curves are not usually published.

If you establish a good relationship with your photo dealer, he or she is likely to sell you a lens with the understanding that you can run your own tests, and trade it for another lens of the same make or another make if it does not perform well. See the article TESTING for details on making a test of a lens.

7.5 mm (fisheye)

28 mm

16 mm

35 mm

17 mm

50 mm

21 mm

85 mm

1548

135 mm

200 mm

400 mm

800 mm

1600 mm

This series of perspective conversion photographs represents the different effects produced by lenses of varying focal lengths. Camera-to-subject distance is the same for each picture. Photos courtesy Minolta Corp.

Other Types of Lenses

Most of this article pertains to camera lenses. However, there are other types of lenses as well.

Enlarging Lenses. Enlarging lenses are similar to camera lenses, and are designed and manufactured in similar ways. There is a big difference between the two types of lenses. Camera lenses (except for macro lenses) are designed to be used at distances from about 10 times the focal length to infinity. The aberrations, especially field curvature, are corrected by the lens designer for this range of distances. When used close, the field curvature changes and the increase in the other aberrations cause the image to deteriorate slightly.

On the other hand, enlarging lenses are used at magnifications of from about 1X to 10X, so they are designed to have a flat field at a magnification midway between these two values. Some early enlarging lenses had triplet ancestry, but most quality enlarging lenses made now are in the symmetrical family. High speed is not a requirement; most maximum apertures range from $f/5.6$ to $f/2.8$. Good contrast and definition are the prime requirements, especially good color correction. Enlarging lenses cover a nearly normal 55-degree field angle—and since they are used at finite distances, usually cover that angle very well.

Important mount features are click stops to make it easier to set apertures in the dark; and in some cases, the *f*-numbers are illuminated indirectly by enlarger light piped through the lens board by a plastic tube.

Some enlargers use condenser lenses to provide even distribution of light across the negative-carrier opening. The diameter of the lenses must be somewhat greater than the diagonal of the largest negative-carrier opening. For example, condensers for 2¼″ × 3¼″ enlargers are usually 4½ inches in diameter. The conventional enlarger condenser design is two plano-convex lenses with the convex sides inward and almost touching. The focal length of the condenser assembly must be such that the condensers image the end of the opal enlarging bulb on the enlarging lens, just filling the aperture. Simple enlargers are made so that the focus is at the lowest position on the lens, and the image overfills the aperture when the lens is closer to the condensers. This wastes some of the light.

Other enlargers have a method of focusing the condenser light on the enlarging lens by moving the condensers up and down. Another approach is to use interchangeable condensers—one for each focal-length lens commonly used. In this case, the lower condenser is usually smaller in diameter and stronger in power in order to focus the enlarger bulb on shorter-focal-length lenses.

Because condensers do not form an image of the negative, but only distribute light, they do not need to be corrected for aberrations.

Projection Lenses. Condenser lenses for projectors are similar in purpose. Small motion-picture projectors do not usually have condenser lenses; reflectors built into the lamps are used instead (*See:* REFLECTORS). However, slide projectors normally do use condensers, because the necessary reflectors would be quite large.

Slide-projector lamps have area filaments. The filament is focused on the rear of the projection lens by the condenser lenses, distributing the light evenly as it passes through the slide. In order to collect the maximum possible light, the *f*-number value of the condenser-lens system must be quite high. For this reason, one condenser element often has a strong, aspheric molded surface to give better light distribution. Nearly all projection condenser lenses are biconvex lenses, in order to increase the *f*-number value. Condensers for projectors are usually coated to increase light output somewhat. With time, however, the coating may lose some effectiveness because of the heat from the projection lamp.

Most single-focal-length projection lenses are relatively high-aperture, narrow-angle lenses. They may be of double gauss, telephoto, or triplet design. Motion-picture projection lenses may have apertures as high as $f/1.4$, while slide-projector lenses are more often $f/3.5$ to $f/2.8$ lenses. Projector lenses are always used wide open, so no diaphragm is required. However, this means that the corrections must be adequate at the relatively wide apertures.

Because slides mounted in plastic or cardboard mounts are usually slightly curved, many slide-projector lenses are designed with field curvature to match the curvature of the typical slide, giving better overall image quality on the screen. Some manufacturers give a choice of flat-field or curved-field projection lenses for slides.

Many projection lenses today are zoom or variable-focal-length lenses—usually of the tele-photo-zoom type. Because projection zoom lenses do not have as great a focal-length range as camera lenses, they generally have fewer elements than camera zoom lenses.

• *See also:* ABERRATION; ACHROMATIC; ANASTIGMAT; APOCHROMATIC; ASPHERIC; BACK FOCUS; BARREL DISTORTION; CAMERAS; DEPTH OF FIELD; DEPTH OF FOCUS; FIELD LENS; FISHEYE LENS; *f*-NUMBER; FRESNEL LENSES; *f*-STOP; KINGSLAKE, RUDOLF; LIGHT; MIRROR LENSES; OPTICS; PERSPECTIVE; PETZVAL, JOSEPH; PINHOLE CAMERA; PINCUSION DISTORTION; PROJECTORS; REFLECTORS; RELATIVE APERTURE; RESOLVING POWER; SUPPLEMENTARY LENSES; TELEPHOTOGRAPHY; TESTING; T-STOP; WIDE-ANGLE PHOTOGRAPHY.

Further Reading: Brandt, Hans-Martin. *The Photographic Lens.* (Focal Library Books) Belmont, CA: Pitman Publishing Company, 1968; Gaunt, Leonard. *The Photoguide to Lenses.* Garden City, NY: Amphoto, 1977; Lahue, Kalton C., ed. *Interchangeable Lenses.* Los Angeles, CA: Petersen Publishing Co., 1975; Neblette, C.B. and Allen E. Murray. *Photographic Lenses.* Dobbs Ferry, NY: Morgan & Morgan, Inc. 1973; Ray, Sidney F. *The Lens and All Its Jobs.* New York, NY: Hastings House Publishers, 1977.

Lens Mounts

The term "lens mount" has two meanings in photography: (1) the barrel or tube arrangement that holds the lens elements in proper relation to one another, and (2) the device or system by which the complete lens is attached to a lens board or camera body.

Lens Element Mounts

The elements or element groups of a lens must be precisely centered on a common axis, with the plane perpendicular to the axis of each element parallel to the planes of all other elements. The elements may be cemented in place in the tube or ring that holds them, held in place with threaded retaining rings, or spun in by a thin lip of metal. The simplest arrangement is a single tube that attaches to the front of the camera; focusing is achieved by moving the camera front (or back) to change lens-to-film distance. (An early improvement of the scheme, used with daguerreotype and similar cameras, consisted of two telescoping tubes that could be locked at a desired extension by a thumb screw. The camera front or back was moved for coarse focusing, the lens tubes for fine focusing.) Aperture stops may be placed in front of or behind the lens, or inserted through a slot in one of the tubes. The shutter may also be mounted in front of or behind the lens, or at the focal plane.

Today, barrel-mount lenses usually have an integral iris diaphragm and are designed to screw into standard-size leaf-shutter mechanisms for use on bellows-type cameras. The elements are commonly mounted in a single rigid ring that attaches to the front of the shutter unit, or in two rings that attach on either side of the shutter unit. Focusing is accomplished by moving the lens standard of the camera.

Lens mounts for rigid-body cameras must incorporate a focusing movement. This is commonly achieved by threaded telescoping tubes. With short-, normal-, and moderate-focal-length telephoto lenses, the forward tube is extended or retracted by a ring that engages a helical thread in the rear fixed tube. This arrangement moves the elements toward or away from the film without causing them to revolve, so that the alignment of a polarizer, matte or mask, or other accessory is not disturbed.

Some very long-focal-length lenses for small-format cameras focus by sliding the front tube back and forth, as in a trombone. In fixed-focal-length lenses, all elements are moved in unison to achieve focusing without changing the spacing between the elements. In zoom lenses, both element-to-film and element-to-element distances change to achieve different magnifications, as well as focusing adjustments.

This is the most common lens board mounting system. (Left) The lower edge of the lens board is engaged behind the fixed retaining lip. The locking bar slides to overlap the upper edge of the board and to secure it. Diagonal slots in the bar travel over fixed pins. (Right) The edges of the board and the opening in the lens standard are rabbeted to prevent light from entering. The lens screws into the threaded flange, fastened to the face of the board, or to the rear, as shown. Metal lens boards may be threaded directly so that no flange is required. Each lens is usually permanently mounted in its own lens board.

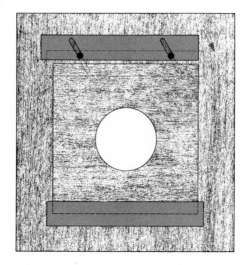
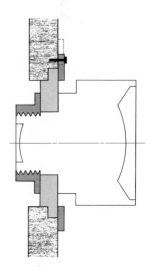

Lenses with built-in focusing movement commonly have a distance scale with a focusing-index mark, and an associated depth-of-field scale. They also usually include an iris diaphragm, which is set by turning a separate ring on the barrel. It is now common for the ring to click into position at full- and half-stop settings.

Some simpler cameras utilize front-crown focusing. The mounts for such lenses are made so that the rear elements of the lens are permanently fixed in relation to the camera body, but the front lens element can be rotated to increase the front air

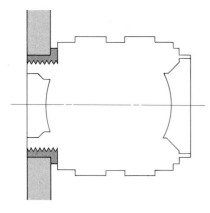

The screw mount is the most basic system. It is highly wear-resistant; but without a locking device, it can allow the lens to twist loose, especially if the focusing movement is stiff. Permanent damage can result if the lens is cross-threaded during mounting.

space. With the increased air space, the lens focuses at close distances. Such mounts may be made of metal or molded of plastic.

Camera Mounts

Most barrel- and shutter-mounted lenses for bellows-type cameras screw into a flange on a lens board. The lens board then locks into position by means of a sliding bar or thumb screws in the lens standard of the camera.

Interchangeable lenses are commonly mounted on small-format, rigid-body cameras by means of one of three systems: screw-thread, bayonet-lock, or breech-ring or modified breech-lock. The accompanying illustrations explain these three mounting methods.

Whichever system is used to attach a lens to a camera, the lens must be held securely with the axis centered in the image area, and exactly perpendicular to the image plane for sharp, distortion-free photography under normal conditions. Cameras that have tilt and swing movements allow these alignments to be purposely changed in order to control linear distortion, perspective, and the placement of focus.

In the simplest amateur cameras, the lens is permanently attached to the camera body and no focusing movement is provided. The camera and lens design insure that all objects beyond a certain distance will be in acceptable focus by utilizing lens apertures that provide considerable depth of field, and focusing them at the hyperfocal distance.

• *See also:* DEPTH OF FIELD; DIAPHRAGM; HYPERFOCAL DISTANCE; LENSES; VIEW CAMERA.

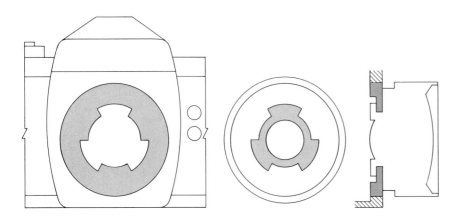

The bayonet-mount system is the fastest method of changing lenses used with small-format cameras. The notched openings in the camera mounting flange (left) accept matching lugs on the rear of the lens mount (center). After the lens is inserted, a quarter-turn engages the lugs behind the camera flange (right). The spring-loaded catch on the camera (not shown) captures the pin or notch on the lens to lock it in place.

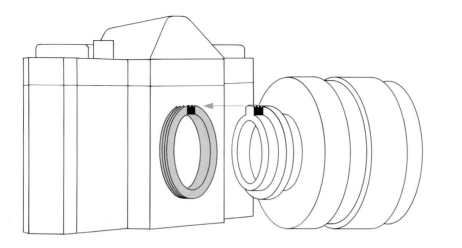
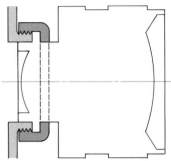

In a typical breech-ring mounting, the threaded flange protruding from the camera (left and center) has a notch to receive an alignment pin or lug on the rear of the lens. (Right) The threaded collar of the lens then screws onto the flange to fasten the lens securely to the camera. The modified breech-lock mount may have multiple alignment pins or bayonet lugs and a collar that makes a half-turn to engage a spring-loaded locking device for quick operation.

Lenticular Systems

A lenticule is a minute lens or lenslet. A number of special-purpose photographic systems use screens composed of lenticules to analyze or break up the image from a conventional lens in order to record it as a pattern of parallel lines or regularly spaced dots. Transparent, or optical, lenticular screens have been used for additive color processes, stereoscopic and apparent-motion images, high-speed photography, and information storage and retrieval. Reflective lenticular surfaces are used for highly efficient, "daylight" projection screens.

Most optical lenticular screens are embossed or molded in the surface of a plastic material. A series of parallel cylindrical lenticules creates a line screen. Embossing the surface in two directions, at right angles to each other, creates lenticules that are spherical segments. Such a lenticular point screen forms an image pattern of dots, rather than lines. The same effect can be achieved—with some loss of image quality—by combining two line screens with their ribs at right angles.

Lenticular Color Systems

A number of additive color systems have used a film with a lenticular line screen embossed on the outer surface of the film base. Such films were used in the early Kodacolor film process (circa 1929—not related to the present-day subtractive Kodacolor film), the Keller-Dorian process, and a number of systems for television transmission of color movies.

In all these systems, the film had a black-and-white emulsion; color analysis or separation was achieved by a three-section (red, green, blue) filter in front of the camera lens. The lenticular surface of the film faced the lens and focused an image of the filter behind each rib. Exposure in each line depended on the light passing through the various filter sections. The film was reversal-processed to a black-and-white positive composed of lines, each of which carried the entire color-separation record. In viewing, the lenticules caused white light passing through each section of a line to be projected through the corresponding section of a matching three-color filter; the result was an image in full color.

In television, the same camera system and film were used, but in transmission, no filter was needed;

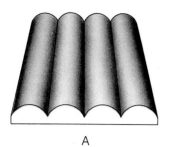

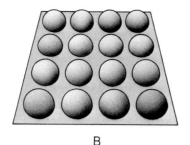

Lenticular Image Formation

(A) Each lenticule sees the entire lens image and focuses it onto a surface such as a film emulsion. Spacing of image elements from the line screen (B) or point screen (C) depends on the fineness of the screen and the optical characteristics of the lenticules. Shifting the screen for a second exposure will focus the next set of image elements in the intervening spaces. In this way, many images can be interlaced without interference. Viewing through a similar screen-and-lens combination will reconstitute each image individually as the screen is shifted.

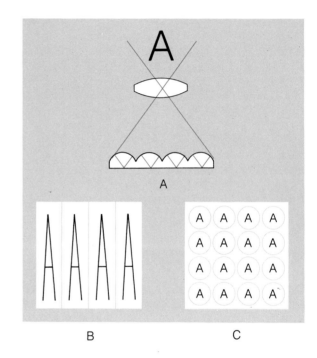

instead, a mirror assembly was placed in front of the projection lens, and beams corresponding to the three primary colors were directed to three camera tubes, each connected through appropriate circuitry to a standard color TV transmitter. The system was tried experimentally with considerable success, but never became commercially practical, mainly because good transmission could be obtained from standard color films, and also because the camera filter caused a great loss of light and film speed.

Lenticular Stereoscopy and Movement

Lenticular-embossed films and separate screens with conventional film have both been used to create three-dimensional images. The function of the lenticules is to separate the left- and right-eye images. The resulting stereogram can be viewed without any auxiliary viewing apparatus. Interestingly, in the case of the separate-screen method, if the screen for viewing has the same spacing as the one used in taking the picture, it is not necessary to place it in exact register with the image. If it is out of register, only a slight change in the viewing angle is required to observe the stereoscopic effect. This fact has made it possible to print three-dimensional images on paper; after printing, the image is covered with a lenticular plastic coating. A number of magazines have experimented from time to time with three-dimensional cover pictures produced in this way.

A variation of this technique is used to produce "movement" between still pictures. The separation between the images and the lenticular screen is wide enough so that the head must be moved or the image turned, to view first one image and then the other. If some elements in both pictures are the same, then those that are different seem to have moved. The method has been used in advertising displays and novelty items to create apparent movement—for example, a girl winking—as a viewer moves past or handles the item.

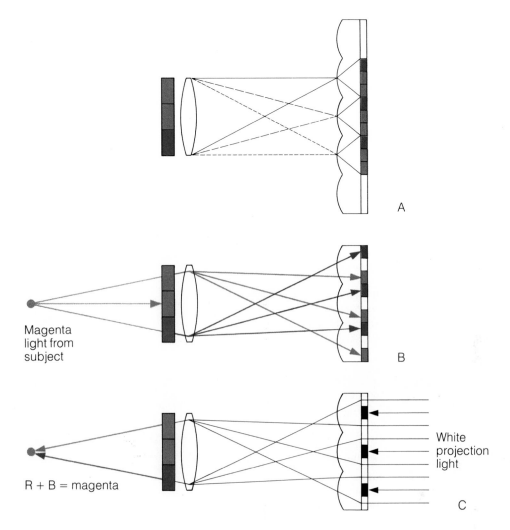

Lenticular Additive Color

(A) Each lenticule on the base of the film forms an image of a three-color filter in front of the camera lens. The scale of the film is greatly enlarged in relation to the lens and filter for clarity in this diagram. (B) Light from each subject point encounters the entire surface of the filter, but each band will pass only its own color. Lenticules see the entire color image passing through the filter, and the film emulsion records it in multiple, duplicate lines of exposure. (C) Reversal processing results in the exposed portions of the film being transparent, and the unexposed portions (green-record lines in this example) being opaque. White projection light passing through the blue-record portion of each film line is directed through the blue filter band; white light passing through the red-record portions goes to the red filter band. The projection lens angles the light rays so that they will converge on the viewing screen to additively reconstruct a full-color image of the original subject point. All other subject points are similarly recorded and reconstructed.

High-Speed Photography; Information Storage

In the diagrams on the following page, a lenticular screen need be shifted only a small distance to focus a new image in the spaces between a previous exposure; thus it can be used for high-speed motion pictures. It is much easier to move the screen a fraction of an inch at a very high rate than to move the entire film from frame to frame. A line screen is commonly used for this application.

(Right) Frame-by-frame high-speed movies require that film be moved a great distance (A) between exposures. A lenticular screen needs to be moved a fraction of the width of a single lenticule (B), so the rate can be much faster. The number of exposures on a single frame (C) is primarily determined by the width of the film area under each lenticule of the line screen. (Below) Shifting a point screen in a regular pattern (D) produces an overall pattern of interlaced images (E) that can later be viewed individually through a similar screen. The diagram is schematic; the number of separate images per frame is not limited to four.

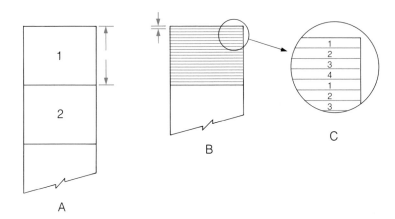

D

2	3	2	3	2	3	2	3
1	4	1	4	1	4	1	4
2	3	2	3	2	3	2	3
1	4	1	4	1	4	1	4
2	3	2	3	2	3	2	3
1	4	1	4	1	4	1	4

E

(Below) A lenticular surface reflects a high percentage of light from the projector (A) into the viewing area. Some ambient light from outside (B) will be reflected into the viewing area, but a significant amount will not (C). At normal viewing distances, the pattern of the screen surface is not perceived.

The same principle can be used with still cameras to store multiple images within a single frame, using a lenticular point screen. The information recorded may be actual scenes, other photographs, pages of printed material, or anything else that can be imaged in a camera.

In either application, viewing is achieved with a projection lens and a matching screen that is moved from image to image as required.

Lenticular Projection Screens

Metallic or nonmetallic reflective materials can be used to make high-efficiency front-projection screens. The ribs of a line-screen pattern act as mirrors that reflect a much greater proportion of projected light back into the viewing area than do conventional beaded or matte screen surfaces. Although ambient light originating within the viewing area will degrade the image, much light from outside the area will be reflected away. The result is a projected image bright enough to be seen easily under lighted or only partially darkened conditions. Some screens for front-projected studio backgrounds have precision lenticular surfaces.

• *See also:* ADDITIVE COLOR SYNTHESIS; FRONT-SCREEN PROJECTION; HIGH-SPEED PHOTOGRAPHY; LINE-SCREEN SYSTEMS; MICROGRAPHICS; PROJECTION SCREENS.

Light

Light is electromagnetic radiant energy to which the eye is sensitive. There are other types of electromagnetic radiant energy that are similar to light, but the eye cannot see them; therefore, they are not light. Ultraviolet radiation and infrared radiation are two such invisible radiations.

Electromagnetic radiation of many types is emitted by the sun; among them are light, ultraviolet radiation, and infrared radiation. All electromagnetic radiant energy travels at a constant speed in straight lines in a given medium, such as space or air. The speed of light in space is over 186,000 miles per second; in air, the speed is just slightly less.

As light and other forms of radiant energy travel, they exhibit two distinct travel patterns. In some ways, light behaves according to the laws of wave motion. In other ways, it behaves as if it were composed of discrete particles, which, in the case of light, are called photons. A photon possesses great energy, but so little mass (weight) that it is unmeasurable. It is useful to think of a ray of light as a stream of photons carrying the energy of light, but exhibiting the characteristics of wave motion.

Energy carried by waves, like water waves, has the characteristics of speed, wavelength, and frequency, and these characteristics are interrelated by the formula:

$$\text{Wavelength} = \frac{\text{Speed}}{\text{Frequency}} \text{ or }$$

$$\text{Speed} = \text{Wavelength} \times \text{Frequency}$$

Wavelength is the distance from the crest, or peak, of one wave to the crest of the next wave. The wavelengths of light are very small, about 1/50,000 of an inch. A metric unit, the nanometre (nm), which is one billionth of a metre, is usually used to define wavelength. The wavelengths of light range from about 400 to 700 nm.

Although the wavelengths of light are very short, there are forms of radiant energy whose wavelengths are even shorter: ultraviolet radiation,

The electromagnetic energy spectrum is composed of both visible radiant energy (light) and invisible radiant energy (ultraviolet and infrared radiation, for example).

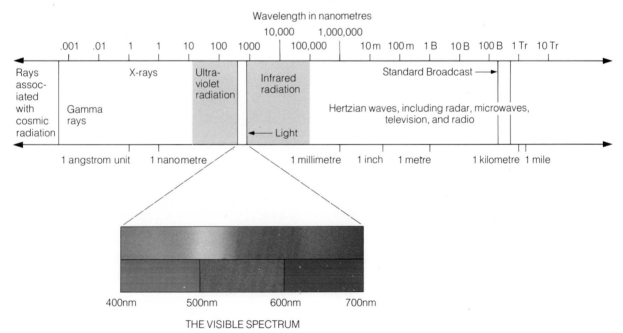

THE ELECTROMAGNETIC SPECTRUM

THE VISIBLE SPECTRUM

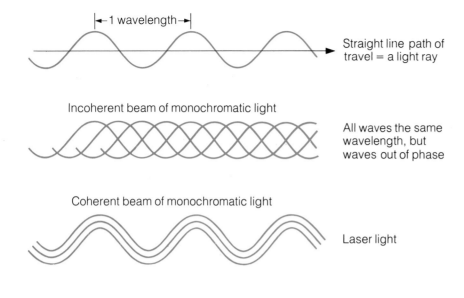

←1 wavelength→

Straight line path of travel = a light ray

Incoherent beam of monochromatic light

All waves the same wavelength, but waves out of phase

Coherent beam of monochromatic light

Laser light

In ordinary light, there is no order to the peaks and valleys of the waves. This type of light is called incoherent light. Light of one wavelength is monochromatic light, and ordinarily monochromatic light is incoherent. Light can be both coherent and monochromatic under certain conditions; this light is called laser light.

x-rays, gamma rays, and the still shorter wavelengths of the radiation called cosmic rays.

There are forms of energy whose wavelengths are larger than those of light: infrared radiation, heat radiation, and many types of radio waves, with wavelengths up to several miles long.

The electromagnetic spectrum is an orderly arrangement of all the forms of electromagnetic radiant energy arranged by wavelength.

Light is a very narrow band in this spectrum. What is unique about light is that it is the form of radiation to which the human eye is sensitive. By definition, light is the electromagnetic radiation by which we see.

The Color of Light

The different wavelengths of light are seen as color. Color is not intrinsic in light; it is a visual perception that is stimulated by light.

If a beam of light contains a relatively even mixture of light of all wavelengths, it is seen as white light. If such a beam is allowed to pass through a prism or a diffraction grating, the light of different wavelengths is spread apart to form a visual spectrum. Although, from one end to the other, the visible spectrum has continuously changing wavelengths, it is seen as bands of color: violet, blue, blue-green, green, yellow-green, yellow, yellow-orange, orange, red-orange, and red. The reason we see bands of color rather than continuously changing color is due to the nature of our color vision. (Not all colors that we see are in the spectrum. The

colors that range from violet through magenta to red result from mixtures of wavelengths that are not created by light of single wavelengths.)

The eye sees color because the retina contains three types of nerve cells called cones, each type of which is sensitive to a band of wavelengths. (*See:* VISION.) One type of cone is sensitive to light whose wavelengths are from about 400 to 500 nm (blue), another type to light of from about 500 to 600 nm (green), and the last type to light whose wavelengths are from about 600 to 700 nm (red). Color film has three sensitive layers; each layer is sensitive to one of these three bands of light. For many photographic purposes, the visible spectrum can be thought to be made up of the three bands of wavelengths described above.

The color of light of mixed wavelengths can be described in terms of the temperature of a glowing, standard black object. (*See:* COLOR TEMPERATURE.)

Emission of Light

Light energy is produced by changes in the speed and direction of charged particles such as electrons and ions. These changes can result from combustion, discharge, fluorescence, or incandescence.

We think of combustion as the creation of fire, which gives off or emits light. In a more technical way, combustion is rapid oxidation in which the original material being combusted is "consumed"—changed chemically into gases, and leaving behind only carbon and ash.

In discharge emission, the moving electrons of electricity move electrons in the orbits of certain gases into other orbits that have higher energy levels. As the electrons move back to their original orbit levels, they release the energy in the form of electromagnetic radiant energy, some of which is light. This principle is used in the types of lights we know as neon signs and fluorescent lights.

In fluorescent lights, the emission of light is more complex. The mercury gas in the tube emits some light by discharge, but much energy is also given off as ultraviolet radiation. This radiation is absorbed by the fluorescent coating on the glass of the tube, which re-emits it as light. Technically, fluorescence is similar to discharge emission. In electronic flash tubes, the light is emitted instantaneously, entirely by discharge, as a single violent pulse of electricity is released from a stored capacitor.

Incandescence is the type of light emission produced when electricity is run through a tungsten wire with high resistance. Because the filament (tungsten wire) gets so hot from the flow of electrons, it could be consumed in seconds if there were oxygen present. For practical light bulbs, the air, with its oxygen, is removed from the bulb so that a vacuum is formed, or it is replaced with gas, such as nitrogen, that does not support combustion.

Behavior of Light

How we see and how we photograph are affected directly by two important characteristics of light as it travels. Light travels in straight lines in a given medium, and it travels at a constant speed in a given medium.

Once light has been created (emitted), it has an independent nature, in that it is no longer dependent on the source for energy. It is independent to a large degree from the medium through which it travels. For example, light travels through relatively empty space and through a vacuum. Water waves and sound waves require a medium with matter in it to exist. Light does not. When light goes from air into a denser, but transparent, medium such as water or glass, it slows down its speed. However, if it leaves the medium and enters the air again, it returns to its original speed. This change in speed is important in refraction, one of the behaviors of light.

Light radiates, or travels, in all directions from its source. Because of this, the energy of light is spread out as it travels greater distances from the

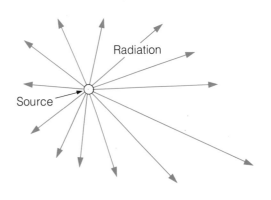

Light starts at an emitting source and radiates in all directions; thus, a change in brightness is seen.

source, so that the energy of the light striking a given area a certain distance from the source is less than that striking the same area closer to the source. We see this as a change in brightness of the light. This effect of the radiant nature of light is described mathematically as the inverse-square law. (*See:* INVERSE-SQUARE LAW.)

The RAT (*Reflected, Absorbed, Transmitted*) Formula. When light is traveling through a constant medium, it may encounter the surfaces of objects. When it does, one of the following things happens to it:

It may be reflected. The surfaces of most objects *reflect* or "bounce" light off the surface.

It may be absorbed. If the object is opaque, the light that is not reflected from the surface will be absorbed by the object, and the light will no longer exist. Its energy will be converted to heat energy within the object.

It may be transmitted. If the object is transparent, some of the light will travel through the object.

The total energy of the light as it strikes the object (the incident light) must equal the total energy of the reflected, absorbed, and transmitted light. (*See:* REFLECTANCE.)

An optical material that transmits light rays in a regular pattern is said to be *transparent.* If a material transmits light, but breaks up the orderliness of the light rays and sends them in all directions, it is said to be *translucent*. If all wavelengths of light are transmitted equally, the medium is said to have *achromatic* (without color) transmission. If it transmits some wavelengths freely but *absorbs* other wavelengths wholly or partially, it will appear to have color, and the transmission is *chromatic*. If a material absorbs all light, it is said to be *opaque*.

Reflection. When light rays are reflected from object surfaces, they follow certain rules. When the surface is very smooth (polished), the reflection is called *specular*. The light from most sources travels in an orderly fashion. *Radiant* light rays are straight, of course, and at very slight angles to each other. When the source is at some distance, they are essentially parallel.

When a light ray strikes a smooth, polished surface at an angle, the angle of reflection equals the angle of incidence. A first-surface mirror is a smooth, polished surface of high reflectance. You can reflect the rays of light from the sun or from a light bulb and see where the reflected beam goes.

However, if the object is not smooth, but is microscopically irregular, the light reflects in all directions. Such a reflection is a *diffuse* reflection, and the light whose paths were orderly (parallel) is now disorderly, or diffuse.

Most object surfaces provide semispecular reflections—part of the light from the surface is reflected specularly, and some of it diffusely.

If the incident light is white—an even mix of all wavelengths—and the reflected light is also white, the reflection is *achromatic* (without color). Nearly all specular reflection is achromatic; only certain metallic surfaces and a few insect surfaces have specular reflections that are not achromatic. Many diffuse reflections are also achromatic; that is, they reflect all wavelengths of light equally. Achromatic reflections are neutral; when the achromatic percentage of reflection is high, the surface is a white surface. When it is low, the surface is seen as black. In-between levels of reflections are called grays.

Many diffuse reflections do not reflect all wavelengths equally. When some wavelengths are re-

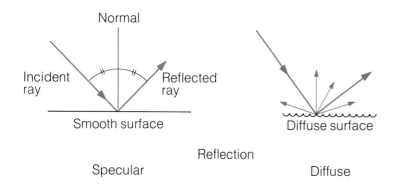

Specular   Reflection   Diffuse

When light rays are reflected from a very smooth object surface, the reflection is specular. Light from most surfaces travels in an orderly manner. When light strikes the surface at an angle, the angle of reflection equals the angle of incidence. With diffuse reflection, the light strikes a microscopically irregular object surface and is reflected in all directions.

Because the speed of light in a material is dependent on its wavelength, the index of refraction of a material varies with the wavelength. Therefore, different colors of light are bent different amounts. Dispersion is the property of changing index of refraction with wavelength. Light traveling through a non-transparent, or translucent, medium becomes diffused. The light rays are scattered over a larger area than with specular illumination, and the resulting light is soft. The degree of softness of the illumination depends upon the diffusing medium—the thicker and more dense the structure of the material, the more diffuse the illumination.

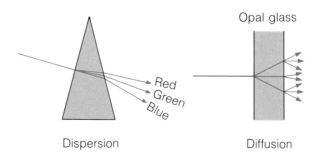

Dispersion   Diffusion

When light encounters a transparent medium such as water, there is always some reflection at the surface; the portion that enters the medium is slowed and refracted. Photo by Seymour D. Uslan.

flected more than others, the reflection is *chromatic*, or colored. Because of the three-color nature of vision (and color photography), the color seen (and photographed) depends largely on the percentage of light reflected in each of the three color bands: blue, green, and red. If the percentage of light reflected in one or two bands is quite low and the other quite high, the color will appear saturated, while if one or two bands have only a slightly higher percentage of reflection than the other, the color will appear desaturated. (*See:* COLOR THEORY; VISION.)

Specular reflections from polished glass surfaces are of importance in photography. When the surfaces are coated with thin metal layers (silver or aluminum), they become mirrors. Mirror lenses are useful long-focal-length lenses with short, overall mechanical lengths (*See:* MIRROR LENSES and MIRRORS.)

Interference. When the two surfaces of a very thin, transparent medium are only fractions of a wavelength apart, the reflections of the light waves interfere with each other and cancel each other out, or reinforce each other. This happens in a thin soap bubble. The spectral colors seen in soap bubbles are caused by interference of a light wave. Lens coating is a very thin layer of a transparent material of such thickness that interference occurs to reduce the reflection losses from the glass lens surfaces. Dichroic

mirrors and filters are made to have chromatic interference in such a way that certain wavelengths are reflected strongly, and others are reflected only slightly, but are transmitted. This makes them filters. Heat mirrors are used in projectors (they reflect light and transmit infrared radiation), while dichroic filters are used in color enlargers.

Refraction. When light enters a transparent medium such as glass, water, or plastic, its speed slows down. Such mediums are said to have optical density. The greater the optical density (related somewhat to the weight per unit volume of the material), the more the light slows down.

The ratio of the speed of light in air divided by the speed of light in the optical medium is called the *index of refraction.* Primarily, then, *refraction* is the slowing down of the speed of light in optically dense mediums.

When light enters a transparent medium through a polished surface along a path perpendicular to the surface (or normal to the surface), it continues on the same straight-line path. Likewise, if light leaves a transparent medium into air along a path normal to the surface, it continues along the same straight line.

However, if a light path is at an angle to the surface of the medium, the light path is bent, and the straight-line path of the light inside the medium is

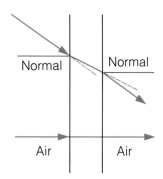

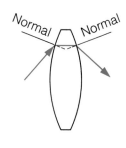

Refraction

In parallel-sided glass   In typical lens

When light enters a material with optical density, such as glass, the light slows down. This is called refraction. If the light path entering the material is at an angle to the surface of the material, the light is bent; if the light path enters the medium perpendicular to the surface, then the light path will continue to travel in a straight path.

at an angle to the path the light traveled in air. How much the light is bent depends on the index of refraction of the material and on the original angle, measured to the normal, of the light path. Further details are given in the articles OPTICS and LENSES.

Dispersion. The speed of light in a material is dependent on its wavelength—short waves are slowed up more than long waves. This means that the index of refraction of a material varies with the wavelength. This, by Snell's law, means that different colors of light are bent different amounts. This property of changing index of refraction with wavelength is called *dispersion.*

A prism creates a spectrum from white light because the glass it is made of has the property of dispersion. The different colors of light are bent at different angles, spreading them out by wavelength to create the spectrum.

Diffraction. The one exception to the straight-line path of light travel is when it travels very near an opaque edge. Light rays passing near an edge are bent very slightly, due to the wave nature of their travel. This bending at an edge is called *diffraction.* Like dispersion, the amount of bend is dependent on wavelength, but in just the opposite direction. Long waves are bent most by diffraction.

Diffraction gratings consist of many fine, parallel, opaque lines with transparent spaces between them, thus creating many edges. When white light is put through a diffraction grating, it is spread out into spectrums.

The light passing the edges of a lens diaphragm is diffracted from its true image-forming paths. When the lens is wide open, the percentage of dif-

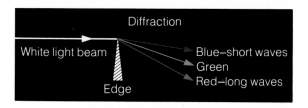

When light travels very near an opaque edge, the rays are bent slightly due to the nature of their travel. This bending at the edge is called diffraction. The amount of bending depends on wavelength; long waves are bent the most by diffraction.

fracted light is very small. However, when the lens is stopped down to very small apertures, the percentage of diffracted light becomes an appreciable amount of the total, and reduces the sharpness of the image.

Scattering. The air is composed of molecules of gases and contains fine particles of other matter such as dust or smoke. As light from the sun travels through the atmosphere, some of it is scattered by the air. The short wavelengths of light are scattered more than the long wavelengths. Because more blue light is scattered than other colors, the sky color is blue.

When the sun is rising or setting, the sun's rays travel through more air. When we look toward the sun, we see the light—from which the blue has been scattered—leaving the longer wavelengths to come through to us. This is what gives the rising and setting sun its reddish-orange color.

Polarization

Normal light beams act as if the waves oscillate in all directions at 90 degrees to the path of travel. Certain materials have the capability of absorbing the energy in certain angles to the path of travel, and transmitting light that, in essence, appears to vibrate in only one direction as it travels. This is called polarization.

Specular reflections at some angles from all shiny surfaces (except polished metal surfaces) are partially polarized reflections. By rotating a polarizing filter in front of a camera lens, the specular reflections from the surface of a glass window or the surface of water can be diminished in intensity.

The color of most objects is in the diffuse reflections, although most surfaces have both diffuse and specular reflections. The specular reflections are both achromatic and partially polarized. Ordinarily, the combination of both types of reflections is photographed, and the chromatic diffuse reflection is diluted by the specular part of the reflection, so the color of the surface is lowered in saturation. If a polarizing filter is used, and rotated so that it stops the polarized portion of the light from reaching the camera lens, the picture taken will show more of the chromatic diffuse light from the surface, which increases the saturation of the color.

A polarizing screen absorbs normal vibrating light energy in certain angles to the path of travel, and transmits light that appears to vibrate in only one direction as it travels. The resulting polarized light is then absorbed by a crossed polarizing screen, resulting in an increase in color saturation in the picture taken.

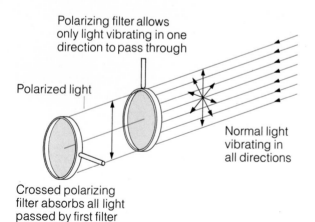

Polarizing filter allows only light vibrating in one direction to pass through

Polarized light

Normal light vibrating in all directions

Crossed polarizing filter absorbs all light passed by first filter

Coherent Light

In ordinary light, the waves travel at a mix of intervals; there is no order to the peaks and valleys of the waves. Such light is said to be incoherent.

Light of one wavelength is said to be monochromatic light. Ordinarily, monochromatic light is incoherent. Under certain conditions, light can be made to be both monochromatic and coherent. Such light is called *laser* light. Because of the coherency, the energy of laser light can be considerable. (*See:* LASER.)

• *See also:* BLACK BODY; COLOR TEMPERATURE; COLOR THEORY; DICHROIC FILTERS; DIFFRACTION; DIFFUSION; DISPERSION; FILTERS; FLUORESCENCE; INVERSE-SQUARE LAW; LASER; LENSES; LIGHT; MIRROR LENSES; MIRRORS; OPTICS; POLARIZED-LIGHT PHOTOGRAPHY; PRISMS; REFLECTANCE; REFLECTORS; SPECTRUM; VISION; WAVELENGTH.

Further Reading: Eastman Kodak Co. *Adventures in Existing-Light Photography.* Rochester, NY: Eastman Kodak Co., 1973. Feininger, Andreas. *Light and Lighting in Photography.* Englewood Cliffs, NJ: Prentice-Hall, Inc., 1976. Life Library of Photography. *Light and Film.* Hastings-on-Hudson, NY: Time-Life Books, Div. of Time, Inc., 1970. Petzold, Paul. *Light on People.* Garden City, NY: Amphoto, 1971.

Light Boxes

The primary purpose of a light box is for viewing transparencies and negatives; however, it can be used for different types of photographic lighting as well. It consists of a box with a light source covered by a translucent sheet of plastic or glass. The lights usually used are fluorescent tubes, which give off little heat as compared with incandescent lamps.

A light box can be purchased from a photographic dealer, or one can be built at home with relatively few materials and a little know-how. Such a box will serve as an all-purpose light source that gives direct light, backlight, transilluminated light, and shadowless light; it is a broad and relatively cool source. Most boxes are corrected for color so they can serve as sources for both black-and-white and color photography.

Instead of being in the standard position on the bottom as in a commercial light box, the lights in the home-built light box described in this article are mounted under the top and illuminate the bottom of the box. The advantage of this lamp position is that it throws an even spread of light down on the bottom of the box for shadowless lighting of three-dimensional objects, as well as for copying and shooting other flat subject matter.

The bottom of the box, in turn, acts as a large reflector, and can serve as a broad light source similar to that created by shining floodlights against a wall or ceiling.

Light Source

The home-built unit shown here is designed around an unusual fluorescent bulb made by Duratest and marketed as the Vita-lite. This bulb is manufactured using a series of phosphors not normally included in fluorescent bulbs. The light is balanced for 5500 degrees Kelvin (K), which very closely matches the color spectrum for most daylight color films. This means that one can shoot daylight-balanced color film without going through the elaborate testing and corrections necessary with most fluorescent lights. The Vita-lite eliminates the green tint that usually results when making color photographs with fluorescent light.

Similar lights are made by both Westinghouse and General Electric. The Westinghouse bulb is balanced for 5000 K and is marketed under the trade name 5000/U (Ultralume). General Electric's bulb is called the C/50 Chromaline™.

The box utilizes four 24-inch 20-watt bulbs in standard fluorescent fixtures. The top is covered with a sheet of white opal or translucent plastic, which can be obtained through most plastic supply houses. Frosted glass can be used instead. The top serves as a platform on which the subject is placed when doing either backlighting or when shooting small transparent or translucent objects.

Assembly. The basic materials needed for the project are shown in the accompanying photograph. All wood, with the exception of the legs and top mounting blocks, can be cut from a 4″ × 8″ sheet of ¼-inch plywood. If a power saw is not available, most lumber yards will cut it for a nominal charge.

The basic box is assembled with a wood glue and brads. Reinforcing strips are glued in each corner, and the "T" nuts are mounted in the strips to hold the legs. Blocks (2-inches square) are glued into each upper inside corner; these also have "T" nuts on their undersides to take the 2-inch bolts used to

---

Materials needed to construct a light box:

A 4′ × 8′ sheet of plywood (¼-inch), cut as follows:
  2 pieces, 30″ × 36″, top and bottom
  2 pieces, 12″ × 36″, front and back
  2 pieces, 12″ × 29½″, sides
  4 pieces, 30″ × 3″, top filler strips
  4 pieces, 11″ × 3″, leg reinforcements
4 pieces pine, 2″ × 2″ × 36″, legs
4 pieces pine, 2″ × 2″ × 1″, top mounting blocks
12 "T" nuts (¼–20)
8 bolts (¼–20, 3-inch)
4 bolts (¼–20, 2-inch)
12 washers
4 fluorescent fixtures (24-inch)
A 30-foot, two-wire electrical cord (#16)
4 Vita-lite or equivalent fluorescent bulbs (24-inch, 20-watt).

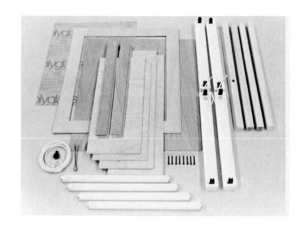

1 toggle switch
1 male plug
Brads, wood glue, and electrical tape or wire nuts
A piece of translucent (opal) plastic sheet or frosted glass (⅛″ × 24″ × 30″)

hold the top on. At this stage, the box is quite flexible, and will not become rigid until the top is bolted in place.

The top to which the fluorescent fixtures are mounted must be cut out so that there is a centered opening measuring 23″ × 29″. The simplest way to do this is with a hand key-hole saw or electric saber saw. The 3-inch-wide filler strips are glued to the upper surface of the top, and serve as a frame to hold the translucent plastic sheet centered in the opening. Keep in mind that the fluorescent fixtures must be wired in parallel. All wiring must follow safety codes to avoid shock or fire hazards. Just follow the accompanying wiring diagram if there are any doubts. Be sure to mount the fluorescent fixtures ¼ inch from the outside of the frame. This leaves a ¼-inch lip around the top so it can be mounted on the box.

Uses

Light Table. The finished box serves as an excellent light table for editing slides or retouching negatives. The interior of the box should be painted a brilliant matte-white to help distribute the light evenly. The edges directly under the lamps have approximately ¼ stop more light than the center. The subject has to be large enough to lie directly under the lights for the exposure to be effected. The opening in the box is covered with the opal plastic

The finished light box may be used as a light table for viewing, editing, and retouching transparencies and negatives. Photo by Harvey Shaman.

(or frosted glass), which helps to even out and diffuse the light.

Shadowless Backgrounds. One of the most useful features of the box is to provide shadowless backgrounds for small objects. This gives the effect of the subject floating in mid-air by eliminating the distracting background shadow created by the main light.

Seamless Backgrounds. By drilling holes in the ends of the legs and inserting lengths of ⅜-inch aluminum rod, a frame to hold a piece of Kodak diffusion sheet or other translucent material can be made (as shown in the photograph on the next page) to form a seamless background for photographing glass.

Place a floodlight behind the diffusion sheet and position it so its intensity is approximately the same as that from the box, and the result will be a basic white background with the glass bowl floating in space.

If the floodlight is moved in close to the diffusion sheet and exposure is made only for this light, a totally different effect is produced. Any number of variations can be achieved by the placement and intensity of the lights. One thing should be kept in mind when shooting glass: Any frontlighting on the

After the filler strips have been glued, the fluorescent fixtures are bolted to the underside of the top. They should be mounted ¼ inch from the outside edge of the frame. This leaves a lip so the top can rest on the sides. The two wires should be wired parallel to each other within each fluorescent fixture. One wire should then be connected to the switch. The edges of the box, directly under the bulbs, tend to have about ¼ stop more light than does the center.

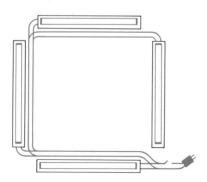

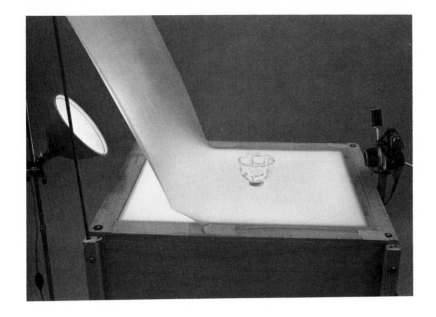

Translucent material for seamless backgrounds used in photographing glass may be held in place by rods inserted in holes drilled in the ends of the table legs. Photo by Harvey Shaman.

glass should be kept to a minimum because of the glare and brilliant highlights that it creates.

Photographing Three-Dimensional Objects. If the top of the light box is removed and a three-dimensional object is placed on the white bottom of the box, a completely shadowless lighting effect is achieved because the bottom of the box is completely surrounded by white light. The effect is equivalent to tent lighting.

Two-Level Shooting Box. It is possible to make a two-level shooting box by covering the box opening with a piece of clear glass. A foreground subject can then be placed on the glass and illuminated from above with floods or strobe (if color is being shot). The lower object is shadowlessly illuminated by the fluorescents and can be held to any degree of sharpness by controlling the camera's diaphragm.

Portraiture. By hanging the box without its opal glass on a wall, or setting it on its side on a table, a relatively broad light source for window effect portraiture is achieved. A black background gives a dramatic look, while a white one gives separation and a more open feeling to the subject.

Copying. For copying documents and other flat objects, the box hung on a wall is an instant lighting setup because broad even light is projected on the back of the box by the four color-corrected fluorescents. Removal of the lower bolts of the four legs permits them to be folded out of the way along the sides of the box.

• *See also:* BACKGROUNDS, ELIMINATING; COPYING; LIGHTING; PHOTOMECHANICAL REPRODUCTION, PREPARING ART FOR; PRODUCT PHOTOGRAPHY.

Facing page, top row: (Left) A tent lighting effect useful for photographing three-dimensional objects may be produced by removing the top of the light box and placing the object on the white bottom of the box. The result will be a completely unshadowed lighting effect. (Right) By covering the box opening with a sheet of clear glass, a two-level box may be created. This will allow the photographing of two differently lighted objects at the same time. Bottom row: (Left) The effect of window light for portraiture may be simulated by use of a light box in a vertical position, with the top glass removed. The background may vary according to the desired effect. (Right) The broad, even light projected on the back of the light box is ideal for copying purposes. The top glass should be removed and the box placed in a vertical position. Photos by Harvey Shaman.

Light Boxes

Light Boxes

Lighting

Photographic lighting is the illumination of subjects being photographed. It comes from both natural and artificial sources, and is controlled by the photographer so that the resulting pictures have the desired effect. Objects are not photographed—only the light reflected by the objects is photographed. Very few subjects emit light by which their pictures can be taken.

The word "lighting" is both a noun and a verb. The above definition of lighting defines the word as a noun. When used as a verb, photographic lighting means the practice of controlling the light on subjects for the purpose of taking photographs. With artificial light, this means selecting the type of lights and arranging them so that they produce the effect the photographer wants. With natural light, it means selecting the type of light (sunlight, open shade, overcast light) and its direction (time of day), and perhaps modifying it by the use of reflectors, gobos, screens, or by adding artificial light (usually flash) to the natural light.

Lighting serves both technical and aesthetic purposes. Its technical functions are to provide enough light for adequate exposure and to adjust the brightness range of the subjects photographed to fit within the limits of the photographic materials being used. Its aesthetic functions are to make the subject clearly and appropriately visible and, often, to create beauty or to express an emotion. Light can be measured, but beauty and feeling can only be sensed. Thus, it is up to each photographer to find and use the practical lighting that is most fitting for the work at hand.

Still, many traditional formulas for lighting—especially product and portrait lighting—are publicly accepted and often treated as hard and fast rules. This is a mistaken interpretation. Such formulas represent an established but optional approach; they are not substitutes for observation, initiative, and choice. Use them when they are right for a particular purpose; depart from them when they are not.

Since the 1950's, advertising photographers have been establishing new kinds of lighting. There is more use of large "soft" light sources and less use of small "hard" ones, such as spotlights. Studio light is no less artificial than before, but it seems much more relaxed now. The expressive range has been enlarged.

Kinds of Lighting

Most *natural light* is sunlight in some form: direct, diffuse, reflected, or in many combinations.

Artificial light comes from any man-made light source.

Available or *existing light* can be either natural or artificial: It is any unchanged light used by a photographer, but the term usually implies dim light.

Direct light goes straight from its source to the subject. It is a "hard" light with sharply defined shadows when the source is small; it is "soft" when the source is large and the shadows are soft-edged.

Diffuse light, which is broken up along the way, reaches the subject from many directions at once. It is a soft light that produces soft-edged shadows and, if it is diffuse enough, sometimes no shadows at all.

Bounce light, which is typically quite diffuse, is reflected onto the subject from a nearby surface, and does not go directly from source to subject—the shinier the surface, the less diffuse the bounce light.

Light from small sources (the sun, a flashcube, a bare light bulb) produces distinct highlights and sharp shadows; light from large sources (the sky, a bank of floodlamps, a reflecting wall, a nearby window), produces large, softly defined shadows and highlights, and minimizes surface textures.

Direct light can travel in a narrow beam (spotlights), but it typically spreads out from its source. Lighting can consist of a single light source or any number of sources. Many professionals feel strongly that no matter how many light sources are used, one of them should dominate. This, too, is optional, but practical for many situations because it more closely matches natural sunlight. Direct light can be polarized—within limits—to suppress unwanted reflections and glare.

Lighting has duration: It is either *continuous* in time as with incandescent lamps or, as with flash photography, *instantaneous.* Continuous and instantaneous light can be, and often are, used together—for instance, flash fill in pictures taken by sunlight.

Lighting techniques are not entirely limited to visible light. The principles can be applied to arranging illumination by infrared and ultraviolet radiation, and even x-rays.

Lighting Factors

Essential factors in lighting include the number of light sources; the direction(s) of the light; the degree of directness or diffusion; the presence or absence of reflecting surfaces near the subject, and their size, texture, reflectivity, and color; the duration of the light; its brightness (and sometimes the accompanying heat) as it affects the subject; and the relative distances, intensities, sizes, and color temperatures of the light sources when more than one is used.

Direction. The direction(s) from which light strikes the subject, relative to the camera, is extremely important. Single-source lighting can come from anywhere—above the subject, below, in front, behind, from either side, or from any position in between. Each basic direction has its name: frontlight, backlight, sidelight, toplight, three-quarter light, and so on. Most natural light comes from above the subject, so most artificial lighting is arranged to do the same. Some subjects, especially people's faces, look unnatural when illuminated from below.

Natural Light. Natural lighting outdoors is "controlled" largely by choosing the time to photograph. It takes an overcast day to produce soft, diffuse light, and a sunny day to produce brilliant, hard light and strong shadows.

Bright Days. Not all sunlight is the same; it is especially important to pick the time of day—low sun with a yellow or orange cast late in the afternoon or early in the morning; high, harsh sun that throws hard shadows and flat light at noon. Noon sun is hotter in temperature, but cooler—bluer—in color than early or late sun. Most photographers prefer low sun over midday sun, and often use filters to adjust the color of the light.

Another way of controlling sunlight is largely a matter of choosing the direction of the light. With a fixed subject such as a building or a landscape, time of day determines light direction. Other subjects can usually be turned or moved so that the light comes from a desired direction. When the subject is between the camera and the sun, it is backlighted. When the sun is behind the camera, the subject is frontlighted. Knowing in advance where the photography will take place often makes it possible to place the subject or background in the lighting that suits it best.

In addition to choosing the type of day and the time of day, natural light can be modified.

Overcast Days. When working in color on a gray day, use a UV filter or a skylight filter to avoid the blue cast that comes with the weather.

Indoors, it is dark on an overcast day, but beside any window looking out on the sky, there is beautiful light for portraiture.

Outdoors, the light of a gray or rainy day is diffuse and soft, and easier to work with than direct sunlight because it is far less contrasty. Mainly, it is skylight from above. Therefore, watch out for deeply shadowed eyes that can look like black holes in the face when printed. The light looks so soft, we tend to assume it will be kind to the subject; this is not necessarily true. To achieve softness and photograph eyes visibly, simply have people turn their faces slightly upward toward the light. This is also good for portraits taken indoors under skylights, and in offices and stores with overhead fluorescent lighting. Scrims are also used for diffusing direct sunlight. They are large frames covered with translucent material and are generally used for softening the light when taking close-ups of faces.

Artificial Light. The greatest difference between natural and artificial light is probably this: With artificial light, the distance from the lamp to the subject becomes crucial—a source of problems and a means of control.

The sun is so far from the earth that for practical purposes its light falls equally brightly even on things that are miles apart. But in the studio, the light on the subject becomes markedly brighter as the lamp moves closer, and dimmer as it moves away. This happens at a regular rate.

Reflection. When sunlight is too contrasty, the harshness can easily be reduced by using a white reflector to throw light onto the shadow side of the subject. The white wall of a house might do. (When working in color, beware of reflections from strongly colored surfaces. Use them deliberately, or avoid them.)

When outdoors on location, many professionals bring along white or silvered sheets or panels that can be hung up or stood wherever they are needed. A silvered board—one covered with aluminum paint or crumpled aluminum foil—produces dis-

On gray or rainy days, lighting is soft, diffuse, and less contrasty than in bright sunlight. Outdoor light such as this is essentially skylight from above; here, the white sand reflects light back onto the boys' faces, eliminating deeply shadowed areas.

tinctly brighter and contrastier fill light than a matte white board. To have both, make one side of each panel white and the other side silver. (If aluminum foil is used, place the matte side out, since the glossy side may produce unwanted hot spots in the fill light.)

Sunlight reflected into a shaded area from walls, reflector panels, the ground, snow, or sand provides a softly directional radiance that can make the subject glow beautifully.

Electronic flash, or a flashbulb or flashcube—preferably bounced rather than used directly—can provide excellent fill light and open up the shadows. When working in color, electronic flash is the right color temperature for daylight film, as are blue flashbulbs. Clear flashbulbs cast a yellowish light. In black-and-white photography, the bulb color does not matter.

Sunlight shining through a window into a white-walled room provides a radiant studio that offers a great variety in lighting, depending on the place and direction of the shooting. But here the timing is critical; the sun shines into a window in a given direction just once a day, for a surprisingly short time. It changes constantly; change along with it to take advantage of light that is as rewarding as it is demanding. Skylight coming in windows is easier to control—it is softer and does not change direction so rapidly. The "north light" of the old-time portrait photographer is an example. The chief disadvantage of this type of light is that it is low in intensity.

The Inverse-Square Law

This is the law that governs the rate at which light falls off with increasing distance between the light source and the subject. Briefly, if two identical lights are at different distances from identical subjects, the closer one throws more light onto the subject than the farther one. If it is twice as close, it lights the subject four times as brightly ($2^2 = 4$). If it is three times as close, the light on the subject will be nine times as bright as the illumination from the other light on the other subject ($3^2 = 9$).

This principle also applies when repositioning a light source or moving a subject to change the light-

(Right) Window light is an excellent source of illumination for indoor portraiture. Here, a white card was used to reflect light onto the side of the model's face away from the window, brightening her dress and casting highlights in her eyes, and on her nose and lips. Photo by Bob Clemens.

to-subject distance. The same inverse-square law can be written as:

$$I_2 = I_1 \times \frac{d_1^2}{d_2^2}$$

where: I_1 is the original intensity of the light at d_1 distance, d_2 is the new distance, and I_2 is the intensity you want to find at the new distance.

Using this example, assume that a light source at a distance of 10 feet gives an illuminance of 3 footcandles on the subject. At half the distance (5 feet) the equation becomes:

$$I_2 = 3\,\frac{\text{ft-}}{\text{cdl}} \times \frac{10^2}{5^2} = 3 \times \frac{100}{25} = 3 \times 4 = 12\,\frac{\text{ft-}}{\text{cdl}}$$

At half the distance, 12 footcandles is 4 times the original 3 footcandles. For a fuller explanation,

see the article INVERSE-SQUARE LAW.

The inverse-square law applies with absolute strictness only to an imaginary source—a point of light that has no area; but it is accurate enough for many studio lights. There are two major exceptions:

1. Light concentrated by a lens, as in a spotlight beam, does not spread outward from the source sufficiently to diminish in intensity according to the inverse-square law.*

---

*This is true only when the subject is so close to the lamp that the light source is the aperture stop of the spotlight system. At greater distances, spotlights obey the same inverse-square relationships as other light sources.

2. The light from a large-area source, such as a bank of floodlamps, thrown on a subject 3 feet away, will be only slightly brighter than the light thrown on a subject 6 feet away.

Most of the light from this large source shines *past* the closer subject, and light from *more of its area*—that is, from more lamps—falls on the distant subject. But as the distance increases, so does the falloff of the light begin to come more into line with the inverse-square law. The best procedure is to use an exposure meter, not a tape measure, to find the correct exposure when working with large light sources.

Studio Lighting

Occasionally, one small bright spotlight is used all by itself in a dark studio to get dramatic light-against-dark effects. This "simple" lighting is, however, difficult to use well and is appropriate to few subjects. Using more than one light source is generally better.

Multiple-source lighting can come from any number of lights and any combination of directions, but in general, as few lights as possible are used—each with its own purpose—and most are placed somewhat above the subject. One light, called the *key light,* is placed so that its light dominates all the others.

Two-lamp lighting is basic to traditional studio portraiture: a strong main or key light, high in front of the subject and to one side; and a weaker fill-in light, as close as possible to the camera on the other side. The key light is the brighter one—either be-

Light falls off with increasing distance between the light source and the subject. (Left) This picture was taken by available light in the room. Because of the overall lighting, the background figures are clearly visible. (Right) Electronic flash aimed at the main subject provides the lighting for this photo. Because of light falloff, the background figures are barely visible. Photos by John Menihan.

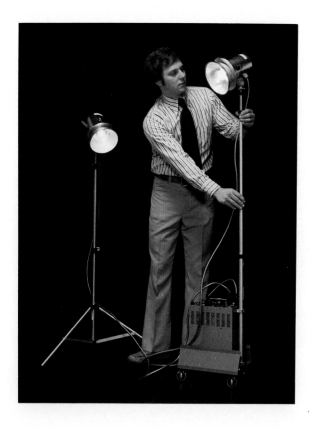

Traditionally, two lamps are used in the basic studio lighting setup. The main, or key, light (at right) is placed high in front of the subject and to one side. A weaker fill-in light is placed on the other side of the subject to lighten shadows cast by the main light. Photo by Neil Montanus.

main-lighted parts of the subject and the shadows, which are lighted only by the fill light. In traditional black-and-white portraiture, it is common to use different lighting ratios for men and women subjects. The usual ratio for women is low, ranging from 2:1 to 3:1 for low contrast and delicacy of tone. In a 2:1 ratio, the highlights are lighted twice as brightly as the shadows; 3:1 lighting puts three times the fill light on the brightest areas. The ratios for men range from 3:1 upward to a contrasty 8:1 in black-and-white portraiture.

In color portraiture, where contrast is restricted to the tonal range of a single grade of printing paper, a 3:1 ratio is customary for both men and women. Color contrast makes up for the unvarying light-and-dark contrast.

A 3:1 ratio can easily be set up without an exposure meter either by using a main light twice as bright (twice the wattage in continuous lighting, or twice the BCPS in electronic flash), with both lamps at the same distance from the subject; or by using equal light sources at different distances.

Light distance can be related to f-stops. Lens f-stops are based on the inverse-square law (with the lens as light source), and the same series of numbers is a useful guide for relative lamp-to-subject distances: 1, 1.4, 2, 2.8, 4, 5.6, 8, 11, 16, 22, 32, 45, 64, 90, 128.

Placement of Key and Fill Lighting. When the fill light is placed one stop farther from the subject than the main light, the lighting ratio will be 1:3 with lamps of equal brightness at the source. If the main light is 4 feet from the subject, place the fill light at 5.6 feet; or do it the other way around. If the fill light is at 8 feet, put the main light 5.6 feet from the subject to get a 3:1 lighting ratio. These distance relationships are the same as $f/4$, $f/5.6$, and $f/8$. Any adjacent pair in the f-stop series in any units of measurement will work: it can be feet, inches, centimetres, or metres. Mathematically, this is equivalent to multiplying or dividing by $\sqrt{2}$ or 1.4.

cause it has a stronger lamp or because it is closer to the subject or both. The fill light is there to lighten the shadows the main light casts, not to obliterate them.

Other lights may be added to throw highlights on hair, to provide tonal contrast between the subject and the background, and so on; but they are incidental to the main light and the fill light.

To adjust the brightness range of the portrait subject to the film and the printing paper, the balance between the main and fill lights is controlled either by adjusting relative lamp-to-subject distances or the relative brightnesses of the light sources.

Using the inverse-square law and equally bright lamps, it is simple to adjust the lighting balance by measured lamp-to-subject distance alone. However, an incident-light exposure meter, or a reflected-light meter used with a gray or white test card, simplifies the job.

The Lighting Ratio. This ratio is the measurable relationship between the light that falls on the

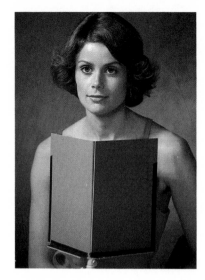

The lighting ratio shows the relationship between light falling on the main-lighted parts of the subject and that falling on the fill-lighted parts. As the ratio increases, so does the contrast. This series illustrates the following ratios: (left) 2:1; (center) 4:1; (right) 8:1. Photos by Andrew W. Purdon.

The light from the fill light at this one-stop-farther distance is just half as bright on the subject as the light received from the main light. The reason this is not 2:1 lighting, but 3:1, is that the main light does not fall on the shadows, but the fill light falls on both shadows and highlights.

Suppose that the fill light throws 50 footcandles on the whole subject, and the main light throws 100 on the highlight areas only. The shadows get a total of 50 footcandles, and the main-lighted parts get a total of 150 footcandles—50 from the fill light, plus 100 from the main light; 150:50 is a 3:1 ratio.

Variations within this type of key lighting and fill lighting include "butterfly lighting," "short lighting," and "broad lighting." In each case, the subject usually faces one side of the camera, in a position about halfway between full face and profile. Ordinarily the nose is not allowed to stick out past the cheek as seen from camera position.

Butterfly Lighting. Here the face is turned directly toward the main light, which is well above the head. It casts a shadow straight down from the nose toward the upper lip, and that is the "butterfly" shape of the nose shadow that gives this lighting its name. The front of the face is uniformly lighted, and the sides, from the cheekbones back, are more or less in shadow.

Short Lighting. The main light is on the side of the face that is turned away from the camera. The cheek that is farther away is strongly lighted, and the near side of the face is largely in shadow. This lighting is used to make wide faces look narrower.

Broad Lighting. The main light is on the side of the face that is turned toward the camera. The farther cheek is in shadow. This light tends to make thin faces look wider, and minimizes skin texture (especially when the main light is large and diffused).

Hair Light. A spotlight above and behind the subject can be used to add a brilliant highlight to the hair. "Barn doors"—adjustable flaps on either side of the lamp—or a "snoot"—a narrow tube that channels the light—can be used to keep the light from shining directly on the camera lens. A "gobo" —a small opaque card or screen on a stand or hand-held—can do the same job.

Kicker Lights. These are other narrow-beam lights like the hair light, used to add small, bright accents of highlight to the hair, the shoulders, and so on.

Rim Lighting. Used against dark backgrounds, rim lighting is just what it sounds like. A very bright light behind and slightly to one side and above the subject makes a very bright outline of the face and head, which are otherwise lighted conventionally. Well-placed gobos are essential here, or flare from the rim-lighting lamp may fog the picture.

Background Light. A milder alternative to the rim light is the background light, which prevents the dark side of the head from merging into a dark background. The background light does not fall on the subject at all; it just lightens part of the background so the dark side of the head stands out against it.

In most modern portrait photography, both the main and the fill lights are diffused to minimize skin texture. The use of small, direct light sources will emphasize skin texture, and pictures taken with this technique may require considerable retouching. (*See:* PORTRAITURE.)

Umbrella Lighting for Portraits. Umbrella lighting was in use by 1900, but has been popular only since the 1950's. White or silvered umbrellas are used as oversized reflectors, usually with electronic flash. Here, one light, placed quite close to the subject, is usually enough. The light source is large enough so the light *wraps around* the face. Three-dimensional form is shown very clearly by the softly defined, yet definite, highlight-and-shadow pattern this light produces. A silvered umbrella produces more contrasty light, and the highlights are more distinct than a matte white umbrella.

As compared to key lighting and fill lighting, umbrella lighting is far less formal, much easier to use, and looks more natural and less contrived. Since umbrellas fold, this is an easy light to carry for work on location. If the flash unit has no modeling light, a small reflector with a tungsten bulb can be clamped onto the umbrella handle next to the flash head. When the relationship of flash-to-modeling light has been established, an ordinary exposure meter can be used to read the modeling light; the reading is then converted to give the correct flash exposure. There is no reason the umbrella cannot be used with flashbulbs or with ordinary photoflood bulbs. (*See:* UMBRELLA LIGHTING.)

Bounce Light. Another informal type of lighting, often used by photojournalists, is bounce light, which is achieved by aiming the light or lights at the

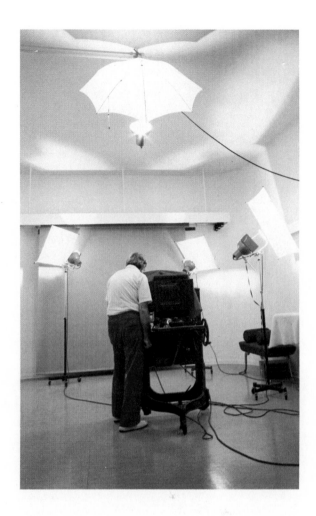

White or silvered umbrellas used as oversized reflectors in combination with electronic flash are commonly used in studio lighting, and may be used easily for location photography as well. Here, the large umbrella suspended from the ceiling provides the overall illumination and determines the exposure level. The mobile umbrella unit at right is the main, or modeling, light. The two smaller umbrellas are backlights to illuminate the hair and help separate the subject from the background. Note that the lights are aimed at the umbrellas, not directly at the subject. Photo by Al Gilbert.

white or light walls and ceiling of a room. Soft light is reflected onto the subject and throughout the room. The direction of the light can be made very definite by aiming all the lights at one spot, or the room can be flooded with shadowless light by aiming several lights at different places all around the walls and the ceiling. Usually the effect is between these extremes.

(Left) A photo taken using direct flash has harsh shadows and reflects too much light from the subject's face. (Right) When light is bounced off the white ceiling, light on the subject's face is flatteringly diffused, and shadows are eliminated. An interesting highlight is also added to the watering can, giving it roundness and texture. Photos by Neil Montanus.

When using bounce flash—bulbs or electronic —in a room of average size with light-colored walls and ceiling, the rule of thumb for black-and-white film is to give four times as much (two stops more) exposure as is required for direct flash with the same light source. In color work, be careful about wall and ceiling colors, which may rule out the use of bounce lighting.

For accurate exposure in an unfamiliar room, shoot and process a test roll, using the estimated exposure and bracketing to two stops more exposure and two stops less than the estimate. If there is no time for this and an electronic flash meter is not available, test shots made with an instant-picture film of known speed can give an accurate measure of exposure.

Another formula that is more accurate than the two-stops-more formula is based on the total distance the light travels:

$$f\text{-Number} = .7 \times \left(\frac{\text{Guide Number}}{d_1 + d_2}\right)$$

The f-number equals .7 times the guide number divided by the sum of the flash-to-ceiling distance and the ceiling-to-subject distance measured along the center light beam from the flash. This formula is valid for a relatively clean, white ceiling. For off-white or light-colored ceilings or walls, give one-half to one stop more exposure.

With bounce flash, it is important to use a deep reflector, and aim the flash unit in such a direction that *no direct light falls on the subject.*

Diffuse Backlight. A large weak frontlight with a diffuser lights the face, while two or four undiffused lights throw approximately four times as much light (by incident-light reading) onto a white background—a wall or seamless paper. Much more background light would produce undesirable flare and degrade the tones of the subject; less light would produce a dull, light gray background. The 1:4 lighting ratio between subject and background is best established by incident-light meter readings. Look for a two-stop difference in indicated exposures, and use the exposure indicated for the subject. No light from the sources that illuminate the background should fall directly on the subject. Trial-and-error testing by varying the ratio will help find the best balance. The 1:4 ratio is given as a starting point.

A more extreme version of diffuse backlighting uses only a white reflecting surface to light the face; all lights are aimed at the white background. Accurate exposure is required, and is best determined by using a reflected-light exposure meter to read the face tones. Use the indicated exposure.

Lighting for Products

The subjects that a product photographer must light differ much more from each other than the people who sit for portraits. Each object dictates its own requirements.

It is essential that the object be lighted so as to emphasize its nature (shiny or dull; angular or round; smooth or rough; light or dark; uniform or varied in tone; opaque, translucent or transparent, and so on); and it must be shown clearly—distinct from its surroundings or background.

One dominant light is used by most good product photographers, usually supplemented by a background light, and by whatever other lights are needed to cast revealing shadows or form revealing highlights. In many product color photographs, the main light is a strong, high-angle backlight. Frontal lighting is provided by reflectors that pick up spill from the backlight. This produces good edge separation from the background, combined with frontal lighting with a brightness range appropriate for color.

With objects that need a light background, a light box or light table can often be used to advantage, in that no cast shadow will interfere with the product's outline.

Alternatively, a sheet of glass or clear plastic strong enough to support the object and placed above a seamless background paper that curves from wall to floor, allows lighting from above or below or both without shadows.
CAUTION: Do not overheat glass with incandescent lamps; it may break.

For most purposes, an opaque sheet of seamless paper curved over a tabletop from a wall will be a satisfactory background.

If the object is shiny, you may want to show that. It is important to note that reflections bounce at the same angle coming and going. Place a small lighted bulb straight in front of the camera lens and move around the object looking for the gleam. Once it is located, simply place the "gleam light" at the point where you saw the gleam. Remove the bulb from in front of the camera, and you will see that the gleam now shows from the camera position and will appear in the picture.

To bring out surface textures strongly, use a small, direct light source and cross-light the surface. Let the light shine across the surface nearly parallel to its plane. Then every bump will acquire its own shadow and, if shiny, its own highlight as well.

Tent Lighting. Polished metal jewelry, machinery, and silverware sometimes defy conventional lighting schemes and are lost in a confusion of detailed reflections. Tent lighting is the best solution for this. The tent can be a cone of translucent plastic or tracing paper coming straight down over the subject from the camera lens at the point of the cone. Or it can be taped or tied to a large, diffused light source placed straight above the subject to form tent

Polished surfaces are best enhanced by tent lighting, which gives an even, luminous glow with no reflected details or distracting shadows. Photo by Neil Montanus.

walls around it. Then the lens looks in through a hole cut just for it. Lights shine on all sides and from above, so there are no shadows, and the light is very uniform and even.

Since there is nothing detailed to reflect—just bright, even, luminous tent walls—the contours of the object and its smooth surface become very clearly visible. Sometimes the contrast is so low that the picture threatens to be dull. Then the resourceful photographer introduces strips of gray, black, or colored paper into the tent and places them where they will form interesting and natural-looking reflections on the metal. (*See:* PRODUCT PHOTOGRAPHY; TENT LIGHTING.)

Copy Lighting. Copying flat pictures or documents requires another kind of even lighting. Every inch of the whole surface should receive exactly the same amount of light, and should be free from surface reflections that would otherwise shine up into the lens and wash out part of the copy material in the photograph. Classical copy lighting uses two or four lights placed at equal distances from the area to be lighted and at an angle from 10 to 45 degrees to the surface being copied. The evenness of the lighting should be checked with an exposure meter, since the eye can be fooled by gradual changes in light that are not easily seen by the photographer while working but are evident in the copy photograph. (*See:* ART, PHOTOGRAPHY OF; COPYING.)

Painting with Light

When a large area must be illuminated by a single source, a "painting" technique can be used. A continuous source can be moved so that its light falls successively on every area of the scene while the camera shutter remains open. Or, a flash unit can be fired repeatedly, aiming it at a different portion of the scene each time. Details of this technique are explained in the article PAINTING WITH LIGHT.

Lighting Equipment

Most of the lighting described here can be done equally well, although not as easily, with either continuous or intermittent light.

The main advantages of continuous light are: (1) you can see the lighting constantly as you work and make changes easily as the need arises, and (2) lamp bulbs and simple fixtures for this type of lighting are relatively inexpensive.

The main advantages of flash and electronic flash are that they use less power than continuous

light, produce much less heat, offer greater comfort to portrait subjects, and make rapid-action photography by artificial light easy and practical. Also, the color temperature of electronic flash closely matches that required for daylight-type color films.

For all these reasons, professional photographers have turned increasingly to electronic flash. The continuously shining modeling lights that are built into most modern studio electronic flash units let the photographers see their lighting as well as before, while the subject is neither baked nor blinded. For some kinds of location work, the flashbulb still has its place. A sack of bulbs and a flashgun weigh a great deal less than the power pack required for equally bright flashes from an electronic flash unit. However, the bulbs must be changed after each shot. Blue flashbulbs are color-balanced for daylight color film.

Continuous Light Sources. Continuous light sources include incandescent photoflood (3400 K) bulbs, reflector flood and spot bulbs, blue photoflood bulbs, 3200 K bulbs, and reflector floodlamps; tungsten-halogen lamps and reflector lamps; and pulsed xenon arc lamps, carbon arcs, and fluorescent lamps.

Photoflood Bulbs. These bulbs are like household light bulbs in most ways, but they burn at a higher-than-rated voltage; this makes them very bright and gives them short working life—from about 3 hours for a 250-watt No. 1 photoflood to 10 hours for a 1000-watt No. 4 photoflood. They burn at a color temperature of 3400 K, which is correct for type A color films used without a filter.

Blue Photoflood Bulbs. These bulbs burn at a warm daylight color temperature of about 4800 K. No correction is normally needed for daylight color film with blue photofloods; the slight added warmth is generally considered attractive.

For a strictly normal 5500 K rendition on daylight color film with 4800 K bulbs, use a Kodak 82A filter and add one-third stop to the exposure. (A camera with a through-the-lens meter can read through the filter; no correction is necessary since the meter adds it automatically).

The life of photoflood bulbs can be prolonged by burning them at about half the normal voltage when not actually taking pictures. Either a variable-voltage transformer or a "high-low" circuit can be used to accomplish this.

3200 K Incandescent Bulbs. Bulbs generally preferable to 3400 K photofloods are 3200 K bulbs, except for working with type A color film. They have a much longer life, and do not dim or change color nearly as much before they burn out. The 3200 K bulbs are color-balanced for Kodak type L and type B (tungsten) color films, which need no filter with these lamps.

In addition, there are a number of incandescent bulbs made with high watt values that have bases for special studio floodlights and spotlights.

Tungsten-Halogen Lamps. A newer form of incandescent light is the long-life tungsten-halogen lamp, sometimes called a quartz-iodide light.

Its tungsten filament is surrounded by a halogen (iodine or bromine gas) atmosphere in a quartz tube.

RATINGS OF TYPICAL PHOTOFLOOD BULBS (110–120 VOLTS)

Bulb	Watts	Lumens	Life (hours)	Screw Base*	Degrees (K)
No. 1	250	8,000	3	Medium	3400
No. 2	500	16,000	6	Medium	3400
No. 4	1000	30,000	10	Mogul	3400

*A medium screw-type base is a household base that fits standard sockets. Mogul is a larger screw base.

RATINGS OF BLUE PHOTOFLOOD BULBS (110–120 VOLTS)

Bulb	Watts	Lumens	Life (hours)	Screw Base	Degrees (K)
No. B1	250	5,000	3	Medium	4800
No. B2	500	10,000	6	Medium	4800
No. B4	1000	19,000	10	Mogul	4800

These bulbs are normally used in aluminum reflectors, 9–16 inches in diameter. But there are also reflector photofloods with a built-in reflector as part of each bulb.

RATINGS OF REFLECTOR PHOTOFLOODS (110–120 VOLTS)

Watts*	Center Beam Candle-power	Beam Spread	Life (hours)	Screw Base	Degrees (K)
200	8,500	Medium	4	Medium	3400
300	11,000	Medium	4	Medium	3400
375	14,000	Medium	4	Medium	3400
375	16,000	Medium	4	Medium	3400
500	6,500	Flood	6	Medium	3400
500	50,000	Spot	6	Medium	3400

*The difference between the two 375-watt bulbs is that one of them is larger, so its reflector throws more light. The 500-watt flood throws a wider-than-normal beam, dimmer in the center than most, but covering a larger area. The 500-watt spot puts about the same amount of light into a narrow, concentrated beam. Flood and spot reflector bulbs are differentiated by the codes RFL and RSP in their designations.

RATINGS OF 3200 K BULBS (110–120 VOLTS)

Watts	Lumens	Life (hours)	Screw Base	Degrees (K)
250	6,500	20	Medium	3200
500	13,650	60	Medium	3200
1000	26,500	60	Mogul	3200

The working temperature is very high, and the filament is regenerated as the lamp burns. Halogen combines with heat-vaporized tungsten and redeposits it on the filament, not on the quartz, so the tube stays clear and the life of the filament is prolonged. The color temperature, whether 3200, 3400, or 5500 K, stays almost unchanged throughout the life of the tube (about 200 hours for a 250-watt lamp).

The relatively higher price of a tungsten-halogen tube is more than offset by its long life, and its ultimate cost is lower than that of conventional incandescent bulbs. Much smaller than a bulb, the tungsten-halogen lamp does not fit household sockets and requires its own fixture.

Most tungsten-halogen lamps are in the 250–1000-watt range, and give about the same light per watt as conventional photolamps. They are used as modeling lights in some studio electronic flash units, as well as being widely used as continuous-light lamps in studios and on location.

Pulsed Xenon Arc Lamps. These are used largely as projection lamps in enlarging and for motion pictures—seldom, if ever, for conventional still photography. In the graphic arts, they are used as copy lights for color work, since their spectral energy distribution is close to that of daylight. The rate of pulsation is controllable, and is sometimes used in place of a mechanical shutter in cinematography. Ordinary exposure meters cannot cope with the light from pulsed xenon arc lamps; special ones called integrating meters are needed.

Fluorescent Tubes. Fluorescent lighting is at times a necessary evil for color photographers, since they cannot always avoid it. A gap in the spectrum emitted by most fluorescent lamps gives an objectionable blue-green cast to color photographs; however, the eye, which has a different sensitivity from that of film, sees nothing wrong in the lighting until it shows up in the picture.

Filtration can provide some, but not full, correction. There is, however, one exception. Some special 5500 K daylight fluorescent tubes are made for indoor gardeners, to stimulate plant growth. Although they are dimmer than most fluorescent tubes, the 5500 K tubes can be used with daylight color films without a filter. There are other special bulbs for color-print viewing that can also be used.

There is no problem with fluorescent light in black-and-white photography.

Instantaneous Light Sources. Flash is the predominant instantaneous light source used in studio and location photography. It may be provided by a flashbulb, a flashcube, or an electronic flash unit. Flash offers the advantages of great portability, freedom from continuous heat and glare that may affect the subject, and—in the case of electronic flash—the ability to stop action beyond the range of the fastest shutter speeds. Flash sources, their use, and exposure are covered in the articles ELECTRONIC FLASH, FLASH PHOTOGRAPHY, and GUIDE NUMBERS.

A stroboscopic light source is essentially an intermittent electronic flash unit that fires continually at a rapid rate. It is usually used to obtain multiple images during a single brief shutter exposure. (*See:* STROBOSCOPIC PHOTOGRAPHY.)

• *See also:* ARC LAMPS; ARTIFICIAL LIGHT; ART, PHOTOGRAPHY OF; BACK-LIGHT; BOUNCE LIGHT; BRIGHTNESS RANGE; BROAD LIGHTING; COLOR PHOTOGRAPHY; COPYING; ELECTRONIC FLASH; FLASH PHOTOGRAPHY; GUIDE NUMBERS; INCANDESCENT LAMPS; INVERSE-SQUARE LAW; NATURAL LIGHT; PAINTING WITH LIGHT; PRODUCT PHOTOGRAPHY; SHORT LIGHTING; STROBOSCOPIC PHOTOGRAPHY; TENT LIGHTING; UMBRELLA LIGHTING.

Further Reading: Bomback, Edward S. *Manual of Photographic Lighting.* Dobbs Ferry, NY: Morgan & Morgan, Inc., 1971; Helprin, Ben and PhotoGraphic Magazine Editors. *Guide to Photo Lighting Techniques.* Los Angeles, CA: Petersen Publishing Co., 1973; Nurnberg, W. *Lighting for Photography,* 6th ed. Garden City, NY: Amphoto, 1968.

FLUORESCENT LIGHT STARTING FILTER CORRECTION TABLE

Kodak Film Type	Type of Fluorescent Light					
	Warm White Deluxe	Warm White	White	Cool White Deluxe	Cool White	Daylight
	Filter and Exposure Adjustment in Stops (S)					
Daylight*	60C + 30M	40C + 40M	20C + 30M	30C + 20M	30M	40M + 30Y
	+1⅔S	+1⅓S	+1S	+1S	+⅔S	+1S
Type A (3400 K)	None	30M + 10Y	40M + 30Y	10M + 20Y	50M + 50Y	85 + 30M + 10Y
	—	+1S	+1S	+⅔S	+1⅓S	+1⅓S
Type B Tungsten (3200 K)	+10Y	30M + 20Y	40M + 40Y	10M + 30Y	50M + 60Y	85B + 30M + 10Y
	+⅓S	+1S	+1S	+⅔S	+1⅓S	+1⅓S

*Includes Kodak Type S films and Kodacolor films, except Kodacolor 400 film, which needs no filter correction.
NOTE: Increase the meter-calculated exposure by the amount indicated in the table. If the exposure times require, make the necessary additional corrections for reciprocity effect, both in exposure and filtration. With transparency films, run a test filter series up to ±CC20 from the given values (usually in the M⟵⟶G and Y⟵⟶B directions) under each lighting condition.
 Filters specified above are Kodak color compensating filters and Kodak Wratten filters. Exposure increases or filters with the same designations from other manufacturers may differ.

Lightning Photography

When lightning occurs at night, it is much easier to photograph than most photographers think. A knowledge of local weather conditions and terrain can be helpful because the most difficult part of photographing lightning is anticipating where it will strike. For this reason it is best to use a normal or wide-angle lens and to try to take the photograph from a high vantage point with an unobstructed view of a large area.

You will need the following equipment to successfully photograph lightning:

1. A camera with shutter-speed settings of "B" or "T."
2. A tripod (or other camera support).
3. A cable release (not essential, but useful).
4. A dark card or lens cap.

Taking the Picture

Once the location of the electrical storm has been determined, follow the steps outlined below:

1. Set up the camera on a tripod and aim it at the storm.
2. Set the camera's distance scale at infinity.
3. Set the shutter speed at "B" or "T."
4. Set the aperture to an appropriate f-stop (see the following section on exposure).

Exposure. If the photography is taking place at night and no light—other than the lightning flashes—falls on the scene being recorded, the shutter can be left open for as long as it is necessary to record a lightning flash. If, on the other hand, the scene being photographed contains lights, such as building or street lights, the exposure must be calculated based on the particular scene. (*See:* AVAILABLE-LIGHT PHOTOGRAPHY.) Use an exposure with as

The highest point on a flat plain, this windmill is the likeliest attraction for lightning during an electrical storm. With the shutter held open, the camera recorded several lightning flashes.

long a shutter speed as possible so that you will have the best opportunity of recording a lightning bolt.

For example, if you are photographing a distant skyline at night and the exposure is 4 seconds at $f/2.8$ with an ASA 64 film, it would be best to set the camera for a longer equivalent exposure. For example, set the camera at $f/16$ and leave the shutter open for as long as several minutes. The actual exposure needed at this aperture depends upon the reciprocity characteristics of the film used. If automobiles or boats are moving within the scene, the lights from those objects will record as streaks of light on the final film when long exposures are used.

Multiple Flashes. To record more than one bolt of lightning on any one frame, do not advance the film between exposures. The easiest way to do this is to set the shutter-speed control to "T" and, with the lens cap *on* the lens, release the shutter. It is a simple matter to remove the lens cap to record successive bolts. A dark card can also be held in front of the lens when the lightning is not flashing.

If you are working at night and there are no extraneous lights that can spoil the photo, leave the lens cap off and let the multiple flashes of lightning record on the film. After you have the desired number of flashes, close the shutter.

Precautions. Be sure to locate in an area where you will be protected should the lightning strike near you. Try to take the photos from inside a building through an open window; photographing lightning from inside a car is also safe. Should you try to record lightning while outdoors, be sure that you are not the highest object in the area.

In addition to protecting yourself, protect your equipment. Lightning storms are usually accompanied by gusty winds and drenching rains, so at the very least the camera should be protected with a plastic bag. Cut a hole in the bag that is the approximate size of the camera's lens diameter and seal the opening around the lens barrel with a rubber band. The bag should be large enough to hold the camera with room for you to reach in to make adjustments.

• *See also:* AVAILABLE-LIGHT PHOTOGRAPHY; BAD WEATHER PHOTOGRAPHY; NIGHT PHOTOGRAPHY.

Light: Units of Measurement

In any given situation, a light source emits light at a certain rate, the light falls on a surface, and some of the light is reradiated by that surface. These are simplified versions of the concepts of *luminous flux, illuminance,* and *luminance.*

Luminous Flux

Luminous flux is the time rate of the flow of light and indicates the intensity of a source. The unit of flux is the *lumen.* A standard light source is the *candela,* which emits 4π lumens. A candela also has an intensity of 1 *candlepower.*

Mean spherical candlepower (usually just called candlepower) is defined as the average candlepower measured *in all directions* and is equal to the total luminous flux in lumens divided by 4π. *Mean horizontal candlepower* is defined as the average intensity of a source measured *in a horizontal plane* and in all directions passing through the source. Horizontal candlepower is often used to measure the intensity of the flash from an uncoiled electronic-

flash tube. In photography, one is usually concerned with the candlepower in a specified direction.

Note that it is a *point* light source that emits 4π (12.6) lumens. In actual practice the figure is closer to 10 lumens for an ordinary tungsten lamp, because the base intercepts some of the light. The term *candle* is no longer officially used as a name for a standard light source, although it is still seen in literature. The official international term is *candela.*

Illuminance

Illuminance can be defined as the luminous flux incident (falling) upon a surface. A typical unit is the *footcandle,* and it is equal to the illumination falling on a surface 1 foot from a 1-candlepower source. This works out to 1 lumen per square foot. A *metre-candle* equals the illumination falling on a surface 1 metre from a 1-candlepower source, or 1 lumen per square metre.

Note that these terms seem dimensionally incorrect; illuminance is calculated by dividing the candlepower of the source by the square of the distance from the source rather than by multiplying, as the terms seem to indicate. This is called the inverse-

Luminous flux (measured in lumens) is the time rate of flow of light and indicates the intensity of a source. Luminous intensity is indicated by the number of candelas (4 lumens = 1 candela).

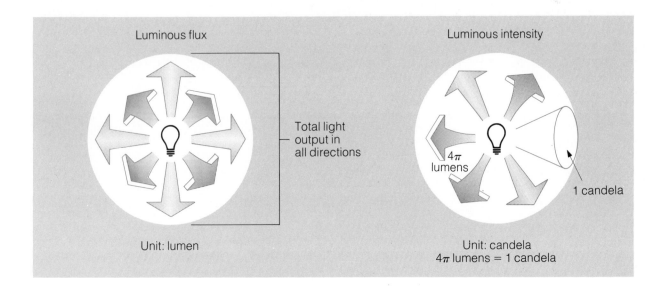

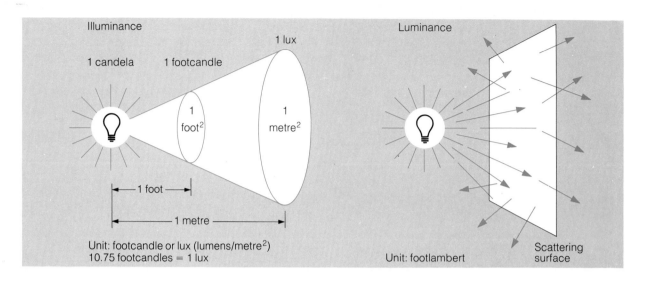

(Left) Illuminance is the amount of luminous flux falling on a surface. The unit of measurement is the footcandle or lux. (Right) Luminance is the brightness of an illuminated surface. For a perfectly diffusing surface, 1 footcandle illumination will result in 1 footlambert.

LUMINOUS FLUX
(Intensity of a Source)

	Candle-power	Lumens	Watts	Ergs/second
Candlepower	1	4π	0.005882π (at 555 nm**)	$5.882\pi \times 10^4$ (at 555 nm**)
Lumens	$\frac{1}{4\pi}$	1	0.001471 (at 555 nm**)	1.471×10^4 (at 555 nm**)
Watts	$\frac{170}{\pi}$ (at 555 nm*)	680 (at 555 nm*)	1	10^7
Ergs/sec.	$\frac{170}{\pi} \times 10^{-7}$ (at 555 nm*)	680×10^{-7} (at 555 nm*)	10^{-7}	1

*True only for monochromatic light at 555 nm. For other wavelengths in the visible region, multiply by the relative visibility factor for that wavelength.
**True only for monochromatic light at 555 nm. For other wavelengths in the visible region, divide by the visibility factor for that wavelength.

ILLUMINANCE
(Illumination Incident Upon a Surface)

	Foot-candles	Metre-candles	Lumens/ft²	Lumens/m²
Footcandles	1	10.764	1	10.764
Metre-candles	0.0929	1	0.0929	1
Lumens/ft²	1	10.764	1	10.764
Lumens/m²	0.0929	1	0.0929	1

LUMINANCE
(Surface Brightness or Reflected Light)

	Candles/ft²	Candles/m²	Footlamberts	Apostilbs***	Lamberts (Lumens/cm²)
Candles/ft²	1	10.764	π	10.764π	$\dfrac{\pi}{929}$
Candles/m²	0.0929	1	0.0929π	π	$\pi \times 10^{-4}$
Footlamberts	$\dfrac{1}{\pi}$	$\dfrac{10.764}{\pi}$	1	10.764	10.764×10^{-4}
Apostilbs***	$\dfrac{0.0929}{\pi}$	$\dfrac{1}{\pi}$	0.0929	1	10^{-4}
Lamberts (Lumens/cm²)	$\dfrac{929}{\pi}$	$\dfrac{10^4}{\pi}$	929	10^4	1

QUANTITY OF ENERGY RECEIVED BY A SURFACE

	Metre-candle-Seconds	Footcandle-Seconds	Ergs/cm²	Watt-seconds/cm² or Joules/cm²
Metre-candle-seconds	1	0.0929	1.471 (at 555 nm**)	1.471×10^{-7} (at 555 nm**)
Footcandle-seconds	10.764	1	15.83 (at 555 nm**)	15.83×10^{-7} (at 555 nm**)
Ergs/cm²	0.680 (at 555 nm*)	0.0632 (at 555 nm*)	1	10^{-7}
Watt-seconds/cm² or Joules/cm²	6.80×10^6 (at 555 nm*)	6.32×10^5 (at 555 nm*)	10^7	1

QUANTITY OF ENERGY EMITTED BY A SOURCE

	Lumen-Seconds	Candle-power-Seconds	Watt-Seconds or Joules	Ergs
Lumen-seconds	1	$\dfrac{1}{4\pi}$	0.001471 (at 555 nm**)	0.001471×10^{-7} (at 555 nm**)
Candlepower-seconds	4π	1	0.005882 (at 555 nm**)	0.005882×10^{-7} (at 555 nm**)
Watt-seconds or Joules	680 (at 555 nm*)	$\dfrac{170}{\pi}$ (at 555 nm*)	1	10^{-7}
Ergs	680×10^7 (at 555 nm*)	170×10^7 (at 555 nm*)	10^7	1

*True only for monochromatic light at 555 nm. For other wavelengths in the visible region, multiply by the relative visibility factor for that wavelength.
**True only for monochromatic light at 555 nm. For other wavelengths in the visible region, divide by the visibility factor for that wavelength.
***Defined as 1 lumen/m²; occasionally incorrectly called metre-lambert.

square law; that is, illuminance (expressed in flux incident/unit area) is proportional to the reciprocal of the square of the distance from the source, as shown by the formula:

$$E = \frac{I}{d^2}$$

where: E is the illuminance in footcandles or metre-candles, I is the intensity of the source in candle-power, and d is the distance of the surface from the source in either feet or metres.

Similarly, illuminance can be calculated by:

$$E = \frac{F}{A}$$

where: F is the incident flux in lumens, and A is the area of the illuminated surface. (This applies only when the area is illuminated evenly.)

ILLUMINANCE AND LUMINANCE VALUES

f-Number	Illuminance (Incident)		Luminance* (Reflected)	
	Footcandles (lm/ft²)	Lux (lm/m²)	Candles/ ft²	Foot lamberts
1.0	2.0	21.5	.36	.11
1.1	2.5	27	.45	.14
1.3	3.2	34	.58	.18
1.4	4.0	43	.72	.22
1.6	5	54	.90	.28
1.8	6.3	68	1.13	.35
2.0	8	85	1.44	.45
2.2	10	108	1.80	.55
2.5	12.5	135	2.25	.7
2.8	16	170	2.88	.9
3.2	20	215	3.6	1.1
3.6	25	270	4.5	1.4
4.0	32	340	5.8	1.8
4.5	40	430	7.2	2.3
5.0	50	540	9.0	2.9
5.6	63	670	11.3	3.6
6.3	80	860	14.4	4.5
7.0	100	1,080	18.0	5.7
8.0	125	1,345	22.5	7.2
9.0	160	1,685	28.8	9.0
10.0	200	2,155	36	11.5
11	250	2,690	45	14.3
12.7	320	3,362	58	18
14.3	400	4,312	72	23
16	500	5,380	90	29
18	630	6,725	113	36
20	800	8,625	144	46
22	1,000	10,750	180	57
25	1,250	13,500	225	72
28	1,600	17,250	288	92
32	2,000	21,500	360	115
36	2,500	26,900	450	143
40	3,200	34,500	576	183
45	4,000	43,000	720	229
50	5,000	53,800	900	286
57	6,300	69,000	1,134	366
64	8,000	86,000	1,440	458
72	10,000	107,600	1,800	572
80	12,500	138,000	2,304	732
90	16,000	172,000	2,880	916

*Average subject, or 18 percent neutral test card.

Luminance

Luminance is the brightness of an illuminated surface. If all of the illuminance falling on a perfectly diffusing surface were reradiated by the surface, then the luminance would numerically equal the illuminance. But, since this does not happen, we must take into account the *reflection factor* or *reflectance* of the surface, which is the ratio:

$$\frac{\text{Reflected Light}}{\text{Incident Light}}$$

Thus,

Luminance = Illuminance $\times$ Reflection Factor
(or Reflectance)

A typical unit of luminance is candles per square foot. Expressed mathematically,

$$B = \frac{KE}{\pi}$$

where: B is the surface brightness in candles per square foot, E is footcandles incident, and K is the reflection factor. To get around having to divide by π all the time, the *footlambert* was invented. It is defined as $1/\pi$ candles per square foot. Thus, the above relationship becomes:

$$B_L = KE$$

and B_L is now expressed in footlamberts. A footlambert is defined as the brightness of a perfectly reflecting surface illuminated by 1 footcandle; it may also be defined as the luminance of a perfectly diffusing surface, 1 square foot of which emits 1 lumen into a hemisphere.

Physicists and photometric engineers use the word *brightness* to designate the visual sensation produced by observing an illuminated surface, and reserve the word *luminance* to designate the physical quantity measured. The term *brightness* has been used here several times to refer to the physical quantity, but only to simplify matters.

Total Quantity of Energy

There are two additional concepts concerning footcandles:

1. *Total quantity of luminous energy emitted by a light source.* This can be defined as Luminous Flux $\times$ Time (lu-

men-seconds), or as Source Intensity $\times$ Time (candlepower-seconds).

2. *Total quantity of energy received by a surface.* We can use either Illuminance $\times$ Time (metre-candle-seconds and footcandle-seconds), or Energy per Unit Area (ergs per cm^2), to compute exposure. This second concept is important, because it is used to measure the exposure received by a photographic film.

Finding Illuminance and Luminance Values

There are occasions when it is useful to measure illuminance or luminance directly; for instance, in order to achieve a desired setup for viewing or photographing. The following method uses an ordinary exposure meter.

Set the meter at a film speed of ASA 100. Take an incident-light reading, or a reflected-light reading from an 18 percent neutral test card placed at 90 degrees to the light path. Note the *f*-number called for at a shutter speed of 1/8 sec., and consult the table on the preceding page.

Conversion Factors for Light Units

To convert any quantity listed in the left-most column of the accompanying tables to any quantity listed to the right, multiply by the factor shown in each column.

• *See also:* LIGHT; WEIGHTS AND MEASURES.

Line-Screen Systems

Many photographic processes use screens placed in front of the film during exposure to break up the image into a series of lines or dots. Screens that produce patterns of regularly spaced, uniform geometric elements are called *line screens* because they are generated from sets of lines that are parallel, or are arranged at angles to produce squares, rectangles, or triangles. Screens that reproduce random patterns of dots are commonly called *mosaic screens*, although a mosaic pattern can also be composed of regular elements. (*See:* MOSAIC SYSTEMS.)

Monochrome line screens are used to prepare halftone engraving plates in which the image is broken into dots of various sizes, or lines of varying width. (*See:* GRAPHIC ARTS PHOTOGRAPHY; HALFTONE; PHOTOMECHANICAL REPRODUCTION.) Three-color line screens have been used in a number of additive color processes in photography. Although at least one such process enjoyed success into the 1940's, the screen approach subsequently remained unused for color photography until the introduction of Polavision self-processing motion-picture film in 1977. (*See:* DIFFUSION TRANSFER PROCESS.)

Screen-Color Principles

A tricolor screen consists of primary-color (red, green, blue) elements that act as color-separation filters for image-forming light passing through the screen. Element spacing is very fine, so that details in every area of the image are analyzed in terms of their primary color content. Modern Polavision film, for example, has approximately 180 parallel lines per millimetre (4500 per inch). Screens with square elements typically have 4900 or more per square centimetre (over 30,000 per square inch).

The screen is used in combination with a panchromatic (black-and-white) film. Each screen element passes only light of its own color, so exposure depends on the primary color content of light reflected from each subject detail. The film is reversal-processed, or a positive is printed on film from the negative. The resulting black-and-white transparency will transmit light in proportion to the image exposure received in each area, and will block light in areas that were originally unexposed.

When white viewing light is passed through the transparency, the screen elements filter it to reproduce the original subject colors.

Screen Formation

A great many ingenious methods have been used to create screens of uniform spacing with no gaps between elements—which would pass white light, washing out colors in the final image—and no overlaps—which would produce black dots or lines in the image. A purely optical method uses a tricolor filter over the camera lens and a lenticular screen at the film to produce tiny duplicate images of the three filter color bands. (*See:* LENTICULAR SYSTEMS.) Physical screens with dyed or inked elements have been produced by machine ruling, photo resists, mechanical printing, embossing, cross-cutting of stacked gelatin layers, and a variety of other techniques.

However it is produced, a screen may be an inextricable part of the film, or it may be a separate plate or sheet. Modern Polavision film has an inseparable line screen; the most successful integral-screen method, the Dufay process, is described in the article DUFAYCOLOR. The major separate-screen process, Finlay color, was rivaled only by the Lumiere Autochrome (integral, random mosaic) process in

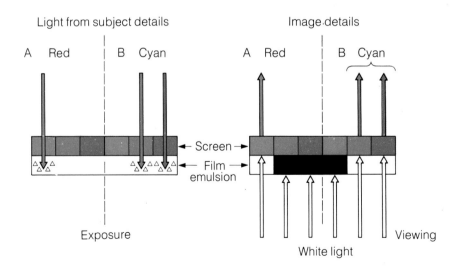

(*Left*) *A screen composed of primary color elements is in contact with the black-and-white film emulsion in the camera; every area is covered by multiple sets of screen elements. (Right) In the processed transparency, those portions unexposed in the camera block viewing light, while the other portions pass light to be filtered through the screen. If the red subject detail (A) had been in shadow, some density would have formed in that portion of the transparency. Then the viewing light would be reduced before passing through the screen element, and the image would be appropriately darker.*

the early part of the twentieth century, until the perfection of the Dufay process.

Finlay Color. The great advantage of the Finlay process was that, because the screen was separate, it could be used with any suitable black-and-white emulsion. This eliminated the extra cost of specially manufactured film, and made it possible to use films of different speeds or contrast characteristics, according to subject requirements. In addition, negative rather than positive film could be used, and any number of positive transparencies could be made by contact-printing onto film.

The Finlay screen was composed of square elements arranged in a checkerboard pattern (see the accompanying diagram), with registration marks at one edge. The screen was placed in contact with the film emulsion in the camera. The marks would expose the film directly if they coincided with a bright area alongside the subject; if the area was dark, an extra exposure was required to insure that they would be included on the film.

The positive transparency obtained by reversal processing, or by printing from the negative, was combined with a matching screen for viewing. The exposed marks in the film border and corresponding marks on the viewing screen made it possible to achieve perfect registration; they were masked off in

Elements of the Finlay screen were squares of primary colors arranged in a checkerboard pattern. Element spacing was 175 per linear inch (30,625 per square inch). This is a 200× magnification.

the finished mounting. Generally, the camera screen was a glass plate, to insure flatness and even contact with the entire film surface during exposure. The inexpensive viewing screen was made of celluloid; it was pressed into contact with the transparency when the two were mounted in glass for projection or display.

The major limitation of the Finlay process was the impossibility of making enlarged positives from the camera negative. The viewing-screen elements had to be exactly the same size as those recorded on the film, and enlargement would have made the screen pattern disturbingly evident.

• *See also:* COLOR SEPARATION PHOTOGRAPHY; COLOR THEORY; DIFFUSION TRANSFER PROCESS; DUFAYCOLOR; GRAPHIC ARTS PHOTOGRAPHY; HALFTONE; JOLY, JOHN; LENTICULAR SYSTEMS; LUMIÈRE COLOR PROCESSES; MOSAIC SYSTEMS; PHOTOMECHANICAL REPRODUCTION.

Lippmann, Gabriel

(1845–1921)
French physicist, mathematician, photographic scientist, and professor

In 1891, Lippmann invented the interference method of color photography, which was of great theoretical interest and found use in scientific work, especially in some microphotographic procedures. For the process, he devised a special panchromatic, extremely thin film emulsion containing very little silver halide, and having exceedingly fine grain. During exposure, planes of silver formed parallel to the emulsion surface and an underlayer of mercury. The spacing between the planes was determined by the wavelength of the exposing light. When viewed, the spacing relationships reinforced the same wavelengths in light reflected by the various planes and canceled others by interference, producing a full-color, saturated image.

Lippmann also suggested a number of lenticular film processes for color photography. He was honored by the Royal Photographic Society with its Progress Medal in 1897, and was awarded the Nobel Prize in 1908.

• *See also:* DICHROIC FILTERS; LENTICULAR SYSTEMS.

Litho Film

Litho (or lith) film is a common term for films used in lithographic or photomechanical reproduction. They have thin emulsions and very high contrast in order to create sharp, clean line and halftone dot images. Maximum contrast is attained with these films when they are developed in special "litho" developers, which usually contain hydroquinone, with paraformaldehyde as an accelerator.

In addition to simple litho films, which are available in ortho and panchromatic types, there are a variety of special films, such as duplicating films that produce high-contrast duplicates of line or halftone negatives without a reversal process. There are similar high-contrast papers that are used for phototypesetting and other graphic arts applications. Nearly the entire printing industry depends heavily on lith films for the making of halftone images and plate negatives of type and line drawings from which the printing plates are exposed.

• *See also:* Graphic Arts Photography; Halftone; High Contrast; Special Effects.

Logarithm

Logarithms are essentially shorthand notations for large numbers. They are most commonly used in photography to express the densities of filters and processed images, units of exposure, and other factors that change exponentially. Characteristic curves, time-temperature, and similar graphs would be less meaningful if plotted from the arithmetic values. (See the section Logarithms and Graphs in this article.) The use of logarithms makes it possible to express the data on an evenly spaced graph of reasonable size, even when very large factors—for example, an exposure range of 1:10,000 or more—are involved.

Principles of Logarithms

Methods for deriving logarithms and for determining the number a logarithm represents are explained later in this article. For practical operating purposes in photography, it is sufficient to know just a few principles.

The logarithm of 2 is 0.3 (log 2 = 0.3). Since *f*-stop and shutter-speed settings change exposure by a factor of 2, a log change of 0.3 in exposure data is equivalent to an exposure change of one stop. Changes of less than one stop are indicated by proportionately smaller log changes:

$$0.3 = 1 \text{ stop change}$$
$$0.15 = \tfrac{1}{2} \text{ stop change}$$
$$0.1 = \tfrac{1}{3} \text{ stop change}$$

Adding logarithms is equivalent to multiplying. For example, each 0.3 increase on the log E (logarithm of exposure) scale of a characteristic curve is equivalent to multiplying the exposure by 2, an increase of one stop.

Subtracting logarithms is equivalent to dividing. A decrease on a log E scale of 0.6 represents dividing the exposure in half *twice,* resulting in ¼ of the original exposure, or two stops less (0.3 subtracted per stop).

Logarithms of numbers less than 1 are commonly indicated by a "bar" or a minus sign written above the first digit. For example, in standard form, log ½ = $\overline{1}$.7. Increases and decreases in such "minus" logarithms have the same meaning as adding and subtracting logarithms.

Densities are logarithmic. A density change of 0.3 is the equivalent of a one-stop change in the light transmission of a filter or a negative area. As density increases, light transmission (and thus exposure) is reduced.

Neutral density (ND) filters are designated by density; for example, an 0.3 ND filter reduces light transmission by one stop. Most other filters are designated by a name or code number; their effect on exposure is specified by an exposure-increase factor. For example, a No. 8 (yellow) filter has a factor of 2 when used with panchromatic film, meaning that exposure must be increased 2× (one stop) to compensate for the amount of reduction in transmitted light. (Color compensating [CC] filters also have density designations; the densities are measured only in terms of the color or colors of light that a particular color filter absorbs. Since this is only a portion of the total composition of white light, CC filter densities cannot be interpreted directly in terms of exposure change.)

DENSITY AND EXPOSURE FACTORS

Filter Density (log)	Exposure Reduction	Exposure Factor	Equivalent Change (in stops)
0.3	½×	2×	−1
0.6	¼×	4×	−2
0.9	⅛×	8×	−3
1.2	¹⁄₁₆×	16×	−4
1.5	¹⁄₃₂×	32×	−5
1.8	¹⁄₆₄×	64×	−6
2.1	¹⁄₁₂₈×	128×	−7

Density and Exposure Factors

The relationship between density and exposure factors is shown in the accompanying table. These data apply to neutral-density filters and to colored filters used for black-and-white photography. The table can be extended indefinitely: For each 0.3 increase in density, the exposure is divided by 2, the exposure factor is multiplied by 2, and the change in stops increases by 1.

In this table, note that the density of a filter is the logarithm of its exposure factor. For example, an 0.9 filter has a factor of 8; log 8 = 0.9. Note also that density divided by 0.3 equals the number of stops the exposure is changed. For example, 0.9 ÷ 0.3 = 3; an 8× factor is equivalent to a 3-stop change.

Logarithms Summarized

Common logarithms, the kind used in photography, are based on the number 10 because our system of numbers is the decimal (1–10) system.

A common logarithm is the exponent or "power" to which 10 must be raised to equal a given number. Powers of 10 have whole-number logarithms; the logarithms of intermediate numbers contain a decimal fraction. For example:

Number		"Power of 10" Form	Logarithm
1	=	10^0	0
4	=	$10^{0.6}$	0.6
10	=	10^1	1.0
55	=	$10^{1.74}$	1.74
100	=	10^2	2.0
132	=	$10^{2.12}$	2.12
1000	=	10^3	3.0
1425	=	$10^{3.15}$	3.15
10,000	=	10^4	4.0

Number	Logarithm
1	0
2	0.3
4	0.6
8	0.9
16	1.2
32	1.5
64	1.8
128	2.1
256	2.4
512	2.7

Common logarithms are written in the form:

$$\log 100 = 2, \text{ or } \log_{10} 100 = 2$$

These forms mean the same thing; the subscript 10 is simply a reminder that the base number is 10. This is sometimes necessary in mathematical applications to distinguish the log from other kinds of logarithms.

A logarithm has two parts, a *characteristic* to the left of the decimal point, and a *mantissa* to the right.

1.75

Characteristic ⟋ ⟍ Mantissa

Depending on the "10-range" of a number, the characteristic is either negative (written with a minus sign above it), 0, or positive, as follows:

Number Range	Characteristic
0.001–0.0099	$\bar{3}$ *
0.01–0.099	$\bar{2}$
0.1–0.9	$\bar{1}$
1–9	0
10–99	1
100–999	2
1000–9999	3
10,000–99,999	4

*There are other ways of writing negative characteristics, but this form is most common and is most easily used on graphs.

When working from a logarithm to determine the number for which it stands (the antilogarithm), the characteristic indicates where the decimal point is located in the answer.

This method of writing logarithms can be more easily understood by examining "scientific notation." In scientific notation, the number is reduced to a single digit to the left of the decimal point multiplied by the appropriate power of 10. Hence, the number 784 becomes 7.84×10^2 and 0.0058 becomes 5.8×10^{-3}. Note from this notation that the logarithm of a decimal has a *negative* characteristic (the power of 10) and a *positive* mantissa.

Log Tables

The accompanying table given for numbers between 1 and 10 is really all that is needed if the scientific notation method is used. However, a more complete table would yield more *significant figures*, which are needed for other than elementary computations or approximations.

Read the table by finding the mantissa at the intersection of the row and column containing the appropriate whole number and decimal. For instance, the mantissa for 5.6 can be found by going down to the row marked 5 under "Number" and across to the column under .6; the mantissa is .75. Since 5.6 is between 1 and 10, the characteristic is 0. If the number had been 5600 (5.6×10^3), the mantissa would be the same but the characteristic would be 3; hence, the logarithm of 5600 is 3.75.

Similarly, for .056 (5.6×10^{-2}), the mantissa is the same but the characteristic is -2. Remember, only the characteristic is negative; the mantissa is still positive. The logarithm of .056 is commonly written as $\overline{2}.75$. The minus sign (or bar, as it is sometimes called) above the characteristic applies only to that part of the logarithm.

The mantissa, or decimal part of a logarithm, can be determined from tables such as the one given here. An electronic calculator determines the entire logarithm; it is not necessary to consult a table. However, as explained later in the text, there are special considerations in working with the logarithms of fractions when using a calculator.

Antilog Procedure. To determine the number a log represents, start with the mantissa (decimal portion). Find the nearest mantissa in the log columns of the table; note the corresponding number. Determine the position of the decimal point from the characteristic (power of 10).

Using a Calculator. A small electronic calculator that has *Log* and X^y functions makes it very easy to determine logs and antilogs of numbers greater than 1. Special attention must be paid to working with logs of fractions.

The log procedure is as follows:

1. Enter the number.
2. Press the *Function* key, if required.
3. Press the *Log* key.
4. Read the logarithm from the display.

LOG TABLE										
Number	0	.1	.2	.3	.4	.5	.6	.7	.8	.9
1	.00	.04	.08	.11	.15	.18	.20	.23	.26	.28
2	.30	.32	.34	.36	.38	.40	.42	.43	.45	.46
3	.48	.49	.51	.52	.53	.54	.56	.57	.58	.59
4	.60	.61	.62	.63	.64	.65	.66	.67	.68	.69
5	.70	.71	.72	.72	.73	.74	.75	.76	.76	.77
6	.78	.79	.79	.80	.81	.81	.82	.83	.83	.84
7	.85	.85	.86	.86	.87	.88	.88	.89	.89	.90
8	.90	.91	.91	.92	.92	.93	.93	.94	.94	.95
9	.95	.96	.96	.97	.97	.98	.98	.99	.99	1.00

The basic antilog procedure is:

1. Enter 10.
2. Press the *Function* key, if required.
3. Press the X^y key.
4. Enter the entire logarithm (characteristic and mantissa).
5. Press the = key.
6. Read the antilogarithm from the display.

Logs of fractions. The method described when a table is used gives a standard log form of negative characteristic (noted by the minus sign written above it) and a positive mantissa. An electronic calculator gives the equivalent, but as a completely negative logarithm.

To transform a calculator negative log into a standard-form fractional or bar log: (1) increase the characteristic by 1 and write it with a bar above, and (2) subtract the mantissa from 1 to determine the new mantissa. For example, find the standard form of log -1.60 from the calculator. Increase the characteristic by $1 = \overline{2}$. Subtract: $1 - 0.6 = 0.4$, the new mantissa. The standard log form of -1.6 is $\overline{2}.4$.

It may be necessary to make this conversion in order to plot exposures of less than 1 exposure-time unit on a graph.

Antilogs of fractions. If a negative log as computed directly by the calculator is used, follow the basic antilog procedure, with one addition: After entering the log, press the *Change Sign* $(+/-)$ key to give it a negative value; then press the = key.

If the standard bar log is used, proceed as follows:

1. Enter 10.
2. Press the *Function* key, if required.
3. Press the X^y key.
4. Enter only the mantissa of the logarithm, preceded by a decimal.
5. Press the = key.
6. Read the number in the display.
7. Move the decimal left to the final position, as described in the procedures for using the log table.

Logarithms and Graphs

The advantage of using logarithms to obtain manageable graphs can be seen in the construction

EXPOSURE AND DENSITY DATA					
Exposure Data			Density Data		
Exposure increase (in stops)	Units of exposure	Log E	% Transmittance	Opacity	Density (Log 0)
—	1	0	70	1.4	0.15
1	2	0.3	70	1.4	0.15
2	4	0.6	61	1.6	0.21
3	8	0.9	46	2.2	0.33
4	16	1.2	30	3.3	0.52
5	32	1.5	19	5.3	0.70
6	64	1.8	13	7.7	0.88
7	128	2.1	8.8	11.4	1.06
8	256	2.4	5.8	17.2	1.24
9	512	2.7	3.8	26.3	1.42
10	1024	3.0	2.5	40	1.60
11	2048	3.3	1.65	60.6	1.78
12	4096	3.6	1.10	90.9	1.96
13	8192	3.9	0.70	139	2.14
14	16,384	4.2	0.49	204	2.32
15	32,768	4.5	0.30	333	2.50
16	65,536	4.8	0.21	478	2.68
17	131,072	5.1	0.14	714	2.85

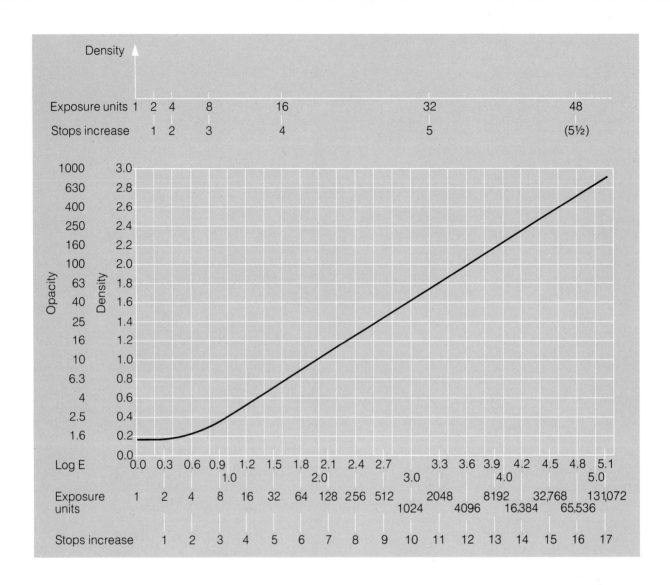

The diagram of the scale for exposures shows the problem of graphing the units of exposure; if each graph line represents one unit of exposure, the number of lines must double from step to step. Setting this up is impossible. The graph shown here uses logarithms to plot the exposure data. In this way, the response curve is of a reasonable size.

of a characteristic curve for a film emulsion.

The exposure data show that a basic exposure of 1 unit was doubled by 1-stop increases for an additional 17 exposures. (This is a greater exposure range than would be encountered with average photographic subjects, but it is typical of the range used to evaluate emulsions.)

The accompanying diagram shows the problem of setting up a scale for the exposures. If each graph line represents 1 unit of exposure, the number of lines has to double from step to step. That would require 256 lines between the eighth and ninth increases, and 65,536 lines between the last two. Obviously that is impossible.

A similar problem would arise in trying to set up a scale for the densities resulting from these exposure changes. If the percent of transmitted light is graphed, at least 700 lines would be required at a value of 0.1 each in order to clearly separate the changes of less than 1 at steps 13 through 17. However, since the exposure and density scales must increase in equal intervals, that would require 10 times more lines for the exposure scale.

If opacity (1/transmission) is used in order to obtain a vertical scale with a value of 1 per line, at least 714 lines would be required. In either case, this too is impossible.

The accompanying diagram shows the use of logarithms to plot the data. The log E values along the horizontal axis are the logarithms of the units of exposure at each step. Thus, the scale numbers represent the relative exposure values. If the actual exposures had been recorded, say, in metre-candle-seconds, the logarithms of actual exposure on the scale would be different, but their spacing would be identical. For conciseness, each graph line represents an increase of 0.2 log units.

The vertical axis has density (log of opacity) values on a scale in which each line also represents an interval of 0.2 log units.

The response curve has been plotted from the log E and the density data for each exposure. It has reasonable size and is easily interpreted.

• *See also:* DENSITOMETRY; EXPOSURE; FILTERS; NEUTRAL DENSITY.

Loupe

A loupe is a simple lens that is held close to the eye so that objects or details may be focused at very close distances to achieve great magnifications. In photography, loupes are often used to inspect the image on the ground-glass screen of a view camera for critical focusing, and to view small-format images. Loupes for technical purposes are often of very high optical quality and may include a comparison scale, or reticle, for direct measurement of, for example, object size or spacing of details in millimetres, or the number of threads per inch in fabric. A normal-focal-length camera lens may be used as a loupe if it is set to its infinity focus position and held very close to one eye.

When any lens is held close to the eye, an object placed at or near the front focal point of the lens can be focused. This is very much closer than the unaided eye could focus the object. The image will be very large because it is proportional to the angle subtended by the object at that distance. Based on an average minimum focusing distance of 250 mm (10 inches) for the unaided eye, the approximate magnification (M) achieved with a loupe is:

$$M = \frac{250 \text{ mm}}{\text{Focal length of loupe (in mm)}}$$

Image size on the retina at close distances is proportional to the angle subtended by the object (shown by colored lines). (A) At a minimum focusing distance of 250 mm, the lens of the eye can just manage to refract (bend) rays from a subject point (shown by the broken lines) sufficiently to bring them to a focus on the retina. (B) The object at a closer distance subtends a greater angle, for a potentially larger image, but the angle at which rays from a subject point encounter the lens is so great that the unaided eye cannot refract them to a retinal focus. (C) The loupe refracts rays so that they are parallel when they reach the eye, and thus can be focused as easily as those from an object at infinity. Image size, however, is still determined by actual eye-to-object distance.

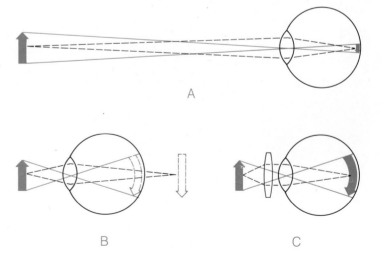

Thus, a 50 mm camera lens used as an improvised loupe would produce a magnification of $250 \div 50 = 5\times$, approximately.

• *See also:* LENSES; MAGNIFICATION; OPTICS.

Low Key

A low-key photograph is one in which dark tones predominate. An overexposed print is not a low-key image. For a true low-key effect, the scale must be complete from black to white, but the darker tones must make up the major expressive part of the picture. Somewhere in the image there should be a small amount of light tone and even pure white: a catchlight in the eyes, or a reflection in some glossy

material, or an actual white object to establish the key of the picture. In any case, a small area of highlight is necessary to provide a reference level for the darker tones; without it the effect will be simply that of an underexposed negative or overprinted picture.

Dark tonal values in both the subject and background are the basis of a successful low-key picture. A normal or a high-key subject will not become low key with reduced illumination, it will simply look inadequately lighted. A meter reading of a true low-key subject will cause overexposure if followed directly because the subject is of less than average reflectance. It is usually best to give one or two stops less exposure than indicated by a reflected-light meter of the averaging type, and with black-and-white films to use a film developer such as Kodak D-76 to bring out full shadow-area detail. To produce low-key pictures in color, the subject must have predominately dark tones, and the exposure must be just adequate to separate the dark tones from the blacks.

• *See also:* BRIGHTNESS RANGE; CONTRAST; HIGH KEY.

Lumière, Auguste and Louis

(1862–1954)
(1864–1948)
French scientists and photographic manufacturers

The Lumière brothers took over management of the dry-plate factory founded in 1882 in Lyon by their father, Antoine, and began the manufacture of roll film in 1887. They carried out joint researches in photography that led to fundamental discoveries and improvements in development and other aspects of photographic chemistry. Interested in the problems of color photography, they produced images by the Lippmann interference process as early as 1892, and invented a color dry plate in 1903. It was commercially marketed as the Autochrome plate in 1906, and is generally considered to be the first prac-

Dark tones predominate in this low-key photograph taken by available light. Light tones of the road markings and the pure white of the car's headlights provide a reference level for the darker tones. Photo by Randall Friedman.

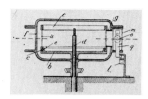
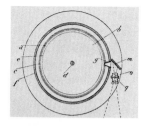

A draftsman's rendition of the Photorama, the 360-degree panoramic projection system introduced by the Lumière brothers in 1900. Photo courtesy International Museum of Photography, Rochester, N.Y.

tical color photographic process in which a single exposure in a regular camera produced a color image.

The Lumière Cinematographe camera and projector of 1895 was one of the first systems to use 35 mm perforated film. The claw mechanism they invented to advance the film frame by frame is still used in various forms in nearly all modern motion-picture equipment. In 1900, they introduced a 360-degree panoramic projection system—the Lumière Photorama.

• *See also:* LUMIÈRE COLOR PROCESSES; PANORAMIC PHOTOGRAPHY.

Lumière Color Processes

The principles of additive and subtractive color and their potential applications in photography had been discovered—notably by James Clerk Maxwell and Ducos du Hauron—and even experimentally demonstrated by 1880. But a practical process of color photography utilizing these principles could not be produced until a truly panchromatic emulsion was available, because all methods depended, then (and now), upon making a record of the primary (red, green, blue) color content of light from the subject. This necessary improvement in emulsion response was achieved in the years 1903–1906, and was immediately applied to color photography.

Louis and Auguste Lumière, French photographic scientists and manufacturers, and their associate Seyewetz, succeeded in creating a single-plate color process in 1903. It was introduced commercially as the Autochrome plate in 1907 and was soon in use throughout the world. Although about 60 times slower than the best black-and-white materials at the outset, it was immediately successful and became widely used for artistic, commercial, and editorial photography.

Single-Plate Additive Color

The Autochrome process used a single plate for additive analysis and synthesis of color. Light from the subject passed through a random mosaic screen, composed of primary-color filter elements, to expose a panchromatic emulsion. The plate was reversal-processed to form a positive black-and-white transparency. When viewed, white light was colored by the filter screen and its intensities were controlled by the transparency in proportion to the original subject brightnesses. The eye blended these effects to complete the creation of a full-color image.

The *Autochrome* Plate. In order for details of the image to be analyzed in three colors, the filter elements of the screen had to be extremely small. They were, in fact, dyed particles that averaged 0.015 mm (0.0006 inch) in size. Various particle materials were used at different times, including yeasts, dried ferments, bacilli, and powdered enamels; but potato starch grains were the most successful in early versions of the process.

The earliest Autochrome plate had a filter screen composed of two layers of cyan, magenta, and yellow starch grains. The combined effect of the screen as seen from either side (detail) was red, green, and blue filter elements mixed with some yellow, magenta, and cyan elements. Light had to pass through the screen before exposing the emulsion; viewing from the other side corrected the lateral reversal produced in the camera.

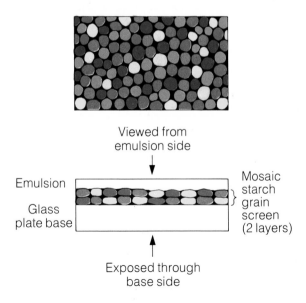

Viewed from emulsion side

Emulsion

Glass plate base

Mosaic starch grain screen (2 layers)

Exposed through base side

Separate batches of particles were dyed cyan, magenta, and yellow, and were then blended to produce a mixture with a uniformly neutral (gray) appearance. A glass plate was covered with a thin layer of transparent varnish and the particle mixture dusted on. When dry, this layer was coated with varnish and a second layer was dusted on. Finally, carbon black (pulverized charcoal) was dusted on to fill any remaining spaces between the colored particles of the second layer.

Although the dyed particles each had secondary (cyan, magenta, yellow) colors, wherever different color grains were aligned between the two layers, their combined effect produced primary-color filtration $(C + M = B; Y + C = G; M + Y = R)$. The particles were so minute and so randomly distributed that surprisingly uniform filtration was produced over the whole surface, although it was not perfect. There were scattered areas where, for example, yellow overlapped yellow, which produced a filter element that was not red, green, or blue. The same occurred with the magenta and cyan starch grains.

The carbon particles blocked any light from passing all the way through the screen in areas where spaces in both layers coincided, or through only the grains of the lower layer below spaces in the upper layer; either case would permit unwanted light to degrade the final image.

When the screen was completed, it was coated with a panchromatic emulsion. Exposure was through the base side of the plate so that the screen could analyze the light before it affected the emulsion. The processed image was viewed from the emulsion side to counteract the left-right reversal produced by the camera lens.

Each Autochrome plate was unique. Although it was theoretically possible to contact-print one plate onto another, or to copy it with a camera, in practice the results were generally unacceptable. Sharpness suffered because the plates could not be placed emulsion-to-emulsion (if they were, light exposing the second plate would not be screened), the grain factors of the two screens multiplied to produce a grainier image, and colors changed because the transmission characteristics of the screens were not perfect and tended to differ from batch to batch. One of the great appeals of the later Finlay process was that it used a separate camera screen so that a

(Right) An early Autochrome. Commercially introduced in 1907, the Autochrome plate remained one of the most popular color processes until the early 1930's. Photo courtesy International Museum of Photography, Rochester, N.Y. (Below) An Autochrome plate mosaic screen, shown here at 600× magnification, has random distribution of color grains. Primary colors are formed by two layers of particles dyed cyan, magenta, and yellow. Black areas indicate where carbon black was dusted on to fill spaces between colored particles.

negative could be made on any emulsion, and as many positives could be printed from it as desired; they were combined with separate screens for viewing. On the other hand, aligning a Finlay screen over a transparency required great care, because either a moiré pattern would form, or the colors would not be right.

The Autochrome plate was rivaled by other processes, especially Finlay color, but it remained one of the most popular color processes until the early 1930's, when both were supplanted by the Dufaycolor process. *All* additive color processes rapidly became obsolete, however, upon the introduction of Kodachrome subtractive color film in 1935.

• *See also:* COLOR THEORY; DUFAYCOLOR; LINE-SCREEN SYSTEMS; MOSAIC SYSTEMS.

Mackie Line

Mackie lines are a development effect related to the Eberhard effect. They are part of what are generally called edge, adjacency, or border effects, and occur when a negative contains a strong highlight adjacent to a lightly exposed area. If the negative is developed with little or no agitation, the soluble bromide released by development of the strong highlight will not be washed away but will slowly diffuse out of the highlight areas into the adjacent middle tones. This retards the action of the developer at these points and results in a lighter area of background immediately adjacent to the highlight. When the negative is printed, the highlights appear to be surrounded by a dark narrow line, which is the Mackie line. In some cases these lines produce the effect of a sharper image, especially when they are very narrow.

Many modern films are designed to produce such adjacency effects with normal development to enhance the apparent sharpness of fine detail.

• *See also:* ACUTANCE; IMAGE EFFECTS; SABATTIER EFFECT.

Maddox, Richard Leach

(1816–1902)
English physician, amateur photographer, and microscopist

R. L. Maddox is credited with having invented the modern gelatin-silver halide emulsion. In 1871, he published the details of his process in the *British Journal of Photography* for unrestricted use. Because he did not patent it, he received no gain from the invention, but it was one of the most significant achievements in the history of photography. The invention was to be the basis for all modern photographic sensitized materials; today's color materials are based on his gelatin-silver halide emulsion.

Maddox had been using the collodion wet-plate process, but suffered severe effects from breathing the alcohol and ether fumes of the collodion; his

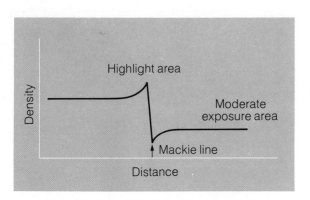

Mackie lines occur when a negative has a strong highlight next to a lightly or moderately exposed area. Due to a retardation in the developer, a lighter area of background occurs adjacent to the highlight in the negative. When the negative is printed, the highlights appear to be surrounded by a narrow, dark line, which is the Mackie line.

gelatin emulsion was odorless. In addition, the emulsion was used after it had set and dried, making it possible for plates to be prepared ahead of time, and for processing to be deferred until a convenient time after exposure. It also made possible the manufacture of prepared plates. Although at first photographers made their own gelatin emulsion following Maddox's process, or purchased prepared emulsion with which to coat their own plates, most photographers preferred to purchase ready-made plates when they became available. In either case, the gelatin plate was vastly more convenient than the collodion wet plate, which had to be coated and sensitized, exposed, and processed on the spot, before the collodion dried—usually within about 20 minutes.

For his invention of a practical dry emulsion, Maddox was awarded the Progress Medal of the Royal Photographic Society in 1901. Although there is no doubt that Maddox contributed to the gelatin dry plate, it appears likely that the term "inventor" should be shared with a number of other contributors to the advancement of emulsion technology during the same period of time.

• *See also:* EMULSIONS; WET-COLLODION PROCESS.

Magnesium Fluoride

A natural-occurring mineral used for making anti-reflection coatings on lenses, filters, and other optical devices.

Formula: MgF_2
Molecular Weight: 62.32

Crystalline salt, often ground to a white powder, that exhibits slight violet fluorescence. Almost insoluble in water, it is slightly soluble in dilute acids. In coating lenses, the purified material is vaporized in a high vacuum by heat. The lenses are supported above the container of magnesium fluoride, which is usually a boat-shaped filament, heated by electricity. Because there is no air to impede the molecules as they evaporate, they move at high speed to the super-clean lens surfaces, adhering to form a uniform coating thinner than a single wavelength of light.

Magnetic Sound for Motion Pictures

Magnetic recording depends upon the ability of a thin coating of ferrous oxide to be differentially magnetized by a varying magnetic field. When the coating on a support is passed by the magnetic heads of a recorder, a magnetic pattern is formed in the coating. This magnetic pattern will remain until altered by the introduction of another magnetic field. Thus, magnetic recordings can be erased and rerecorded. When the coating is passed over a "play-back" head, a magnetic field is induced in the head to produce a signal for a play-back amplifier.

When discussing magnetic-sound recording on film, the format is either motion-picture camera film that has been edge-coated with magnetizable emulsion such as ferrous oxide, or what is called a "full-coat" film. The latter is a plastic film base that is completely coated with magnetizable emulsion and is used during the sound track production process for editing purposes. The former is used in "single-system" motion-picture production. It is called single-system because photographic emulsion and magnetic emulsion are on the same film, and images and sound are recorded simultaneously in the camera.

The application of a magnetic stripe on motion-picture film can be done either before (prestripe) or after (poststripe) processing. Sound is recorded on this stripe, which consists of metallic oxide coated along the edge of the film, by running it past a magnetic recording head that selectively magnetizes the metallic particles in the coating.

A second, much narrower stripe of the same thickness, and usually the same material, is often coated between the perforations and the edge of the film opposite the edge used for the sound stripe. This stripe serves to balance the film mechanically and keep it from telescoping and binding against the reel flanges during projection and rewinding. The balance stripe can also be used for recording a cue or sync signal, although this is not a common practice.

Magnetic-sound films have proven to be very durable. Magnetic tracks are not susceptible to dust distortion and are degraded very little by scratches. In fact, a metallic oxide sound track would have to be gouged deeply, almost to the base material, before the scratch damage would be deemed objectionable.

(Left) Magnetic recording depends upon the fact that ferrous oxide can be differentially magnetized. Here, iron filings are lined up to form a magnetic pattern. (Right) A magnetic pattern of sound is illustrated on this magnification of a quarter-inch magnetic recording tape. The pattern will remain unaltered until the introduction of another magnetic field.

Because magnetic-sound prints are coated with a stripe on each edge of the film, they offer two additional advantages over optical-sound prints. The dual stripes raise the emulsion image area off the base side of the next convolution of film on the reel and thus protect the picture area from frictional damage, emulsion-to-base sticking, and other contact problems such as foreign material. They also act as narrow "rails" in the projection gate, allowing the film to be transported through the projector with a minimum of friction and gate-to-film contact.

Original Sound Recording

There are basically three methods of recording original sound on photographic film: (1) single-system recording, (2) double-system recording, and (3) postrecording.

Single-System Sound Recording. Single-system refers to the recording of both picture and sound track simultaneously on film in the camera. A magnetic single-system sound camera is equipped with a built-in sound recording device, with a microphone and recording amplifier in the camera, or connected by a cable to the recording head in the camera body, and requires the use of prestriped film.

In a single-system camera, the amplifier usually has inputs for microphones (usually two) and provisions to mix them. It may also have auxiliary inputs for phonographs or other sources but these are seldom used in single-system filming. In the camera, the film first passes through the picture gate, and then over the sound head. The displacement is necessary because the film moves a frame at a time in the picture gate, but must travel at a perfectly steady rate through the sound unit. The slack loop between the two allows for the change. In today's cameras, the sound head is 28 frames below the aperture in 16 mm machines, and 18 frames below on super-8 mm. Thus, the sound appears ahead of the picture on the film. In the best cameras, the sound head contains a flywheel that smooths out the film motion to eliminate all traces of flutter or other irregular motions.

The playback equipment is arranged in much the same way; to secure proper synchronization and also to allow for smoothing out the film motion, the sound head is below the film gate by the same distance as in the camera. It is essential that the magnetic head be in tight contact with the running film for best resolution of the higher frequency sounds.

The fluctuating magnetic field in the running film is thus converted into an electrical signal, which is then fed to an amplifier; this, in turn, drives a loudspeaker in the usual way.

Once an optical track is printed onto a projection film and processed, it cannot be changed. For some uses, this is an advantage of optical sound. With a magnetic-sound track, however, it is possible to make alterations after a film has been made. Super 8 magnetic-sound films can be updated and edited easily with magnetic record-and-playback projectors whose sound systems operate much like the everyday tape recorder. Once the new track has been recorded, it can be played back immediately. If the new narrative is not exactly what was intended, it can be erased easily by rerecording a second, more refined commentary. Thus, you can use a single film with magnetic track to satisfy several requirements by modifying the narrative to fit each particular audience.

This high degree of flexibility can also be extended to include the silent titles many film collectors and filmmakers have stored in film libraries. They can be sent to laboratories offering striping services for the addition of the extra dimension of sound and the added protection of the dual tracks to extend the life of the films.

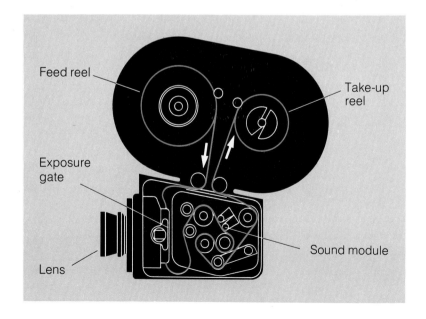

One of the methods of recording original sound on photographic film is through the use of the 16 mm single-system sound camera. This diagram shows the film path through the system.

Feed reel

Take-up reel

Exposure gate

Sound module

Lens

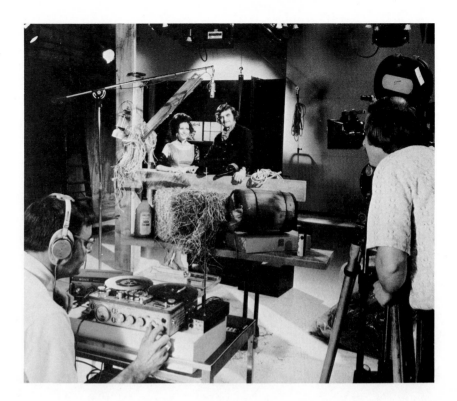

In this studio set-up for double-system sound recording, sound is recorded separately from the film. This is the technique usually employed for professional productions, where a variety of audio techniques may be combined.

Double-System Sound Recording. In double-system recording, sound is usually recorded separately on ¼-inch tape. The magnetic tape is later transferred to a perforated magnetic (full-coat) film so that the picture and sound track can be synchronized during editing. This technique of sound recording is usually employed for professional productions where it may be desirable to combine a variety of audio techniques, such as "voice-over" narration, "wild sound," and lip synchronization, as well as background music.

Postrecorded Sound. In one method of utilizing this silent-camera technique, the camera operator shoots the picture without sound, but uses magnetically prestriped film in the camera. After processing and editing, the footage is run through a projector with a built-in recording head. Narration can then be recorded, voice-over, on the film to match the visual presentation of the event. The audio portion can be erased easily and rerecorded, if necessary, without harming the film image. This type of postrecording is often used in television stations for news coverage.

A second method involves recording sound at the scene with a standard cassette tape recorder—which is not synchronized to the camera—and then rerecording some or all of the sound onto magnetically striped film. With this method, wild sound—consisting of authentic background and atmosphere noises at the scene—can be added to the film behind the narrator's voice. In addition, with some effort, sound can be postrecorded to obtain adequate lip synchronization.

The frame-for-frame synchronization of sound and picture usually begins to fade as the recording of the scene progresses. This is because there is no simple way to lock together the tape recorder and camera (and later, the recorder and projector) to be sure that the film and tape will run at exactly matching speeds. (Such things as battery strength, motor design, and film or tape load affect the transport speed, and these variations rarely are equal in camera, recorder, and projector.)

If lip synchronization is necessary, a technique that professionals often use can be employed. Record voice at the time of filming; then, at a rerecord-

City and traffic noises are recorded here for background. Some or all of this sound will later be rerecorded onto magnetically striped film to be used behind the voice of an actor or narrator.

ing session, have the same person record onto the film track the sound he or she previously recorded on tape—in sync with the lip motion on the screen. This technique, known as *postsynchronous sound,* becomes easier to do with practice.

There are also ways to achieve the *effect* of lip synchronization using a silent camera and a tape recorder. When a lack of synchronism occurs as the scene progresses, a few frames of blank recording stock or wild sound can be inserted between short sections of dialogue to maintain good synchronism. (While on location, record more sound effects than actually needed. The excess can be used in connection with titles and scene changes created in editing.) This type of double-system *nonsynchronous* sound (coincident recording), although not suitable for recording lengthy dialogue, can be quite satisfactory where there are short sentences and frequent changes in camera angle—especially if the films are informational rather than dramatic.

Other methods of achieving the effect of synchronized sound without actually producing it include the following:

Make long shots—any lack of sync will not be so apparent.

Use reaction shots—that is, close-ups of the *listener,* rather than the speaker.

Film the sound action *after* it starts and *before* it stops. For example, show a hand and switch starting a machine (sound source) instead of a machine starting; then film the machine in motion, but pan or cut *away* from the sound source before it is turned off.

Frame Rates. Ordinarily, the rate of 18 frames per second (fps) is selected for filming and projecting silent subjects as well as for much normal sound picture-taking (such as home movies, industrial, and educational filming). However, there are other occasions in which it may be desirable to shoot sound film at 18 fps. Examples are if the sound film is to be intercut later with other 18-frame-per-second footage for projection purposes, and if you wish to economize film usage.

The rate of 24 fps is used to shoot for television projection (many TV stations do not handle 18-fps footage), most sports photography, and motion analysis. At 24 fps, a higher linear film velocity is achieved, which usually results in better quality sound and a steadier projected image. Of course, you should shoot at 24 fps if the film is going to be intercut with other footage shot at the rate of 24 fps.

When choosing speed settings, keep in mind that filming speed should match the speed of the equipment you will be using to project the film. Camera speeds faster than projection speeds will result in slower-than-normal action and low-pitched, slow sound in the projected film; and camera speeds slower than projection speeds will produce a faster-than-normal action and high-pitched, rapid sound.

Sound Displacement. In both original recording, and in reproduction in a projector, the sound signal must be located a specific number of frames ahead of the picture frame to which it corresponds, as shown in the accompanying chart. This sound displacement is necessary because it is mechanically impossible to place the camera recording head or the projector reproducing head in the same area where the picture is being exposed or projected.

FRAMES OF SEPARATION BETWEEN SOUND AND PICTURE

Film Size		Super 8	16 mm	35 mm
Frames preceding action	Magnetic track	18	28	28
	Optical track	22	26	20

With single-system sound, the frame advance, which causes the picture and sound to play back in synchronism when projected, can create some limitations in editing. For example, it may become necessary, as is often the case with television news interviews, to edit the sound track only and disregard the picture, which is one of the reasons for continuing to record the picture after the audio portion has finished. Otherwise, complete words or phrases can be inadvertently omitted. The use of *displacement recorders,* however, can facilitate the editing of single-system sound.

Basically, a displacement recorder repositions the sound track of a single-system recorded film to

A displacement recorder can facilitate the editing of single-system sound by realigning the sound track and corresponding picture for editing purposes. It can later reposition the sound track ahead of the picture for projection. Photo courtesy Magnasync/Movieola Corp., North Hollywood, Calif.

editor's sync sound, with the corresponding picture frame *in line.* That is, the sound track and corresponding picture are no longer displaced but, rather, in alignment. After editing has been accomplished, the displacement recorder can be used to reposition the sound track to *projection sync* (the proper frame advance ahead of the picture) for immediate projection, which is often required by television and documentary producers.

Planned Sound Filming

In sound films, the sound reinforces the visual display. The sound should be pertinent to the action, and it should not be intrusive. Care must be taken to use good microphone technique to avoid extraneous sounds. Unplanned action and "wild" sound may be appropriate for some scenes, but sound films are usually much more successful when they are the result of planned filming and sound recording. Complete scripting of camera techniques, action, sound, and dialogue will provide the best method of achieving consistent results.

Subjects. For the scripted film, subjects ought to be well rehearsed before shooting commences. A well-prepared narrator will require fewer retakes during shooting; this reduces material costs and production time. "Dry runs" and trial run-throughs on the set can also save money. They allow the performers and production crew to check the dialogue, action, and technical aspects of each shot before filming.

For the beginning of a scene, the subjects should be instructed to wait for several seconds after the camera begins before speaking. At the end of a shot, they should "freeze" the action for at least 2 seconds after the last sound. This 2-second camera run after the sound concludes will provide the pause needed to facilitate editing. An additional 1- to 2-second pause (3 to 4 seconds total) is usually desirable to provide a smooth finish to the final scene in the film.

The verbal content of each shot can be printed on large sheets of poster board to be used as cue cards. Cue cards are handy references for the subjects; they can study their lines from the cue cards between takes. However, the dialogue should be memorized, so the speaker can look directly at the camera lens. Eye contact or lack of it is very noticeable on film.

Actors (professional or nonprofessional) who appear in a film to be shown publicly should be asked to sign a model release form. Legal release forms are available, through which the performer agrees to allow the film to be used in any manner for any purpose.

Locations. Locations should be scouted prior to shooting to check noise conditions. Listen for background sounds, such as air conditioning, telephones, machinery, and traffic. Most rooms contain basic ambient noise, sometimes called *room tone*. Room tone normally provides a desirable presence on a sound track; it fills the "holes" during pauses, but it can be distracting if it is too loud.

As mentioned, each location has its own distinctive room tone. Therefore, if close-up shots are used, the voice should be recorded on location as the close-up is filmed, regardless of whether the speaker is on camera. (The voice could be added later through a recording projector, but the room tone would not match that of the other scenes.) When recording over close-up shots, the speaker should maintain a normal volume and distance from the microphone so that the voice quality will match that of long shots on-camera.

The area where you film and record can influence the sound quality of the film. Rooms with carpeting and heavy draperies help deaden echoes, thereby improving the quality of recorded sound. If you are shooting in small rooms with highly sound-reflective walls, unwanted sounds from the camera and other sources may sometimes be recorded at a noticeable level. Keeping the microphone at least 3 ft (approx. 1 m) from the camera will help to minimize pickup of camera sounds. In noisy environments, camera noise is not usually a problem.

As a general rule, the closer the microphone is to the subject, the better the sound quality will be. You may decide to have the on-screen narrator hold the microphone in the scene. Another option is to conceal the microphone within the scene. Or you can attach the mike to a stand and position it just outside the field of view of the camera lens.

The microphone is sensitive to sounds from many directions and to handling noises. Handling of the microphone or rubbing the cord during filming will produce excessive, distracting noises on the sound track. Decide upon a location (concealed, if desired) for the microphone in a scene, and leave it there until you change scenes. If the subject is hand-holding the mike, the person should hold it steady and be careful not to brush the mike or the cord against anything.

Microphones. There are several types of microphones used in recording, broadcasting, and sound amplification. Their differences stem mainly from the attribute known as acceptance angle or pattern of sound pickup. The diagram on the next page shows the various acceptance patterns.

Omnidirectional. This is the most common type of microphone in use today, since it is supplied as standard equipment with most amateur single-sound cameras and home tape recorders. The pickup pattern is spherical with a field roughly 300 degrees around the front or face of the microphone.

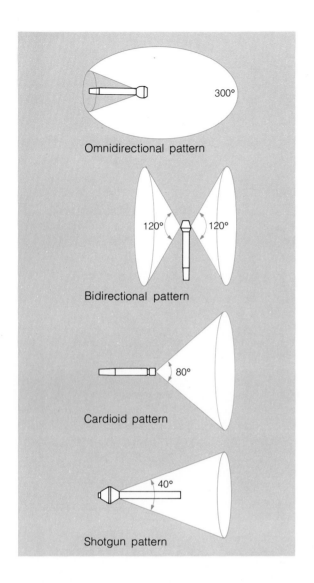

300°

Omnidirectional pattern

120° 120°

Bidirectional pattern

80°

Cardioid pattern

40°

Shotgun pattern

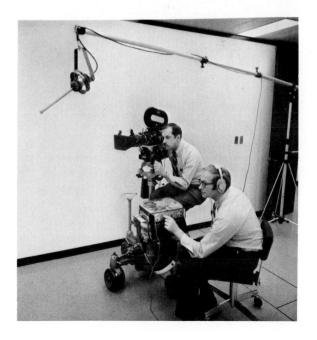

(Above) Differences in microphones used for recording stem mainly from the various acceptance patterns. Omnidirectional microphones pick up sound in a spherical pattern; bidirectional microphones are sensitive to all sounds in a pattern shaped like a figure eight; cardioid microphones pick up all sounds in a heart-shaped pattern; and microphones with the shotgun pattern have the narrowest angle of acceptance.

The photos illustrate two types of omnidirectional microphones. (Above right) A lavaliere microphone allows the user considerable freedom of movement. However, because of its placement, it is out of the best pickup area; it also tends to pick up clothing-rustle noises. (Right) The boom microphone is the most popular method of recording location sound. It is suspended on a boom or a "fishpole" near the speaker's head but outside of the picture's frame.

A wireless or radio microphone setup uses a mini-VHF transmitter that broadcasts its signal to a receiver plugged into a tape recorder.

Bidirectional. These microphones are sensitive to all sounds in a pattern that is shaped like a butterfly wing or a figure eight. Bidirectionals were developed for radio use and are popular for interview situations but not usually for filmmaking.

Cardioid. Cardioid microphones are used widely in filmmaking because they pick up all sounds in a heart-shaped pattern and are most sensitive to sound that is directly in front of them plus some ambient (peripheral) sound, but not nearly as much as the bidirectional.

Ultradirectional or Shotgun. These microphones have the narrowest angle of acceptance and are designed to isolate selected sound in front of them from ambient sound. They are useful to the filmmaker, particularly to pick out narrative in noisy locations.

General-Purpose. Most general-purpose mikes are omnidirectional and are especially useful when the sound to be recorded may be coming from a variety of sources. When you want to exclude specific sounds, you might use another type of microphone. Before using a different mike, be sure that its impedance matches that of the amplifier with which it will be used. (Refer to the manufacturer's specifications for this information.)

Windscreen. A windscreen is a device that is usually put to good use outdoors (it cuts down wind noise) and can often serve well indoors. It is made of foam-type material to fit over the mike like a hood. Indoors, the windscreen will cut down on room ambience and can screen out the sounds that are made by the mouth and lips between words.

In addition, the windscreen will provide some protection for the mike if it is dropped. If a windscreen is not available, cover the mike with a handkerchief or a knitted mitten. As a last resort, put it in your pocket. Even the slightest breeze can be troublesome.

Postrecorded Sound

Postrecorded sound can be used to improve prestriped camera-original films or to add sound to silent films after a sound stripe has been applied. With a projector that is capable of reproducing *and* recording sound, it is a relatively simple procedure and can be accomplished with a minimum of additional equipment.

With postrecording techniques you usually have better control over recording procedures. For instance, you can record music only, commentary only, alternate commentary and music, or commentary *and* music together.

The choice of postrecording methods includes the use of prerecorded sound transferred electronically to the sound stripe from a tape recorder or record player and live sound recorded through a microphone.

A windscreen, made of foam material, fits over the microphone like a hood. Used outdoors, as shown here, it cuts down wind noise and also offers some protection if the microphone is dropped.

Electronic Transfer. This method is used primarily for placing background music on the sound stripe; however, sometimes it is used to record both background music and commentary on tape before transfer to the sound track. Electronic transfer, when used with equipment of suitable quality, usually provides the best sound and is not affected by extraneous noise.

For electronic transfer, connect the output jack from the amplifier on the tape recorder or record player to the input jack on the projector. This requires a "patch cord." It is possible to exceed the range of the automatic gain control on the projector when recording in this manner; set the gain manually while observing the VU meter (see the projector instruction manual for detailed instructions on the correct procedure).

Live Recording. Basically, recording live before the camera and postrecording "live" onto the sound track require similar technique. Observe proper microphone placement and handling, avoid unwanted extraneous noise, and use the correct recording procedure.

The biggest problem in live recording is projector noise. There are several ways to minimize the possibility of picking up projector noise.

Use a directional microphone that will exclude some of the extraneous noise.

Always get the mike as close to the sound source (minimum, 1 foot) and as far from the projector as possible. If the mike cord isn't long enough, use a mike extension cord.

Record in a room that has natural sound deadeners, such as drapes, carpeting, and padded furniture.

Place padded screens or furniture around the projector or microphone—to isolate one from the other more effectively.

Project from one room to another, placing the projector and microphone in separate rooms. The walls on either side of the doorway will act as baffles and prevent some of the noise from passing through.

Sound-On-Sound. Sound-on-sound is the recording of voice *and* music simultaneously on the sound stripe. There are a variety of ways in which to record sound-on-sound. Play music as background for narration, or record music on one track of a stereo tape recorder and voice on the other track —then transfer them electronically to the sound stripe.

Recording music and voice at the same time seems like the easiest method of producing sound-on-sound; however, if a mistake is made in either music or voice, both must be rerecorded. Also, achieving and maintaining a good volume balance between the two is more difficult.

The most control over the recording process is achieved by placing music on one track of a stereo tape and commentary on the other, and then transferring them electronically to the sound stripe. This eliminates the need to rerecord both parts if something goes wrong with either part.

Music. For legal reasons, no music records or tapes should be rerecorded without proper clearance, or "use rights." Recorded music for which clearance can be obtained is available from music libraries.

Catalogs from music libraries usually list titles, themes, moods, and the exact playing time for individual musical segments.

Listings of producers, processing labs, film distributors, and sources of sound effects can be found at a local public library. One reference book carrying such information is the *Audiovisual Marketplace,* a multimedia guide used in the industry.

Editing Sound Films

Normally, in super 8 sound production, the original (the film used in the camera to record picture and sound) is edited and then used for screenings. Editing and screening the original film is not the procedure normally used in 16 mm and 35 mm professional productions; a duplicate print is edited and release prints are produced for projection.

Although it is possible to project the original film, each time the film is handled or projected, the possibility exists that it can become scratched and/or dirty. Therefore, only a limited number of screenings should be expected from the original film, and it should be carefully cleaned and stored. If numerous screenings are required, it is wise to use a duplicate of the original film. Of course, the best time to make duplicate prints is *before* the original becomes damaged. Film laboratories can provide good-quality duplicate prints of edited super 8 sound films.

Basic editing is usually required to remove unwanted sound. Every camera takes a fraction of a second to reach its normal running speed. Often the sound that is recorded in that split second is garbled. So even if the scenes are shot in the proper order and if each take is good, editing may still be required to remove a few frames of garbled sound and make scene changes smooth. Also, the pauses provided by

the narrator at the beginning and end of each scene may need to be shortened to suit the pacing of the film.

The script and storyboard cards are helpful as references in editing. The footage should be screened with a projector when it returns from the processing lab. Each roll should be numbered and the takes to be used recorded in a written log.

Editing with Sound Displacement. When the picture and sound are recorded inside the camera, they are recorded in two different places. There is a distance between a frame of picture and the sound that matches it, so the pauses provide the extra picture and sound needed to make scene changes smooth.

In the diagram on the opposite page, if you were to cut at the *picture*—Frame B—the words "Hello, I am Hal . . ." would be lost. In addition, so would the 18 (or more) frames of Hal's silent smile, which resulted from the pause at the beginning of the scene during filming. As a consequence, the scene would have lip movements without the accompanying sound. Except for special effects, always cut at the *sound*—Frame A—for the beginning of a scene. The usual practice is to make the cut a few frames *before* the first sound, to establish the scene in the viewer's mind before the sound begins.

The cut to end a scene should be made *at the picture* (except for special effects). If the cut were to be made at the *sound*—Frame C—Hal's "Goodbye" would be heard, but the picture would conclude before the viewer saw his lips form the word. By cutting at the *picture*—Frame D—both sound and picture are included in the segment of film.

Remember that had you been shooting *uncontrolled* action, the film probably would not have the pauses between scenes. Therefore, at each cut it is possible to have a 1-second carry-over of sound from the preceding scene. Careful planning and, whenever possible, in-camera editing will help to minimize these occurrences.

In practice, editing may not be as precise as these drawings indicate, unless scene changes were planned at places where there was a natural break— such as at the end of a sentence or paragraph. It is a good idea to include a few extra frames at cutting points. Extra frames provide a margin for error in splicing, which will help to prevent the elimination of desired sound at the beginning of a scene.

Single-System Super 8 Sound Film

When editing with sound displacement, always cut at the sound (Frame A), or a few frames before, for the beginning of a scene. Otherwise, if you were to cut at the picture (Frame B), the words "Hello, I am Hal..." would be lost, as would the 18 or more frames of the silent smile, which resulted from the pause at the beginning of the scene. The cut to end a scene should be made at the picture (Frame D). By cutting here, both the sound and the picture are included in the segment of the film to be retained. In this film footage, there is a distance between a frame of picture and its sound, so the pause gives the extra sound and picture needed to make smooth scene changes. If the action were uncontrolled, there probably would not be pauses between scenes; planning and in-camera editing help minimize the possibility of 1-second carryover of sound from the preceding scene.

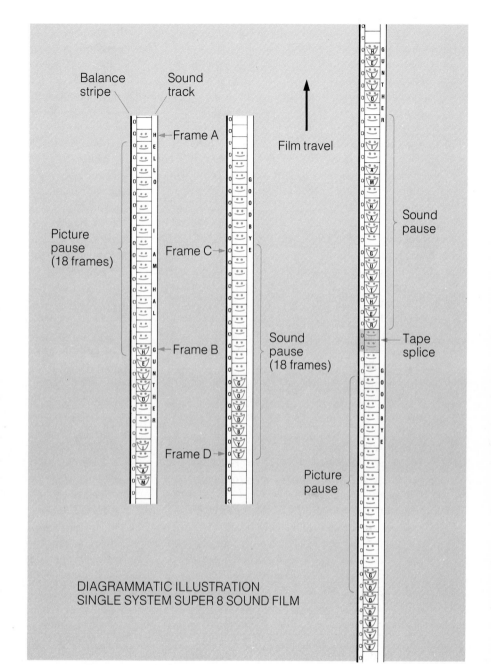

DIAGRAMMATIC ILLUSTRATION
SINGLE SYSTEM SUPER 8 SOUND FILM

Undesired sound in a scene can be removed by passing an ordinary small magnet over the section of the sound track containing the unwanted sound. The magnet will act as a sound eraser. First, mark the area to be erased; and then, use care not to eliminate adjacent sound that you wish to retain.

You can also use an electromagnet of the type used for demagnetizing the sound head on tape recorders.

Either method involves a relatively low level magnetic field, but normal caution should be used to avoid contact with the film and possible accidental erasure of the sound track.

NOTE: As with any magnetic-sound recording material, this film should be kept away from strong magnetic fields, such as those created by large motors and generators.

Editing Equipment. A wide variety of sound film editing equipment can be purchased from commercial suppliers, or it can be built by modifying existing components and assembling them into an *editing bench*.

For super 8 editing on the editing bench, the soundhead is located 18 film frames to the right of the viewer/editor picture gate because the sound precedes the picture by 18 frames (ANSI Standard PH22.164-1975). This 18-frame separation is necessary because of camera and projector design considerations—the images must be photographed intermittently (series of still images) and the sound must be recorded on the sound stripe as smoothly as possible; these simultaneous actions must be mechanically separate.

A *splicer* is attached to the editing bench, in front of the viewer/editor. Editing gloves, grease pencil, scissors, masking tape, extra reels, white leader, and film cleaner (with lubricant) should also be available during editing.

Film with magnetic-sound stripe can be spliced satisfactorily by normal cement-splicing methods. A minimum amount of cement should be used for each splice to prevent smearing of the magnetic track. If the steel scraper or cutter in the splicer becomes magnetized, a noticeable click will be heard in films on which the sound has been recorded magnetically prior to the time the splice was made. If this becomes a problem, have the splicer demagnetized or do all editing before the sound is recorded.

Adding Sound to Silent Films

A magnetic-oxide coating can be applied along the edge of processed 8 mm, super 8, and 16 mm motion-picture films. The stripe can be placed on color or black-and-white films. Film perforated along one or both edges can be striped. Once this coating has been applied, live or recorded speech, music, and sound effects can be recorded on the magnetic stripe with a sound projector designed for magnetic recording and reproducing. The sound track can then be played back immediately, erased, rerecorded, or edited.

One of the greatest advantages of a magnetic track is that the sound can be changed to meet the requirements of different audiences, such as groups of different ages or educational backgrounds, or to people who speak a language different from that originally recorded.

The best results are achieved when sound striping is applied to film with no splices, such as an uncut original film or a duplicate film made from an edited original camera film. If edited original films are to have a magnetic stripe coated on them, splices are best kept to a minimum. Splices (cement or tape) that are adequate for use in some projectors may not easily pass through the coating equipment.

Cement splices in film that has a recorded magnetic track can cause some loss in signal level due to the mechanical separation of the coated film from the magnetic head at the splice. This effect is minimized by making splices as shown.

Care and Storage of Magnetic-Sound Films

Magnetic-sound films should generally be stored in the same manner and under the same conditions as motion-picture film. In addition, they must not be placed near a powerful magnetic field, such as that emanating from a transformer or other electromagnetic device. Electromagnetic fields will alter the molecular alignment in the ferrous-oxide emulsion on magnetized films (erase or partially erase it). Here are some storage and handling tips:

1. Store magnetic-sound films in cans, in a cool, dry place. Avoid extremes of temperature and humidity.
2. Be careful with cleaners. Some cleaners will remove or damage the magnetic iron oxide stripe or emulsion.
3. Keep films away from magnets and any other source of electromagnetic fields, such as loudspeakers, power transformers, degaussers, or tape erasers.
4. Clean all projection equipment and editing bench gear before and after each use. Some oxides leave a residue of particles in the projector gate, the soundheads, and other points of contact.
5. Avoid getting oil or other liquids on the film. Liquids will damage the sound track just as they do an emulsion.
6. Project or rewind stored films occasionally, even if not for viewing. This helps relieve winding tensions and prevents film distortion.

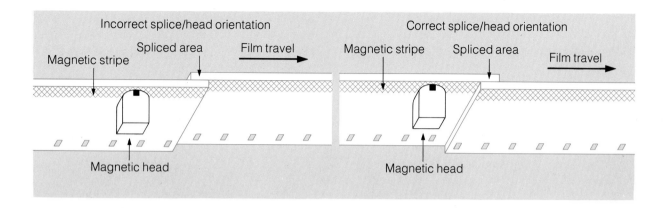

Incorrect splice/head orientation

Magnetic stripe   Spliced area   Film travel

Magnetic head

Correct splice/head orientation

Magnetic stripe   Spliced area   Film travel

Magnetic head

With film that has a recorded magnetic track, cement splices can cause some loss in signal level due to the mechanical separation of the coated film from the magnetic head at the splice. This loss can be minimized by making the splice as shown.

7. Make sure that film to be stored is wound evenly on the reels.
8. Periodically clean and lubricate films.
9. Never tighten a wound reel by pulling the loose end. This could scratch the film.
10. Avoid winding the film too loosely or too tightly on the reels. Loose winding often causes slipping and cinching with resultant scratches and abrasions. Winding the film too tightly will cause strains and tensions that produce film distortion. Tape the outside end of the film so that it will not become loose.

• *See also:* EDITING MOVIES; HOME MOVIES; MO-TION-PICTURE PRODUCTION; MOVIE FILMS, STOR-AGE AND CARE OF; PROJECTION, AUDIOVISUAL; SOUND STRIPE; SYNCHRONIZATION.

Further Reading: Bensinger, Charles and PhotoGraphic Magazine Editors. *Guide to Video Tape Recording.* Los Angeles, CA: Petersen Publishing Co., 1973; Harwood, Don. *Everything You Always Wanted to Know about Video Tape Recording,* 2nd ed. Syosset, NY: VTR Publishing Co., 1975; Rilla, Wolf. *A–Z of Movie-Making.* New York, NY: Viking Press, Inc., 1970; White, Gordon. *Video Recording: Record and Replay Systems.* New York, NY: Crane-Russak and Co., Inc., 1973; Yulsman, Jerry. *The Complete Book of 8 mm Movie Making: Super-8, Single-8, Standard-8.* Scranton, PA: Barnes & Noble Books, Div. of Harper & Row Pubs., Inc., 1974.

The sound track for any motion picture is extremely important—in many cases at least as important as the visual story.

Magnification

Magnification is the degree to which the image of an object differs from the actual size of the object. This difference is often expressed as the *reproduction ratio* between the image (I) and object (O) sizes, in the form I:O. Since the ratio sign (:) indicates division, I:O means I ÷ O. When the division is carried out, the resulting quotient is called the magnification (M), or scale. The magnification number is commonly written along with a multiplication sign (×) to indicate that the image size is the indicated multiple of the object size.

For example, if in a close-up, the image size = 100 mm, and the object size = 25 mm, then:

Reproduction Ratio = 100:25, or 4:1, and
Magnification = 100 ÷ 25 = 4×.

That is, the image is four times larger than the object.

In most normal camera systems, the image is smaller than the object; therefore, the magnification is a fraction, or less than 1. If I = 30 mm, and O = 90 mm, then:

Reproduction Ratio = 30:90, or 1:3, and
Magnification = 30 ÷ 90 = ⅓× = 0.33×

In some cases, such as copying or graphic arts, it is useful to compute the reduction [R], which is the reciprocal [1/M] of the magnification: O ÷ I.

Thus, if I = 30 mm, and O = 90 mm, then: R = O ÷ I = 90 ÷ 30 = 3. Object size must be *divided* by R to discover the image size.

Determining Magnification

The most direct way to determine magnification is to measure the object (or place an item of known length at the object position), measure the image size on the camera focusing screen, and divide *I* by *O*. When the screen is not directly accessible, its known dimensions can be used. For example, in a 35 mm single-lens reflex viewfinder, the long dimension is usually about 34.2 mm.* If about 100 mm of a ruler placed alongside the object is visible across that dimension of the viewfinder, *M* is about 0.33×. However, if only 16 mm is visible, *M* is about 2×. The dimensions of the viewfinders or ground glass for other formats can be used similarly.

Magnification can also be determined from other factors in a situation:

$$M = \frac{\text{Lens-to-film distance}}{\text{Lens-to-object distance}}$$

$$M = \frac{\text{Lens-to-film distance} - \text{Focal length}}{\text{Focal length}}$$

$$M = \frac{\text{Focal length}}{\text{Lens-to-object distance} - \text{Focal length}}$$

With symmetrical lens designs, distances can be measured from the diaphragm. Focal length and distances must be in the same units. With telephoto and wide-angle retrofocus lens designs, magnification should be calculated from image and object measurements for accuracy.

Magnification and Close-up Exposure

In close-up situations, when the magnification becomes greater than about 0.2× (ratio = 1:5), the lens is far enough from its infinity position so that the marked aperture is no longer correct. The effective value of the marked *f*-stop settings is reduced. As a result, the exposure must be increased to compensate for the smaller effective aperture.

The basic formula for close-up exposure compensation with a symmetrical lens is:

$$\text{Exposure Factor} = (M + 1)^2$$

For example, when M = 1 (life-size, or 1:1 close-up), the required exposure increase is $(1 + 1)^2 = 2^2 = 4\times$. When M = 3×, the factor is $(3 + 1)^2 = 16\times$, or the equivalent of four stops more exposure.

For close-ups with asymmetrical lenses, such as telephoto designs, the basic formula should be adjusted by the pupillary magnification of the lens.

---

*The normal safety factor used by many manufacturers is to display 95 percent of a 24 × 36 mm camera frame in the viewfinder, or an equivalent of 22.8 × 34.2 mm.

(Wide-angle, short-focal-length lenses are seldom used for extreme close-ups because of the exaggerated proportions they produce in images and because lens-to-object distances become impractically short. For example, when $M = 2\times$, the lens-to-object distance from the front surface of most 35 mm lens designs is less than 25 mm, or 1 inch.)

Pupillary Magnification

The diameter of the diaphragm as seen through a lens is called the pupil. In asymmetrical lens designs, the pupil as seen from the front of the lens (entrance pupil) is not the same as the pupil seen from the rear (exit pupil). This is because the front and rear lens elements or element groups have different magnifying powers. The ratio of the exit pupil to the entrance pupil is the *pupillary magnification* (P), or pupil enlargement, of the lens.

A simple method for determining P is to remove the lens from the camera and close the diaphragm one or two stops from the maximum opening so that its diameter is clearly visible—a light background will help. Hold a ruler or scale across the face of the lens and measure the diameter of the entrance pupil. Turn the lens end-for-end and measure the diameter of the exit pupil at the same f-stop. Then:

$$P = \text{Exit Pupil} \div \text{Entrance Pupil}$$

If P is less than 0.9 or more than 1.2, compute close-up exposure compensation for a lens mounted in normal position (rear of lens toward film) as follows:

$$\text{Exposure Factor} = \left(\frac{M}{P} + 1\right)^2$$

If the lens is used in reversed position (front of lens toward film) for better image definition, the reciprocal $1/P$ must be substituted for P, and the formula becomes:

$$\text{Exposure Factor} = (MP + 1)^2.$$

Magnification of a Lens

To compare the magnifying powers of camera lenses for a given format, it is useful to define the relation of the lens focal lengths to that of the normal focal length for that format. If a 50 mm lens is normal, a 150 mm lens has a $3\times$ magnifying power, meaning that it will enlarge objects three times as much as the normal lens when both are used at the same distance from the subject. Similarly, a 400 mm lens has a power of $8\times$ for the same format.

When lenses of different focal lengths are used at distances proportional to their focal lengths, they have equal magnification. That is, a 400 mm lens at 80 feet and a 150 mm lens at 30 feet will produce the same image size as a 50 mm lens at 10 feet.

Magnification in Enlarging

In making enlargements, the size of a detail in the negative is the *object size,* and its projected size is the *image size.* Enlarging magnification is determined by linear measurement, not by the increase in total image area. It is sometimes expressed in diameters (the linear measurement of a circle). If an object 1 inch long in a negative is 10 inches in the image, the print is a $10\times$, or a 10-diameter, enlargement.

The usual requirement in enlarging is to make a print at a certain magnification. A simple way is to insert a scrap piece of film marked with a line of unit length—for example, 1 cm or 1 inch—in the negative carrier, and adjust the enlarger until the projected image measures the same number of units as the desired magnification (12 cm, or inches, for a $12\times$ enlargement). The image must be sharply focused when measured; as a little investigation will show, size changes significantly during focusing. Once the enlarger is adjusted, replace the scrap film with the negative to be printed, taking care not to move the enlarger head closer to or farther from the easel. Refocus critically before making an exposure.

In common usage, "enlarging magnification" is the relative magnification between the negative and the print. The *true magnification* of an object is the relation of its print image size to its actual physical size. If these can be measured directly, the formula $M = I \div O$ can be used. An alternate method is:

True Magnification = M in Negative $\times$
Relative M in Enlargement

For example, an object recorded at $0.25\times$ in the negative and printed at a relative enlargement of $12\times$ has a true magnification of $0.25(12) = 3\times$. That is, it is three times life size in the print.

It is often important to indicate true magnification in photographs to be used for scientific and record purposes, for testing and evaluation, or for presentation as legal evidence.

• *See also:* CLOSE-UP PHOTOGRAPHY; LENSES; PHOTOMACROGRAPHY; REPRODUCTION RATIO.

Makeup

Photographic, television, and even stage makeup techniques have undergone great changes over the last decade. Greasepaint is no longer in general use, and pancake makeup is largely a thing of the past. The trend today is toward a natural, translucent look, and the best result is agreed to be a face that does not look made up. For photography or television makeup, only a few products are necessary in most cases; and the kinds of products needed are widely available in cosmetic departments serving the general public.

Study the Face

The objective of good makeup is to show the person. The first step requires standing back and studying the face and its shape. Note good points that should be accentuated as well as defects that should be remedied or minimized. The general principle to keep in mind is that lightness accentuates, and darkness makes features appear to recede.

The Skin

Evaluate the condition of the subject's skin. The first job—before applying any makeup—is to make the skin look healthy, pliable, and elastic. Skin condition can obviously vary with age; it can also vary with life-style. For example, an 18-year-old leading an outdoor life in the sun may well have dry skin and fine lines that might generally be seen in an older person. The subject may also have skin blemishes such as pimples or scars.

Moisturizer. A good-quality moisturizer is called for when the skin is dry, leathery, or has lost its elasticity. Some makeup artists *always* use a moisturizer prior to applying foundation to the skin.

Foundation. Three colors of foundation are needed: The basic color should closely match the natural color of the model's skin; a lighter color and a darker color will be needed when the makeup artist begins to contour the model's face. As mentioned,

the lighter color is used where features need to be brought out or emphasized; the darker color is used to minimize a feature, such as softening the look of a very strong jaw or prominent cheekbones. A light-color foundation can also be used to cover such things as circles under the eyes.

Powder. The trend today is to use a very fine, sheer translucent powder, which is applied by dipping the makeup brush in the powder, shaking off the excess, and making several very light applications over the foundation. Powder helps set the foundation; it should never be darker in tone than the foundation. The powder should be applied so that the skin retains its natural look and bleeds through the foundation and the powder. To maintain the lightness in powders, some makeup artists place a pair of razor blades in the powder and shake the container vigorously before beginning the application. Pressed powder should never be used as it tends to streak, change color, and eventually takes on a heavy appearance.

Eye Makeup

Eyeliner. Makeup artists have very individualistic approaches to their job—there is no one "right" approach to the art. However, depending on the evaluation of the face and the effect that is sought, eyeliner may be applied to the top of the eye. The lower lash of the eye may be lined as well. It should be fuzzed out and smudged with a cotton swab until a blended, soft line is achieved. The eye may be "winged" with the same lining to achieve a wide-eyed look. Consider using two colors if the model can wear this effect.

Eyeshadow. Next, shadow is applied above the eye and brought out to the crease of the eyes. It may be desirable to wing it lightly from the corner toward the hairline. The effect should be very delicate and muted. (The eye makeup is not fuzzed out on top; a sharper line looks better there.) The eye then appears wide open, alive, and somewhat mysterious.

Mascara. Mascara is then applied. Most makeup artists avoid mascara with fibers and opt for a plain mascara in cake form. Again, this is applied in sheer, gossamer layers. Often four or five light applications are given and then brushed out in an effort to separate the eyelashes and present a soft and natural look.

Eyebrow Pencil. Shaping the eyebrow is usually done with an eyebrow pencil. Dark brown, charcoal gray, or even navy blue is more often preferred than black because black gives a rather hard line. Black eyebrows, even in models with jet-black hair, photograph with a harsh look. Following the penciling of the eyebrows, a stiff toothbrush should be used to soften the penciling and leave a subtle, natural look to the eyebrows.

Contouring the Face

Professionals differ as to when contouring is to be done in the process of making up, and a lot depends on the type of makeup that is used. The general rule is that with liquid or cream, contouring is done before powder is applied to the model. With compressed powder, the contouring is done after the translucent powder has been applied. Do not confuse contouring powder with regular compressed powder; the latter is never used for contouring.

Contouring is an art in itself. Noses and jawlines are frequently contoured by makeup artists. The rule again is that light colors reflect light and fluff out dark areas, while dark colors reduce a feature's prominence by making it appear to recede into shadow. Many women use too much makeup in attempting to contour their faces, and they fail to blend makeup to eliminate harsh lines. Blending and allowing the natural skin to bleed through the makeup is paramount. The intent is to show a natural person and to make the viewer or camera unaware of the use of makeup.

Lip Makeup

Lip makeup is most often started by outlining the lips—shaping and contouring them with an eyebrow pencil or lip liner. Then the outline is filled in with lipstick, lightly applied with a lip brush. Application of lipstick directly from the tube results in a very heavy look. Lip gloss or super-shine lipsticks are seldom used by professionals, as their holding power and color are not as good as cream lipstick followed by an overcoat of petroleum jelly. Plain petroleum jelly over cream lipstick stays in place better, is more natural looking, and lasts longer under photographic lights.

Makeup for Men

Makeup for men is important, and there is a trend today for men to be made up.

Many men appear to have a five o'clock shadow; sometimes this can be corrected on the spot by a quick shave. A dark, loose powder worked into the area that appears dark will help to eliminate shad-ows. This is the same kind of translucent powder used in making up women, but men's powder can be darker than their natural skin because of the hint of shadow left from a beard. A scar or other blemish can be reduced in effect by using a white "erase" stick or, perhaps, a light liquid makeup in a nude or porcelain color. Circles under the eyes can be corrected with white or a very pale liquid makeup foundation, or an erase-type stick.

For the best effect in men's fashion photography, a foundation is applied to the entire face, followed by a light application of loose, translucent powder. When making up models for photography, motion pictures, or television, the loose aerated powder helps prevent moisture from forming and controls a greasy look of the face. The powder should be brushed out of the man's eyebrows, and a small amount of petroleum jelly may be used on the eyelashes and lips. Hairspray is useful in hairstyling for men as well as women.

Obtaining Makeup Supplies and Advice

The varieties of makeup used for photography today are to be found at any good makeup counter. The people attending the counter are often experts in makeup and will be glad to help you select the necessary products. In many cases, these professionals will do the makeup for you if you take the model along. Additionally, many of them can be retained to come to the studio in their free hours.

A Makeup Kit

The trend in makeup is to use a minimum of products. Foundation is used sparingly; only a little contour color is applied. These products plus a lip pencil can change a whole look. Many things can be done with only one or two items. A good supply of makeup might consist of the following:

Moisturizer and foundation—three colors
Erase stick, contouring cream, or powder
Gloss
Eyebrow pencil
Eyeliner (pencil preferred)
Mascara
Loose, translucent powder
Sponges for applying foundation
Cleanser and toner
Cotton balls and swab sticks
Set of makeup brushes (good-quality)
Toothbrush.

(Above left) Eye makeup may be used to create any number of effects. Here, a dark gray crayon was used to outline the upper and lower lids. It was then fuzzed and smudged on the lower lid for a smoky, exotic look. Highlighting shadow on the center of the bone below the eyebrow was blended into a darker shadow on the inner and outer edges for further contour. (Above) A wide-eyed look was achieved by application of several light layers of cake mascara. The lashes were then brushed out and separated to present a soft and natural appearance. (Left) The basic foundation color should closely match the natural color of the model's skin. It is used to give a smooth, overall color and to cover any blemishes or unevenness in skin tone. Sheer, translucent powder is applied over the foundation and should allow the skin to retain its natural look; it should never cake over the skin itself. Photos by Robert Farber.

Makeup

(Right) A completely natural look is the result of meticulously applied makeup, used sparingly. Foundation, a little contour color, and a lip pencil can change or improve a whole look. (Below) Contouring the face is an art in itself. Dark colors are used to model cheekbones, nose, and jawline. This must never be overdone, or it will appear harsh and artificial. (Below right) Eyeshadow winged lightly from the corner of the eye gives an alive and slightly mysterious look. Lips are carefully defined by lipliner before the fill-in color is applied. A light foundation under the eye minimizes circles and emphasizes the shadowed cheekbones. Photos by Robert Farber.

Before Shooting

As a rule, models should be made up wearing a robe. They are more comfortable, and spills are less of a problem. After being made up, the model's face and hair should be draped in a scarf so that makeup and clothing are protected while the model is dressing. While on the set, shine is controlled with an application of loose translucent powder. It must be continually fluffed and aerated in its container. Compressed powder should not be used.

It bears repeating that today's look is sheer, natural, and see-through in makeup. Application of makeup should not begin before you have made a thorough study of the person's face. Help is available at most good cosmetic counters.

Manly, Thomas

(?–1932)
English photographer

Manly invented the Ozotype and Ozobrome processes. The first was an improved method of gum-bichromate transfer printing. The second, introduced in 1905, involved the transfer of a silver image from bromide paper to a pigment sheet where the silver caused local hardening of the pigment. From this, Howard Farmer developed the Carbro process, which was used for many years, both as a monochrome process for pictorial purposes and in tricolor for high-quality color prints.

• *See also:* CARBON AND CARBRO PRINTING; GUM-BICHROMATE PROCESS.

Mannes, Leopold D.

(1899–1964)
American musician, co-inventor of Kodachrome film

Mannes' collaboration in the invention of Kodachrome film is described in the entry for his coworker, Leopold Godowsky. Their subsequent work at the Kodak Research Laboratories laid the basis for a method of dispersing color couplers throughout the emulsion layers of a film. The couplers are enclosed in globules that prevent interaction with the gelatin or the silver halide; this makes it possible to incorporate couplers in the emulsion during manufacture rather than introducing them during processing, as is the case with the Kodachrome film process. The integral-coupler method developed from their research was introduced in Kodacolor film and prints in December 1941.

Mannes left the Kodak Research Laboratories in 1939, but returned for wartime research in 1942–43. He subsequently returned to his musical career as a concert violinist and as co-director and then president of the Mannes College of Music, which had been founded by his family.

• *See also:* GODOWSKY, LEOPOLD; KODACHROME FILM AND PROCESSING.

Marey, Etienne Jules

(1830–1904)
Pioneer in scientific photography

In about 1882, Marey, who was a French physiologist, began experiments in photographing animals in motion for analytical purposes. Marey and Eadweard Muybridge were acquainted and corresponded with each other about their work. Marey invented a camera (the "ophymograph") for recording heart action, another camera in the form of a gun for photographing birds in flight, and one using flexible film (designed in cooperation with Demeny) that was the forerunner of the motion-picture camera. Marey and Demeny also worked on projection equipment. Marey built several "slow motion" cameras that worked at speeds up to 700 frames per second (such as the one he built in 1894).

Marey's *chronophotography* devices produced multiple images on a single plate or film, which created a record of the path or flow of a continuous movement, much like that of modern stroboscopic photography. However, Marey's equipment used a revolving, slotted-shutter plate, not a repeating light source. Muybridge's method produced individual images on separate plates or films, which allowed each stage of a movement to be clearly seen and analyzed.

Marey founded the Marey Institute in Paris for further research in the photography of moving objects. After his death in 1905 the Institute was reorganized and carried on his work with funding from the French Government and others. There, early in the century, M. Lucien Bull made high-speed motion pictures at rates up to 2000 frames per second.

• *See also:* HIGH-SPEED PHOTOGRAPHY; MOTION STUDY; MUYBRIDGE, EADWEARD.

⊏C Masking

Masking, in photography, is a system in which a negative and a positive image, or sometimes two negative or two positive images, are fastened in register, so that a print or copy negative can be made from the combination. The second image, made from the original image for this purpose, is called a photographic mask.

One purpose of masking is to reduce, or in rarer cases, to enhance, the contrast of an image. Obviously, if you bind a negative in contact with a less contrasty positive printed from it, the positive will partly cancel the negative image, and the end result will be a less contrasty negative. The converse is also true; you can, for example, bind two negatives together to get a negative image having more contrast than one alone.

This can be done in either black-and-white or in color; in the latter case, the mask, or opposing image, need not also be in color. A black-and-white mask added to a color image will increase or decrease the contrast of the color image without having too great an effect on the color saturation. This is an important point; if, for instance, you had a color transparency that was too contrasty to print, and chose to make the print by lowering the contrast of the print material, then the final print would possibly have improved gradation, but partially desaturated colors. By using a mask, however, the contrast of the print can be greatly lowered, yet the strength of the colors remains nearly the same as in the high-contrast original.

It is very important that the mask image be identical in size to the original image, and that they be very precisely registered. If this is not the case, the result will be to form an outline around some parts of the image, or in extreme cases, to produce a bas-relief or tone-line image. (*See:* BAS-RELIEF; TONE-LINE PROCESS.)

Securing the required size and registration accuracy is a very difficult problem. Early workers in this field found it necessary to produce all their masks on glass plates, and even then, if the original size changed between the time the mask was made and the time it was used, registration was still difficult or impossible.

A simple solution has been found for this problem: Make the mask image deliberately unsharp, either by printing it through the back of the film, by using a diffusion sheet between original and mask film, or by using a rotating turntable type of mask printer. An unsharp mask is easy to register with the original image, and a slight mis-register has little or no effect upon the final result. The degree of unsharpness depends upon the size of the image. For 35 mm originals, the mask need be only slightly soft-edged; for large originals, more diffusion may be needed.

It might be thought that the use of an unsharp mask would degrade the definition of the final image. In actual practice, the opposite is true; an unsharp mask actually makes the masked image appear sharper. This is because the mask image, when diffused, is of lower contrast at the edges of image details than over large areas, and thus it has less effect upon edge contrasts than it does on massed tones. The result is that edge contrasts are actually enhanced in proportion to the overall image contrast, and this results in enhanced sharpness.

As previously mentioned, masking can be used for black-and-white negatives, but this is seldom done. There are other and easier ways to control print contrast in black-and-white. Likewise, additional masking is seldom if ever used for color negatives, except in isolated cases where the lighting of the original is too contrasty and must be reduced.

Masking as a means of contrast control, then, is mainly used with color transparencies. This is because color transparencies naturally have both high contrast and long scale, and this contrast must be compressed in making color prints or separation negatives from the transparency.

Color Correction Masks

There is a second type of masking, used mainly with color transparencies to be reproduced; here masking is done, not merely for contrast control, but

(A) An unmasked print. A contrast reduction mask (B) used to make a print (C). Note that highlights have been greatly reduced, resulting in loss of brightness and a generally "dull" appearance. A highlight mask (D), used to make a contrast reducing mask (E), restores brightness to the print (F) without excessive contrast. Note the improved highlight and midtone rendition. Original photograph by Steven Kelly for the Schlegel Corp. Prints from masks by Ken Star.

A

B

C

D

E

F

also to improve color rendition. This is done by making one or more masks through filters of different colors, so the effect of the mask is to hold down the contrast of some colors while leaving the contrast of other colors unchanged. The effect is to enhance the brilliance of the latter colors.

If only a single mask is made, the effect is merely to brighten certain colors while leaving others uncorrected. For instance, if a contrast control mask is made for a color transparency, and a red or magenta filter is used to make this mask, the result will be that the greens and blues will be lightened in the final print, while other colors remain much the same as they are.

If several masks are made, and each is used while printing a single color, as in making color separation negatives, then it is possible to improve both the overall contrast and the purity of the colors in the final print.

The reason such correction is necessary is because the dyes used to form the image in a color film are to some extent imperfect. In theory, each dye should absorb one color and transmit two. Thus, the yellow dye absorbs blue light and transmits green and red light. The magenta dye should absorb green and transmit blue and red. And the cyan dye should absorb red and transmit blue and green. As it happens, most yellow dyes are fairly satisfactory in this respect. Magenta dyes tend to lack density to green light, thus transmitting some light that they should absorb while absorbing some of the blue that they should transmit freely; however, their red transmission is satisfactory. Cyan dyes absorb some of the blue and green that they should transmit freely, while transmitting a good deal of red light that should be completely absorbed.

Therefore, if one tries to copy an image produced with such imperfect dyes on a color film, or print it on a color paper, one will find that the colors of the copy are degraded. The unwanted absorption of the cyan and magenta dyes results in these images being represented to some extent in layers other than the one in which they should lie. This has the effect of adding the complementary color to a given hue, which simply adds black or gray to it.

What masking amounts to is producing additional images representing the unwanted densities of the dyes. These images are in negative form when used with a positive transparency, and hence they add the unwanted density wherever it is *not* present in the original. Thus, they combine with the unwanted densities of the image to form a uniform, overall density covering the whole image area. The end result is to neutralize the unwanted absorptions of the dyes, at the cost of an overall addition of gray density, which merely serves to increase the exposure required to make the copy. In the case of color transparencies, the minimum requirement is for two masks, correcting for the unwanted absorptions of the magenta and cyan dyes. As a rule, no mask is needed for the yellow dye layer, but a mask may be made for it merely to keep its contrast the same as that of the other two layers.

In the case of color negative films, a different system of masking can be used, and this is built right into the negative emulsion. This comes about because, unlike a color transparency, there is no need for the dyes in a negative to have any particular visual appearance. They are there only to act as a color separation device in printing.

The masking system used in color negative films is based upon the use of color couplers, which are themselves colored. For instance, since the cyan dye has some unwanted density in the blue and green, the color coupler in this layer is reddish, and its original density is adjusted so that its blue and green density is as nearly as possible equal to the unwanted density of the cyan dye. When this layer is developed, cyan dye is produced to form the image, and the reddish color is eliminated in proportion to the amount of cyan dye formed. Therefore, the more cyan dye produced, the less red remains, and the result is to balance out the unwanted blue and green density of the cyan dye.

In the case of the magenta layer, since there is practically no unwanted red density, but some spurious density in the blue, the coupler used is yellow in color and works in exactly the same way; it adds a blue density (yellow-colored) mask that corrects for the unwanted blue absorption of the magenta dye.

The yellow image layer needs no masking, and its contrast is adjusted to match that of the two masked layers. So the final color negative contains the three image dyes (magenta, cyan, and yellow) and two mask dyes (reddish and yellow). The visual effect is to cover the image with an orange color, which makes it difficult to judge visually but improves its printing quality considerably.

More recent color negative films have greatly improved dyes, which have less of the unwanted absorptions. The masking of Kodacolor II and Kodak Vericolor II professional negatives is much less dense, and tends to a brownish tone rather than the strong orange hue of the previous color negative films.

Some variation in color is needed in the masking layers, depending upon the purpose of the film. Therefore, the masking layers of internegative films are adjusted to compensate both for color errors inherent in their own dyestuffs, and for the absorptions of the dyes in the transparency to be copied.

Masking in Photomechanical Processes

Masking is used in photomechanical work for the same reasons as in color photography, but the mask also has another function. Because in photomechanical work four colors (magenta, cyan, yellow, and black) are used, the masking is designed to make proper allowance for the black image.

In mixed colors—that is, colors having some gray in their makeup—the final image in color films is produced by differing amounts of all three dyes. In photomechanical work, however, part of the dark grays in the image come from the black printing plate, and a given color must be rendered by the use of only two of the three primaries, plus black. The masking used for this purpose is intended to eliminate part of the third color at any point in the dark parts of the image, and to add a corresponding density to the black plate. The engraver's term for this is "undercolor removal."

While there have been some purely photographic methods of accomplishing this aim, early engravers and lithographers did a good deal of this color correction by handwork on the negatives, and even by selective etching of the metal plates. This latter, however, made color plates exceedingly costly, and in the case of offset printing, no handwork can be done on the printing plate itself.

Today, many offset color plates are made by the use of an electronic scanner that produces the four negatives in a single operation. The scanner contains a computer that analyzes the composition of the image at every point, and calculates the amount of third color that is to be removed and added to the black image. Thus, color separation, color correction, and undercolor removal are all done in a single, automatic operation.

However, this does not concern the photographer. He or she may have occasion to use the photographic masking methods given below, but may not be concerned with the processes used in the final reproduction of color on the printed page.

Highlight Masking

The effect of masking, even for color correction, is also to reduce the contrast of the image. Since, in many cases, highlight contrast is already fairly low, masking may make the highlights excessively low in contrast and density. The remedy for this is to make a "highlight mask," which merely places a high density over the highlights of the image while the main masks are being made. This mask is then removed when the final copying is being done with the main masks. The result is to improve the contrast and brightness of the highlights, which remain substantially unmasked in the final negatives.

Making Masks

Because specific instructions for making masks change somewhat as the color materials themselves change, it is best to get up-to-date information on such details. For the reader who is interested, the following Kodak publications are suggested as aids in making masks:

1. Masks for color negative contrast control—pub. No. E-66, *Printing Color Negatives.*
2. Masks for color transparencies—pub. No. E-80, *KODAK Dye Transfer Process.*
3. Masking for color photomechanical reproduction—pub. No. Q-7A, *Silver Masking of Transparencies with Three-Aim-Point Control;* pub. No. Q-7B, *Camera-Back Silver Masking with Three-Aim-Point Control;* pub. No. Q-10, *Fundamental Techniques of Direct-Screen Color Reproduction.*

• *See also:* BAS-RELIEF; COLOR PRINTING FROM NEGATIVES; COLOR PRINTING FROM TRANSPARENCIES; COLOR SEPARATION PHOTOGRAPHY; DYE TRANSFER PROCESS; GRAPHIC ARTS PHOTOGRAPHY; TONE-LINE PROCESS.

Further Reading: Borosky, Irvin J. *Handbook for Color Printing.* Philadelphia, PA: North American Publishing Co., 1974; Eastman Kodak Co. *Creative Darkroom Techniques.* Garden City, NY: Amphoto, 1976; Hedgecoe, John and Michael Langford. *Photography, Materials and Methods.* New York, NY: Hastings House Pubs., 1975; Nadler, Robert. *The Color Printing Manual.* Garden City, NY: Amphoto, 1977.

Matte Box

The matte box is a device used on moving-picture and still cameras as a combination sunshade, filter holder, and masking device for multiple exposures. In its original form, it contained several mechanical masking devices, such as a circular iris, similar to the diaphragm in a lens, and a set of movable blades that divided the frame into quarters. Eventually, these gadgets were abandoned as they were difficult to position for a given effect, and the matte box was simplified to its present form.

As fitted to a motion-picture camera, the matte box contains a compartment that will accept filters, usually 3 inches square. This compartment is deep enough to hold two or three filters, depending upon their thickness, and various masks as well. Masks are usually cut from cardboard as needed. The front or subject side of the box is usually made in the form of a short truncated pyramid and acts as a sunshade when the device is moved back against the lens. This unit (sunshade and filter holder) slides along a rail fastened either to the tripod head or to the camera front, and the space behind it is taken up by a short bellows that prevents light from falling on the back of the filter or mask in use.

Moving-Picture Photography

In movies, the device is used for effects such as having one actor play two parts. In this case, a mask is made to cover one half of the film, and the actor is photographed on the other. The film is then rewound to the starting point, the actor changes costumes and moves to the opposite side of the scene, the mask is reversed, and the second exposure is made. If the mask is properly made and placed at the correct distance from the lens, there will be no visible dividing line between the two exposures.

Obviously, any accident or error in shooting either half of the scene will spoil both. For this reason, in today's moving-picture photography, the two shots are made on separate films and no matte box is employed on the camera. The two shots are

(Left) This combination lens shade and matte box is attached to the front of the lens with an adapter. The rear standard accepts gels and special effects devices; the front standard will hold special masks and vignetters. Photo courtesy Ambico Inc. (Right) Masks of various shapes are commercially available to accommodate most needs; blanks may also be purchased for individual uses. The lens shade shown here has five slotted positions to permit masks to be used singly or in combination. Photo courtesy Jack Curtis.

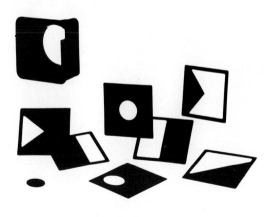

later combined into one print by the special effects laboratory, which uses an optical printer to accomplish the job.

Still Photography

This method is often used by creative still photographers to produce combinations of two images on a single film negative. Again, the result may be obtained by double-printing in the darkroom or by sandwiching two negatives in the enlarger. However, by careful planning and the skilled use of a matte box, the photographer can accomplish the same thing in the camera, producing a single combined negative ready to print. This is particularly convenient when a great many prints are needed and combination printing is too time-consuming.

Fantasies. In wedding photography, pictures called "fantasies" are often used. A common example is an extreme close-up of the hands of the bride and groom forming a framing archway for a long shot of the bride and groom standing in front of the altar; or a diminutive bride and groom apparently inside a wine goblet. The wine-glass effect involves using a registered pair of plastic masks—an opaque center oval with a clear surround, and the exact opposite of this, a clear center oval with an opaque surround.

To make this wedding "fantasy," a registered pair of plastic masks was used. First, the couple was photographed through the transparent oval in the opaque mask. Then, the same film was double-exposed to photograph the wine glass and background through the clear mask with the opaque oval. Photos by Al Gilbert.

Matte Box

Simply photograph the couple through the transparent oval, change masks, and then double-expose the same piece of film, photographing the wine glass through the second mask.

If a 2¼″ × 2¼″ camera with interchangeable backs is being used, these two exposures can be made hours or even days apart. Just insert the dark slide noting the frame to be used, and put this negative aside for the subsequent exposure. Various shaped masks are commercially available, or they can be made with Kodalith film.

There is a fairly critical lens aperture that will give a pleasing "blurred blend" of the two images. The exact aperture depends somewhat on the focal length of the lens and the distance the matte-box mask is in front of the lens. Try an aperture of *f*/5.6 or *f*/8 for a start. Smaller apertures will result in a line of demarcation that is too sharp; larger apertures will cause this line to be excessively broad and blurry.

Maxwell, James Clerk

(1831–1879)
Scottish physicist and mathematician

Maxwell is generally credited with the discovery that light is essentially an electromagnetic phenomenon, partaking of the nature of waves. Thus, he effectively added to Newton's theory that light was made of concrete corpuscles. Following the work of Young and Helmholtz on color analysis and sensation, Maxwell demonstrated the fundamental basis of three-color photography in 1861.

Maxwell had theorized that any color could be created by the additive mixture of red, green, and blue light. He had slides made through red, green, and blue filters, and projected the slides through the same filters, superimposing the images on a screen. The result, although crude, was the first color photograph in 1861.

His discoveries that relate directly to photography are only a small part of the monumental advances he made in the theoretical physics of electromagnetism and gases. Although he died at the age of 48, Maxwell's career was probably the most brilliant in all of nineteenth-century science. One of the well-known Maxwell equations defines the index of refraction, basic to the design of lenses.

Medical Photography

Medical photography is as broad and diverse as the field of medicine itself. A current directory lists over 30 medical subdivisions that range from aerospace medicine to veterinary medicine. And, of course, within the ranks of medical practitioners the specialties and subspecialties continue to proliferate.

It is helpful to consider all of the imaging techniques—photographic and electronic—as related to medical photography. The only qualification, perhaps, is that the image is reduced at some point to a photographic reproduction.

Thus, a hastily exposed instant print of a fetus within its mother's womb, visualized by ultrasound waves, may be considered a medical photograph. On the other hand, the infinitely complex work to show what the retina "sees" or to record the appearance of the interior of the aorta—a technique pioneered by Lennart Nilsson—requires detailed photographic knowledge.

Medical photographs may, at times, appear mundane, yet they are valuable to the clinician, the researcher, the pathologist, and the patient. However, medical photographs as seen in the work of

Medical photography is invaluable for a number of purposes: recording, comparing, teaching, examining, and describing. This photograph, for example, illustrates a simple arm lesion that would require over 100 words to describe.

Nilsson or Fritz Goro often require highly complex theoretical considerations and one-of-a-kind equipment. These photographs often have both medical value and true artistic qualities.

A considerable number of practicing physicians are highly skilled photographers in their own right; they are as much at home with photography as they are in their medical practice. Most teaching hospitals and medical schools consider photographic equipment and staff as necessary, full-time elements of the institution. And, as in medicine itself, medical photography makes use of generalists and specialists. The same is true of photographic equipment, which may consist of entirely conventional cameras or may require specially constructed photographic apparatus.

Medical photographers may make a rough distinction between clinical work and biomedical laboratory photography. Clinical photography often deals with full-size subjects such as surgical operations, patients at various stages of treatment, morphological and pathological conditions, or demonstrations of medical techniques and procedures.

Biomedical laboratory photography most often encompasses the making of images of smaller subjects—tissue specimens; gross anatomical specimens; culture plates and tubes; gel slabs; parasites; instruments; and generally, images of phenomena that require magnification. (*See:* Biomedical Photography; Bright-Field Illumination; Cathode-Ray Tube Recording; Clinical Photography; Close-Up Photography; Dark-Field Illumination; Dental Photography; Electron Micrography; Fiber Optics; Motion-Picture Production; Photomacrography; Photomicrography; Scientific Photography; Ultraviolet and Fluorescence Photography; X-Ray.)

Patient Photography

Releases. The concepts of privacy and contract as they relate to medical photography are subject to differing interpretations in various countries and states. In general, clinical photographs should not even be made without permission of some kind. Even if only a part of the body that does not reveal the identity of the patient is photographed, the right to privacy is involved, and this affects the photographer as well as the institution. The photographer should make sure that a general hospital admission release includes permission for his or her activity. If it does not, then a photographic release must be prepared. Nonprofessional observers must be kept out of the studio.

The patient's consent, or that of a parent or guardian, should be obtained and constitutes a valid contract. The form should be short and couched in simple lay language, because many people are wary

---

SOME MAJOR FUNCTIONS OF PHOTOGRAPHY IN MEDICINE

Diagnosis	Radiographs, nuclear medicine.
Documentation	Pathological gross specimens, photomicrographs, electron micrographs, plastic surgery, dermatology, surgical procedures, eye photography, lab source.
Patient Progress	Dental procedures (orthodontia, endodontia, restoration), orthopedic (gait studies), radiation therapy.
Patient Monitoring	Heart catheterization, cardio-pulmonary, cine-fluoroscopy.
Research	Electron microscopy, optical microscopy, as well as those techniques mentioned above.
Education and Training	Audiovisual techniques with materials from the previously mentioned applications.
Staff Communication	Pathology, radiology, conferences, recording rounds.
Patient Communication	Diet, physical therapy, administering medication, home care.

---

of signing legal-looking statements they cannot understand. It is reassuring to have incorporated a sentence stating that the patient's name will not be revealed when the photograph is used. It should also be made clear that the photograph is made for medical purposes only. For photographs to be used in commercial applications, a professional model release is needed.

Anatomical Standardization. The photographer and the physician need a common language for establishing the best viewpoint. It is for this reason that the photographer should know the rudiments of anatomy, pathology, and terminology. The forms used for ordering photographs usually have outline drawings for indicating body regions. In some departments, reference charts are prepared for use by the photographer and the medical staff. In that way, better standardization can be obtained, and less time is spent in communication. Such convenient aids are vital in special programs.

Surgery. In the photography of surgical operations, whether for stills or for motion pictures, two opposing factors confront the photographer. On the one hand, graphic and tidy photography can be a time-consuming procedure. On the other, surgical photography has to be carried out swiftly, without hindrance to the surgeon, because the safety of the patient is paramount. Furthermore, the surgeon

Displacements from the main body planes are indicated by directions in space and by anatomical reference points. Standardization is essential in communication between physician and photographer.

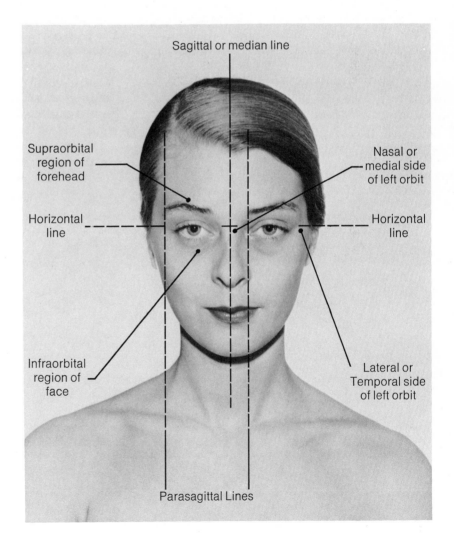

Sagittal or median line

Supraorbital region of forehead

Nasal or medial side of left orbit

Horizontal line

Horizontal line

Infraorbital region of face

Lateral or Temporal side of left orbit

Parasagittal Lines

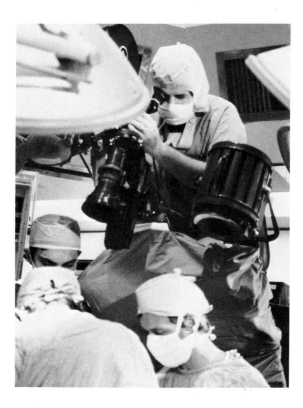

Motion pictures and still photographs are often required during operating-room procedures, and the photographer must be well versed in methods for setting up, lighting, and exposure. He should also be familiar with the special equipment available for this work. Here, a cinematographer is seated with the camera positioned well over the surgical field. The stand can be raised or lowered by a motorized drive. Photo by Allan Boatright; © Herbert R. Smith.

a similar operation should be observed beforehand, and steps to be illustrated should be discussed with the surgeon. Hazards and safety precautions must be discussed with the surgical staff. Tripods, light stands, and stepladders must be draped. The photographer will be gowned, capped, and masked, and must not allow him- or herself or the equipment to touch anything in the sterile area. Above all, should such an accident occur, the photographer must immediately call it to the attention of the surgical team.

In the operating room, the surgeon, of course, designates the area of interest and significant details. Responsibility for selecting the proper angle and position for the camera falls primarily on the photographer. Since the photographer should also hold him- or herself accountable for tidiness in the finished illustrations, he or she should always be alert to the appearance of the background and incidentals seen in the viewfinder as well as the focusing of the main subject. However, the photographer will not be able to make changes, and here the understanding and cooperation of the surgeon are imperative, because only a neatly arranged field does full justice to the skills of both surgeon and photographer. Often, extra care, such as the addition of a fresh drape, or a more orderly grouping of instruments, is all that is needed.

Special Techniques

Ultraviolet Photography. The ultraviolet photography of living subjects is a valuable supplementary technique for the clinical photographer. Electronic-flash ultraviolet records can reveal details invisible to the eye and record fleeting visible fluorescence patterns for study and reference.

The clinical examination of dermatologic and other lesions under ultraviolet radiation is a frequent and informative application of ultraviolet technology. Recording the ultraviolet appearance of patients has the same function in clinical routines—patient progress, research, science, and education—as recording their appearance under ordinary lighting.

Ultraviolet Reflection Records. The usefulness of these records comes from the differential reflection of white and slightly pigmented skin. Tone and color differences so slight that they may not be discernible to the eye become exaggerated when recorded in the ultraviolet region. The accompanying

cannot always anticipate the need for photographic records, and the photographer may not be summoned until the lesion is exposed or some unexpected condition is discovered. Therefore, the photographer's greatest asset will be the ability to work systematically with speed and accuracy. He or she must be extremely familiar with all the adjustments on the cameras to be used and be able to make them automatically.

Since there will be no time for experimenting during surgery, the photographer must be well versed in methods for setting up, lighting, and exposure. (Practice in the autopsy room will enable development of this technical facility.) When possible, illustration shows how a slight depigmentation (vitiligo) is clearly mapped in a photograph. The normal skin pigment absorbed the ultraviolet rays, while the affected areas of the epidermis reflected this radiation.

Fluorescence Studies. The examination of patients under a lamp that emits ultraviolet radiation has long been an invaluable clinical procedure. Healed and incipient lesions that are missed during visual inspection often become apparent from the colors and intensities they exhibit under ultraviolet irradiation. The extent of current dermatoses and active cancer lesions (see the accompanying illustration) can be readily traced, recorded, and followed.

It is also possible to detect a patient's past history of conditions like lupus erythematosus, syphilis, psoriasis, neurodermatitis, erythemas, dysvitaminosis, and patch testing. In forensic medicine, evidence of plastic surgery performed to hide identity can be discovered.

Incipient, subclinical, and early conditions can often be revealed. Notable are tinea capitis, glossitis, pterygia, and jaundice.

Induced Fluorescence. Many of the most valuable fluorescence techniques involve the use of fluorescein. This dye has been used in checking and following the fit of contact lenses. Retinal photography involving injections of fluorescein coursing through the blood vessels of the eye has been investigated.

Occlusions of vessels in the exposed brain have been located advantageously and quickly by injecting fluorescein into pertinent arteries. The diffusion through the smaller arteries and the return through the veins was studied under ultraviolet radiation and sequential photographs made.

Ultraviolet reflection records are especially useful in distinguishing very subtle tone and color differences in the skin. Here, the depigmented patches of vitiligo have reflected the ultraviolet irradiation, but the normal skin has absorbed it.

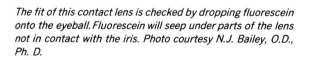

The fit of this contact lens is checked by dropping fluorescein onto the eyeball. Fluorescein will seep under parts of the lens not in contact with the iris. Photo courtesy N.J. Bailey, O.D., Ph. D.

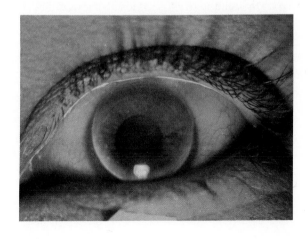

Infrared Photography. In general photographic practice, it has been found that infrared radiation between the 700 and 900 nm wavelengths can penetrate the human skin to a depth of about 3 mm. The translucency of tissues and detail size govern delineation and tone value in the reflected infrared radiation. For example, the superficial venous system records darker than the body in an infrared photograph. The skin and superficial tissue reflect most of the infrared falling on, and penetrating, a short distance into the body, whereas the blood in the veins absorbs much of the infrared. This provides tone separation. In an infrared color transparency, the veins appear blue as well as dark, because they lie under a scattering layer.

Photography of Gross Specimens. The camera requirements depend upon how permanent the setup is to be and how much work is planned. An efficient and versatile camera has a ground glass for focusing, and long bellows extension that allows making photographs up to actual size (1:1). However, large workloads, cost, and time requirements may make working with a 35 mm single-lens reflex camera more practical. A lens hood is desirable for shielding against stray illumination, because lights are often used close to the front of the camera.

Films. The color of tissue provides vital information, and such color variations can be recorded realistically by using color films.

There are some instances, however, where black-and-white photography will provide a useful record if handled properly. These instances fall into three main groups:

1. To record dark-red areas with light or normal bordering tissue. This requires panchromatic film.
2. To record brightness values in about the actual tones of the specimen. This calls for panchromatic film plus a correction filter.
3. To record subtle variations of red tones with enhanced contrast. This requires an orthochromatic film, or panchromatic film plus a green filter.

Lighting Equipment. Flood lighting is generally used for specimen photography. The subject will not move during the exposure interval, so time expo-

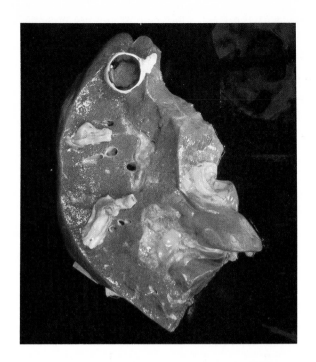

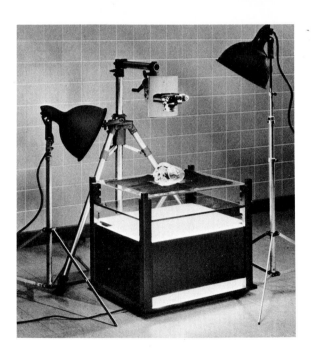

Shown at top is a gross specimen of a liver, photographed using a set-up similar to that in the bottom photo. Two flood-lamps are usually adequate for lighting. A plate glass base mounted on standards, with another shelf below for holding a background, served to display the specimen.

sures can be made, which allows the use of small apertures to provide adequate depth of field for overall sharpness of the image. (Occasionally, flash may be used to avoid excessive heating of the specimen.) Two lights are usually adequate to light the subject, although a third is sometimes needed for background illumination. A small light source is desirable to keep specular reflections small in size.

Supplementary Equipment. An important accessory is an appropriate base on which to arrange the specimen. A piece of ¼-inch, flawless, polished plate glass, about 18″ × 24″, will serve the purpose well. This glass should be supported on standards or wooden blocks 6 to 12 inches high, so that a suitable background can be placed below it. If a large volume of work is to be done, it is better to construct an illuminator. The glass can be separated from the background material, or placed directly above and in contact with it if the background is opaque.

When a black background is used, reflections of the camera unit in the glass support must be prevented. This can be done by suspending a stiff black card between the lens and the subject. A piece about 13″ × 15″ will do, with a hole cut in the center for the lens.

Props are also needed to support the specimen on the glass so that the desired aspect will be displayed to best advantage. Blocks of wood, wads of cotton, modeling clay, and curved strips of ⅟₁₆-inch lead of various lengths and widths are practical.

When the size of the specimen is important, a ruler should be included in the picture. Its use gives the viewer a quick grasp of the subject's size regardless of whether the picture is projected on a screen or published in a journal. A dull, light-toned ruler with black indices photographs more legibly than a shiny, white one. A clear plastic ruler with contrasting indices is unobtrusive. Some workers prefer to include an object of familiar size.

Before placing the specimen in position, it is wise to have the film and filter ready, and to have an idea of the size of image desired, the subject-to-film distance, the illumination, and the number of exposures to be made.

With careful planning in advance, the photography can be carried out efficiently and promptly, and there is less likelihood that the specimen will be dried out by long exposure to the heat of the lamps during lighting, composing, and focusing.

Image Size. As a rule, the image size (called scale or magnification) is determined by the relation of the size of the specimen to the negative size. For example, at 1:1 scale, only a very tiny object or a small portion of a larger one can be photographed on 35 mm film. On the other hand, 4″ × 5″ film can accommodate a much wider range of specimens at 1:1 or at least 1:2 scale. Whatever the scale, it should be definitely known, because this information makes the photographs more comprehensible to anyone who views them. The scale can be automatically established in the photograph by including a ruler or a familiar object of known size. Whenever feasible, adopt definite scales such as 1:2, 1:5, 1:10, and so forth.

Disinfecting Photographic Equipment

When the camera and other equipment are used for photographing autopsies or for photographing gross pathological specimens, the camera may become accidentally contaminated. Preferably, equipment should be reserved for these activities and not transported to areas such as the patient studio. The photographer will normally use all of the precautions advised for medical personnel for their own safety, including the wearing of masks, gowns, and rubber gloves. The clothing can be discarded, but the equipment must be suitably treated before it is reused.

Most cameras, with the film in them, can be sterilized by the gas sterilization method. The following cycle is suitable: 27 inches of vacuum, relative humidity 30 to 50 percent, 54.4 C (130 F), 2 hours. Four hours at 37.8 C (100 F) with the same factors are also effective. Black-and-white films do not show any noticeable effects. However, with color film, a slight increase in latitude, but not speed, is encountered. The camera should be wrapped in a polyethylene bag having 3 to 4 mils thickness. Sterilization fluid should not be allowed to come in contact with plastic parts of the camera because it is likely to attack them.

In some hospitals, a routine load, especially one wrapped in a freely pervious cover, is processed for 4 hours at 54.4 C (130 F) or for 2 hours at 60 C (140 F). Sometimes also the relative humidity is raised above 50 percent. A camera should not be included with such loads. A time should be chosen when the rest of the load in the sterilizer can also be treated by means of a cycle suitable for the camera,

SUGGESTED GERMICIDAL SUBSTANCES FOR DISINFECTING PHOTOGRAPHIC EQUIPMENT

| Product and Concentration | Treatment time 5–10 min. | | | | | Comment |
	Plate Glass	Glass or Steel Trays and Vessels	Exterior of Camera and Lens	Hand Rinse	Floors and Furniture	Most products have lowered activity in the presence of organic matter, so surfaces should be washed prior to disinfection. (Use capital X when feasible.)
Vesphene, 2.5%	X	X	x	x	X	Residual action
Amphyl, 2–2.5%	X	X	x	X	X	Residual action
Flexosan, 2–2.5%	X	X	x		X	Wetting and residual
Wescodyne, 150ppm	x	X	x	x	x	Temporarily colors
Betadine, 75–150ppm	x	X	x	x	x	Temporarily colors
Hypochlorite, 10–2500ppm					x	Inactivates organic matter
Roccal, 0.2–1%	x	x	X		x	Active on viruses,
Zephiran, 0.2–1%	x	x	X		x	less on bacteria
Formaldehyde, 8%, alcoholic	x	x				Sporocidal
2% Activated glutaraldehyde	x	x	x			Sporocidal

Tabulation courtesy of Leon J. LeBeau, Ph.D. From a paper presented at the 41st Annual Meeting of the Biological Photographic Association, 1971. Adapted from Block and Lawrence, "Disinfection, Sterilization and Preservation," Lea and Febiger; 1968 PHS Pub. 2054, *Isolation Techniques for Use in Hospital.*

or else the camera can be sterilized separately. Any treatment that is more intense is likely to harm the camera or affect the film. This does not mean that the photographer cannot try out a specific cycle in the event that its use would be more practical in a particular institution. In order to safeguard photographic equipment the photographer could increase the schedule in easy steps.

• *See also:* BIOMEDICAL PHOTOGRAPHY; BRIGHT-FIELD ILLUMINATION; CATHODE-RAY TUBE RECORDING; CLINICAL PHOTOGRAPHY; CLOSE-UP MOVIES; CLOSE-UP PHOTOGRAPHY; DARK-FIELD ILLUMINATION; DENTAL PHOTOGRAPHY; ELECTRON MICROGRAPHY; EXPOSURE; FIBER OPTICS; INFRARED PHOTOGRAPHY; MICROPHOTOGRAPHY; MODEL RELEASE; MOTION-PICTURE PRODUCTION; PHOTOMACROGRAPHY; PHOTOMICROGRAPHY; RADIOGRAPHY; SCIENTIFIC PHOTOGRAPHY; TELEPHOTOGRAPHY; ULTRAVIOLET AND FLUORESCENCE PHOTOGRAPHY; X-RAY; ZOOM LENSES.

Further Reading: Currie, Donald J. and Arthur Smialowski. *Photographic Illustration for Medical Writing.* Springfield, IL: Charles C. Thomas Pubs., 1962; Gibson, H. Lou. *Medical Photography; Clinical-Ultraviolet-Infrared.* Rochester, NY: Eastman Kodak Co., 1973; Korff, H., ed. *Colour Photography for the Medical Photographer.* New York, NY: Elsevier-North Holland Publishing Co., 1974.

Mees, Charles Edward Kenneth

(1882–1960)
Photographic scientist

Early Studies
C. E. Kenneth Mees was born in Wellingborough, England. During his study at St. Dunstan's School he met Samuel E. Sheppard, with whom he had a scientific alliance until Sheppard died in 1948. In 1900, Mees and Sheppard entered the science school at University College, London, headed by Sir William Ramsay, who had done pioneer work in rare gases. Mees and Sheppard were so well advanced in chemistry that Ramsay suggested they do some elementary research rather than follow the usual laboratory courses. Mees and Sheppard had by then become seriously interested in photography, and sought to determine what happened when light struck the silver bromide-gelatin mixture, as well as the rules governing development and tone reproduction; Ramsay encouraged this line of endeavor.

With the classical papers of Hurter and Driffield (1890) in hand, Mees and Sheppard proceeded. Their investigations were first centered on the field

of sensitometry; and in 1903, they published their first papers in the *Photographic Journal.* These reports discussed gamma, and the concept of gamma infinity, a term they invented to describe the maximum contrast a given film-developer combination could attain.

In addition to their work on sensitometry, they studied the statics and dynamics of development, including the chemistry of the ferrous oxalate developer, the microstructure of the developed image, the theory of fixation, and the effect of oxidizing agents upon the latent image. Eleven papers were published between 1904 and 1907, and these formed the bases for their doctoral dissertations, and also for a book that is still a classic in its field: *Investigations on the Theory of the Photographic Process,* known ever since as "Sheppard and Mees."

Research in Photography

Mees eventually became associated with Wratten and Wainwright, a small manufacturer of photographic plates at Croydon. The owners offered to incorporate the firm and sell Mees a share in the company; he became Joint Managing Director with the younger Wratten.

Under the direction of Dr. Mees, wide research into color sensitizing of emulsions was under-

taken, and Wratten and Wainwright soon became the leading source of color-sensitive materials and the filters used with them. Through its publications, the firm also became known as a primary source of knowledge in the proper use of photographic materials. Mees was proud of being a pioneer in the publication of what are now called data books, instruction manuals, and technical booklets. Mees was with Wratten and Wainwright for six years and found a certain amount of time for special studies, such as the screen-plate process of color photography, and for further work on photographic theory, the resolving power of emulsions, and the graphic arts.

In 1912, George Eastman visited the Wratten and Wainwright factory at Croydon; he suggested that Mees come to the United States and work for Kodak at Rochester. Mees accepted on condition that Eastman buy the Wratten and Wainwright company.

In 1913, the Royal Photographic Society awarded Mees its Progress Medal, the highest honor in photography, for his researches, discoveries, and publications; in 1953 he received this award a second time.

Applications in Practical Photography

Mees moved to the United States in 1912 and established the Kodak Research Laboratory with a staff of about 20 people (the staff now numbers well over 1000). The laboratory was independent of the Kodak factory management, and it was not intended that it concern itself primarily with manufacturing problems. It set as its main objective the study of the theory of the photographic process and its application to practical photography. Mees pointed out that in the case of photography, unlike the other sciences, there was no general academic source for the advancement of knowledge of the theory of the process. Therefore, the research laboratories of the photographic industry had to develop into institutes devoted to the advancement of scientific knowledge, as well as to its application to the technology of photography.

During the first world war, Mees devoted the efforts of the laboratory largely to military problems. Work was done on the production of graticules, on colloidal fuels for the Navy, on aerial photography and reconnaissance, on the camouflage of ships at sea, and on a variety of other subjects. Laboratory efforts were intensified during World War II.

A side effect of World War I was a serious shortage in the United States of research chemicals that had formerly been obtained from Germany. In order to supply chemicals to laboratories and universities, Mees established a department of synthetic organic chemistry, which later became a major source of chemicals for photographic research.

New divisions were added to the laboratory as needed, and laboratories were established in England and France, as well as in Panama, to investigate the problems of photography and the behavior of materials in the tropics.

History of Photography

In the late 1930's, Mees became interested in the history of photography, and encouraged the collection of historical material. When the home of George Eastman became available in Rochester, Mees supported the idea of making it into a photographic museum and educational institution. George Eastman House was established, and Mees was the first chairman of its board. The International Museum of Photography at George Eastman House is an educational institution chartered by the N.Y. State Board of Regents and operated by a board of representatives of industry and education; it is the most outstanding organization of its kind.

Photographic Literature

Mees also encouraged the publication of a large part of the results of the work of the laboratories, both scientific and practical, as *Scientific Communications from the Kodak Research Laboratories.* Abridgments of many of the papers were published in an annual *Abridged Scientific Publications.*

In 1915, Mees started the *Monthly Abstract Bulletin,* in which abstracts of the world's photographic and related literature were brought together. This was primarily intended for use by workers in the laboratories and by interested people in other departments of the company, but it also had wide outside distribution.

In 1942, Mees made his greatest contribution to scientific literature with the publication of *The*

Theory of the Photographic Process, written with the aid of many of his associates. It brought together the state of knowledge on the theory of photography, and it was intended to form a comprehensive survey to stimulate work on photographic theory. The fourth edition was edited by Mees' colleague, T. H. James, and published in 1977. It continues the extensive revision and addition of material to maintain its position as one of the leading scientific reference works in photography.

Dr. Mees retired from Eastman Kodak Company in 1955, and settled in Hawaii, where he died in 1960.

Méliès, Georges

(1861–1938)
French motion-picture pioneer

Beginning as a conjuror and illusionist, Méliès became manager of the Theatre Robert Houdin in Paris, where he presented shows with mirror illusions and other magical tricks. When the Lumiere brothers first showed their motion pictures, Méliès acquired some film apparatus and proceeded to make a variety of trick films. Some of his effects were unsurpassed even a quarter century later; they involved double exposure, stop motion, and other camera manipulations. D. W. Griffith is said to have credited Méliès with everything he knew. Two of Méliès' most successful films are "The Voyage of Gulliver" (1902) and "A Trip to The Moon" (1902). An extensive biography, with autobiographical sections, was written by Maurice Bessy and Lo Duca, 1961 (original publication, Paris, 1945).

Mercuric Chloride

Bichloride of mercury, corrosive sublimate

Bleaching agent used in mercury intensifiers.
Formula: $HgCl_2$
Molecular Weight: 271.52

White powder or colorless crystals, freely soluble in water, alcohol, and ether. Mercuric chloride is a dangerous poison, and must be handled with great care. Its solutions are unstable to light.

DANGER: If ingested, give powdered charcoal, egg white, flour, or starch mixed with water. Then give a mustard emetic followed by strong tea or coffee. Finally, give demulcent and alkalizing drinks. *Call a physician at once!*

Mercuric Iodide

Red iodide of mercury, deutoiodide of mercury, mercury biniodide

Used as an intensifier in photography.
Formula: HgI_2
Molecular Weight: 454.47

Scarlet red powder, only slightly soluble in water, but very soluble in solutions of potassium iodide, sodium sulfite, or hypo. It is unstable to light in solution. Very dangerous to use, extremely poisonous.

DANGER: If ingested, give powdered charcoal, egg white, flour, or starch mixed with water. Then give a mustard emetic followed by strong tea or coffee. Finally, give demulcent and alkalizing drinks. *Call a physician at once!*

Mercury-Vapor Lamp

A mercury-vapor lamp is an electric lamp containing a pair of electrodes in an atmosphere of mercury vapor. The source of light, primarily, is an electric arc, maintained through the vapor and passing between the two electrodes. In some lamps, a phosphor coating, which glows when excited by the ultraviolet radiation produced by the arc discharge, forms a secondary light source. The light from the phosphor coating not only adds to the overall output, it also provides the missing colors in the mercury spectrum, when desired. The output of such a composite lamp will be a continuous spectrum, upon which the characteristic spectral lines of mercury are superimposed.

Early Forms

The early forms of mercury-vapor lamp were the Cooper-Hewitt types; they consisted of a long glass tube with a bulb at one end. The bulb contained

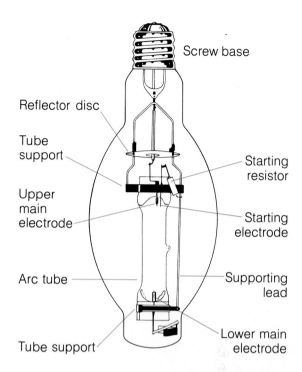

A mercury vapor lamp has a pair of electrodes in an atmosphere of mercury vapor. The light source is primarily an electric arc maintained through the vapor and passing between the two electrodes. In most mercury lamps, the arc tube is enclosed in an outer bulb. In some lamps, a phosphor coating forms a secondary light source.

two electrodes and a small pool of liquid mercury; at the far end of the tube was a third electrode. The two electrodes immersed in the mercury pool were used to start the arc by vaporizing the mercury. When sufficient conducting vapor was produced, the arc transferred to the far electrode and one of those in the bulb.

The light of these lamps was a blue or blue-green color with considerable ultraviolet content. They were used a great deal in the early days of photography, where their light output matched the sensitivity of the color-blind films and plates of the period.

Modern Mercury Lamps

Modern forms of the mercury lamp do not have the pool of liquid mercury, and do not need a starting electrode. They are usually started by a high-voltage pulse produced by the inductive "kick" from the ballast coil, which is required to limit the maximum current through the tube in any case. The basic mercury lamp with clear glass or quartz bulb has about the same spectrum as the older types.

"Color-improved" mercury lamps, as mentioned above, have a phosphor over part of the glass, which adds its light to that of the mercury arc. "White" mercury lamps are completely covered with a phosphor coat, and most of the light output comes from the phosphor layer; only a small contribution is made by the arc. Except in shape, these lamps are quite similar to the ordinary household fluorescent lamp, and work on the same principle. Their light output has a continuous spectrum with some traces of the mercury lines added, but the resulting color quality is not the same as that of a black body having the same visual color temperature. Such lamps are used mainly for street lighting and factory illumination; they are not used to any extent in photography. A big advantage of these modern forms of mercury-vapor lamps is their high efficiency. They give out many more lumens of light per watt consumed than incandescent lamps.

Black-Light Lamps

The so-called "black-light" lamp is a mercury lamp designed for greater emission in the near ultraviolet (320–400 nm) region. These rays cause many substances to glow. The process is used for stage and decorative lighting, as well as for industrial inspection, mineralogy, detective work, medical investigations, and other purposes.

Since these lamps also emit light in the blue and green regions of the spectrum, they must be used with some kind of filter that absorbs the visible light and transmits only the ultraviolet radiation.

In some types, the filter is the glass envelope of the lamp itself; other types have clear envelopes, and must be used with a separate filter. Fluorescent black-light lamps are also available; they have a higher output than the plain mercury lamps, but require more space. The BL types require filters; the BLB types are made of special filter glass.

Sunlamps

While almost any mercury lamp can be used as a sunlamp, there is a special type, known as the RS lamp, which is the same size and shape as a reflector photoflood lamp, but contains a mercury tube inside the reflector. This lamp also contains a special ballast device in its base, so no auxiliary equipment is required; it can be used in any convenient socket.

The RS lamp can be used in certain photographic processes where an intense source of blue and ultraviolet light is needed. It is often used to expose small offset plates for office duplicators, and also can be used to expose printing-out paper, blueprint paper, and other materials requiring simulated daylight for printing.

Capillary Lamps

The capillary lamp is a very small tube containing mercury with an electrode at each end. It is made of quartz, and is about ¼ inch in diameter and about 3¼ inches long. One model of this lamp burns at 1000 watts and requires water cooling; for this purpose it is operated inside a glass water jacket through which water is pumped at all times while the lamp is burning. The other type, also a quartz tube and having the same dimensions, burns 900 watts and requires forced-air cooling. These lamps are used to expose diazo films in high-speed microfilm duplicating machines. Their spectrum is a combination of a continuous one with the characteristic mercury lines superimposed, and the light is visually white.

Composite Lamps

Some experimental work has been done in making mercury lamps that can be used for certain color processes where a continuous spectrum is not necessary. These processes require not only the blue and green output of the mercury lamp, but a fair amount of red light as well. This is accomplished by adding some cadmium to a mercury lamp; the main emission line of the cadmium spectrum is red in color, and provides the missing element in the illumination.

Color Photography with Mercury-Vapor Lamps

Photographers are sometimes required to expose color film in large interiors or under streetlights illuminated with the newer "white" mercury-vapor lamps. While it is obvious that color correcting filtration is necessary to achieve proper color balance, no information is yet available on what filters to use. One of the complicating factors is that even with the same type of lamp there is considerable variability in color output between bulbs of different voltages. Studies are being considered to investigate this problem. If a photographer is faced with taking color pictures under such illumination, he or she should run tests with various color compensating filters to achieve a balance. If it is possible to use color negative film, where further balancing can be done in the printing step, the photographer stands a better chance of achieving good balance than with a transparency film.

• *See also:* INCANDESCENT LAMPS; LIGHTING.

Metol

Elon, Pictol, Rhodol, Photol

Chemically, *p*-methylaminophenol sulfate. Developing agent used alone or in combination with hydroquinone, and occasionally combined with pyro.
Formula: $(CH_3NHC_6H_4OH)_2H_2SO_4$
Molecular Weight: 344.38

White to yellowish powder soluble in cold water; solubility increases with heat. However, metol does not dissolve in strong sodium sulfite solutions. Hence in preparing a developer, the metol is first dissolved and the sulfite added afterward. Metol has low fog tendency and builds image detail rapidly. It stains hands and fingernails, but does not stain the gelatin of the film. Its reduction potential is 20.0.

• *See also:* ELON DEVELOPING AGENT, KODAK.

Metric System

The metric system has evolved as an attempt to incorporate the measurements of length, volume, mass, and time into a simple decimalized system. The modernized version of the metric system has been established by international agreement as the International System of Units (abbreviated simply as SI after the French version of the name). For everyday use, the main units are the metre (m) for length, the litre (l) for volume, and the gram (g) for mass (weight).

Prefixes are used to designate decimal divisions or multiples of the basic units. Commonly used prefixes are milli- (as in millimetre) to indicate one thousandth (0.001), centi- (as in centimetre) to indicate one hundredth (0.01), and kilo- (as in kilometre) to indicate one thousand times (1000). Therefore,

$$1000 \text{ millimetres} = 1 \text{ metre}$$
$$100 \text{ centimetres} = 1 \text{ metre}$$
$$1000 \text{ metres} = 1 \text{ kilometre}$$

Although the SI system designates the Kelvin as an absolute unit of temperature, the Celsius temperature scale is more commonly used. On the Celsius scale the freezing point of water is 0 C and the boiling point is 100 C with the interval between divided into 100 segments. For precise work, such as in some photographic color processing, Celsius temperatures may be measured to 0.1 degree.

The basic unit of volume can be considered as the cubic metre, but the litre (l) is more commonly used, especially for liquid. The millilitre (one thousandth of a litre, 0.001 l) is equivalent to, and has replaced in common usage, the cubic centimetre. For measurement of mass (weight), the milligram, the gram, and the kilogram are usually used.

In most cases it is best not to make conversions between metric and U.S. customary measurements. This can lead to confusion when mixing photographic solutions in such proportionality equivalents as grams per litre and ounces per quart. (See the articles on MIXING PHOTOGRAPHIC SOLUTIONS and WEIGHTS AND MEASURES for further discussion of this problem.)

It is important to recognize approximate size of the metric units. For photographic purposes, mass (weight) need only be given to tenths of a gram. Equipment for measuring photographic chemicals is seldom more accurate than this, and the precision required in photographic formulas is almost never this high.

By the same token, length measurements are usually expressed to 0.1 mm (about 4/1000 inch) at most. A fairly accurate ruler will be marked in centimetres and whole millimetre divisions, and liquid measurements will most commonly be used to the nearest whole millilitre.

• *See also:* MIXING PHOTOGRAPHIC SOLUTIONS; TEMPERATURE SCALES; WEIGHTS AND MEASURES.

Microfiche; Microfilm

Microfiche, or "fiche," are typically 105 mm × 148 mm sheets of film with rows of images in a grid pattern. Other sizes are also available. They can contain up to 98 full-color or more than 300 black-and-white page-images. Because they are easily mass-duplicated, fiche are widely used as a publishing medium for parts lists, catalogs, research reports, training materials, and other such reference items. In addition, computer output is frequently generated via computer output microfilmers onto 105 mm film, which is cut into standard 105 mm × 148 mm microfiche.

Microfilm consists of photographically recorded, reduced document-images on film. In the broad sense, microfilm can result from any conventional photographic process. However, the commonly accepted meaning of "microfilm" is film containing microimages that have been exposed in a microfilmer and are viewed on standard readers.

At one time, almost all microfilm was retained on small reels of 30.5-metre (100-foot) lengths of 16 mm or 35 mm film, each capable of containing thousands of images. Most of it still starts out that way, but a variety of microformats now exist that permit the tailoring of a microfilm system to specific needs.

A typical microfiche, shown here actual size — 105 × 148 mm. This particular microfiche contains 84 full-color page-images in 7 rows of 12 page-images each. Other internal formats are available.

Micrographics

Micrographics is a class word which, simply defined, covers all methods, materials, and equipment for the reproduction, duplication, dissemination, storage, and use of documents that have been photographically reduced to a very small size.

Modern micrographics in the United States began in the late 1920's with what was originally called "microfilm." By means of microfilm, large collections of documents could be sequentially recorded in greatly reduced form on rolls of 16 mm or 35 mm film. A single roll of film had a capacity of many thousands of such "micro-images" as they came to be called.

Today, microfilming has found wide application because of its many benefits. Foremost among these are the speed and convenience of retrieval possible with microfilm. Compatibility with computer systems is another advantage: Microfilm can be generated from magnetic tapes by high-speed computer output microfilmers and can be retrieved through the use of computer-interfaced retrieval terminals and computer-generated indexing. Security of information and savings in space, labor, and equipment have all contributed to the increased use of microfilm in business and industry.

Microfilming in the United States evolved directly from motion-picture technology. The film sizes used by the motion-picture industry—35 mm and 16 mm—were destined to dominate micrographics in the United States for several decades. But meanwhile, another micrographic concept was being developed in Europe—the production of micro-images on small sheets of film instead of rolls of film. In 1935, Dr. Joseph Goebel invented the first "step-and-repeat" camera for recording micro-images in a series of successive rows on a sheet of film instead of the linear sequence used with roll microfilm. Thus, what later was to become universally known as the "microfiche" was born. "Fiche" is a French word that means "card."

Microfiche did not enter American micrographic technology until the early 1960's. Since then, microfiche have rapidly grown to be the most widespread microform in active use throughout the world in innumerable document reproduction systems in business, industry, government programs at all levels, and in libraries.

Microforms

A great many microforms have been introduced in the past 40 years. There are two important classes: transparent microforms (film) and opaque microforms (micro-images printed on paper). The former require transmitted light for viewing. The latter require reflected light. Among the transparent microforms, other subdivisions need to be noted. As has been mentioned, they exist in roll form and in sheet form. One further subdivision is between negative images (reversed image tone) and positive images.

Micro-opaques. Micro-opaques, as they are called, have been produced in three different formats and by two different methods. The micro-opaques were in sheet form. They have now largely been superseded by microfiche.

Microprint. The first important micro-opaque was called "microprint," and was produced by a highly precise combination of roll microfilming and photolithography. A microprint sheet measures $6'' \times 9''$ and usually contains 100 pages arranged in 10 rows of 10 images each. The negatives for microprint were produced by recording images on rolls of 35 mm microfilm, which were then cut into strips to make a master from which a photolithographic printing plate could be made.

Microcard. The second important micro-opaque was the microcard—a sheet of $3'' \times 5''$ photographic paper containing up to 48 micro-images contact-printed from roll film.

Microlex. The third micro-opaque was designed for the reproduction of large collections of materials in the field of law, and hence was called "microlex." The sheets measured $6\frac{1}{2}'' \times 8\frac{1}{2}''$ and contained 200 pages on each side. Microlex enjoyed only brief popularity among the microforms.

Microstrip (Microtape). Another form of micro-opaque is what was called "microstrip" or "microtape," in which copies of documents photographed on 16 mm microfilm were contact-printed on photographic paper and then pasted in rows on $3'' \times 5''$ cards.

Micro-opaques vs. Microtransparencies. One of the serious drawbacks of micro-opaques, when compared with microtransparencies, was the difficulty of making reproductions from them, either in equivalent size in the form of a duplicate, or in the form of an enlarged print. Making duplicates or enlarged prints from microtransparencies was much easier, cheaper, and superior in quality.

Microformats

The first internal format for micro-images developed in this country was a variable-length frame format on 16 mm film, which the Recordak Corporation first developed for recording bank checks and then expanded for the recording of other business documents of a larger size. The most enduring format for 35 mm film was the result of Eastman Kodak Company's invention of the models C, D, and E microfilm cameras. These cameras use non-perforated 35 mm film and are capable of producing document images ranging in size from 1¼″ × ⅜″ to 1¼″ × 1¾″. For many years, these cameras have been in worldwide use.

Along with 35 mm film, 70 mm and 105 mm film have been extensively used for the reproduction of vast quantities of engineering drawings.

Microformatting for sheet microfilm (microfiche) has gone through a great many changes.

After several years of discussions and much experimentation concerning the overall size of microfiche, a standard was finally agreed upon. The size chosen was a standard European metric document size measuring 105 × 148 mm. This corresponds very closely to 4″ × 6″. But, while the overall size of the microfiche format was thus established, internal formatting in terms of micro-image size proved to be quite another problem and still continues to be a problem.

When microfiche first came into widespread use in the United States, two standards were adopted for the size and placement of micro-images. The first had 60 frames arranged in 5 rows with 12 images per row. The second had 98 frames arranged in 7 rows

Shown here are various microformats and roll or magazine systems for these formats. (1) Color microfiche containing 84 page-images. (2) Black-and-white microfiche showing 98 page-images. (3) Two-up 16 mm roll microfilm. (4 and 5) Aperture card film folios. (6) 35 mm roll microfilm. (7, 8, and 9) Self-threading magazines for 16 mm microfilm.

with 14 images per row. For each of these, a fixed reduction ratio range was established, as were the dimensions of the micro-image, the interframe spacing, and other dimensions. But as micrographic technology inevitably progressed, additional internal formats began to appear. Several of these were brought about through improvements in film technology —in particular, by a remarkable "marriage" between two hitherto unrelated technologies: micrographics and the computer.

Two other microformats are important to mention. One is the so-called "aperture card" format, in which one or more frames of microfilm are mounted in "windows" in IBM-type EAM (Electronic Accounting Machine) cards, which, by means of punched holes, can be machine sorted for rapid retrieval. This application has proven to be very useful in micrographic systems for engineering drawings. Another widely used method is what is called "jacketed" film. Jacket film corresponds in size and format to standard microfiche. The jackets are made up of plastic sleeves into which strips of roll microfilm can be inserted to produce the equivalent of a microfiche.

Reduction Ratio

The number of images that can be recorded on a roll of film or a sheet of film depends first of all on the size of the documents being filmed and secondly on the film size used. For example, reduction ratios for documents filmed on 35 mm film may range from a minimum of 8 times to a maximum of around 30 times. The first microfiche used in the United States were filmed in the 60-frame format previously described, at a reduction ratio of 18 to 20 times. The reduction ratio used for the 98-frame microfiche format was pegged at 24 times. The advent of Computer Output Microfilm (COM) pushed reduction ratios much higher. COM microfiche are often produced at a reduction ratio of 48 times. At this reduction ratio, well over 200 standard-size documents can be recorded on a single microfiche.

The search for the technology for producing excellent quality micro-images at very high reduction ratios has gradually evolved over many decades. From its inception, one of the primary goals for microphotography was to counter the immense and rapidly growing bulk of records on paper. To be able to reduce several hundred large newspaper pages to a few cubic inches was rightfully hailed as a major accomplishment. But as paper records continued to proliferate, an even greater compression was needed. This eventually led to the development of "ultramicrofiche."

Ultramicrofiche (often simply called "ultrafiche") are produced at very high reduction ratios, ranging from 55 times to well over 200 times, depending on the technology used. Modern ultrafiche technology was pioneered by the National Cash Register Company (NCR), in which, because of their extremely high resolving power, photochromic coatings were used instead of the usual silver coatings of traditional photographic films. At reduction ratios ranging from 150 times to well over 200 times, NCR was able to produce 105×148 mm microfiche containing as many as 3200 micro-images. Another important ultramicrofiche system was later developed by UMF Systems, Inc., primarily for library applications, in which 1000 micro-images arranged in a grid of 10 rows and 10 columns were precisely reproduced on a $3'' \times 5''$ sheet of film. Still another company—Microform Data Systems—developed a technology for industrial applications, employing a reduction ratio of over 200 times, which, for purposes of rapid data retrieval, is linked to a computer system. A linear reduction of 200 times is a reduction in area of 40,000 times. Even higher reduction ratios are presumably possible.

Production Equipment

Cameras. Roll microfilm is produced by means of two different types of cameras.

Rotary Camera. The first is called a "rotary camera" because it has a rotating drum that transports the document being filmed into the view of a camera lens that records it as it moves over the drum surface. The film in the camera is precisely geared to the movement of the document. Modern rotary cameras, much like printing presses, are equipped with automatic-feed devices and operate at very high speeds. Some can photograph both sides of a document simultaneously.

Planetary Camera. The second type of camera used for roll-film microrecording is called a "planetary camera." It is essentially a large copying stand having a vertical column on which a camera is mounted, and which can be moved up or down in accordance with the size of the document being

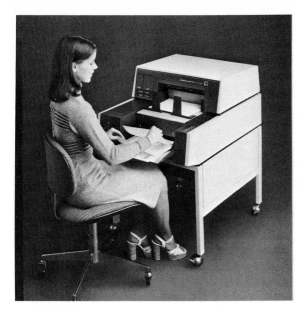

A planetary camera is a large copying stand with a vertical column on which a camera is mounted; the column may be moved up or down to accommodate size of document being filmed.

◀ A rotary camera is equipped with a rotating drum that transports the document into the view of a camera lens.

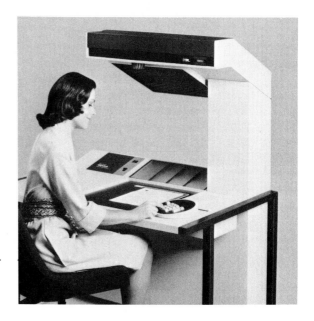

▶

filmed. Planetary cameras are extensively used for the microrecording of library materials in bound form that cannot be taken apart to be run through a rotary camera. Planetary cameras are also used extensively for the microrecording of engineering drawings.

Book-holder. In the microfilming of library materials in the form of bound volumes, an important ancillary piece of equipment, called a "book-holder," is needed. A book-holder, at its simplest, is a box containing a spring-loaded support platform surmounted by a sheet of glass. Its purpose is to press the two facing pages of an open volume upward against the glass surface to flatten them as much as possible so that a sharp image of the text can be recorded.

Continuous Processing Machine. Roll microfilm is developed in what is called a "continuous processing" machine, which transports long lengths of roll film through tanks containing the necessary chemical solutions. These machines are very similar in type to the processing machines used in the motion-picture industry. Some are "darkroom giants" that can process thousands of feet of film at high speeds and require skilled technicians. Others today, such as the Kodak Prostar processor, are small desktop units that can be operated under ordinary room-light conditions by office personnel.

Positive Printer. Roll microfilm is duplicated by means of a "positive printer," in which a roll of negative images rapidly moves in contact with an equivalent roll of positive film stock past a narrow slit of light that exposes the negative image onto the positive film stock. The exposed positive stock is then developed in a continuous processing machine much like the original camera film master.

Step-and-Repeat Cameras. Some microfiche are produced by means of what are known as "step-and-repeat" cameras, which function in a manner similar to a typewriter. The first row of images is recorded along the top row of a sheet of film. When this row is completed, the camera returns to its start-

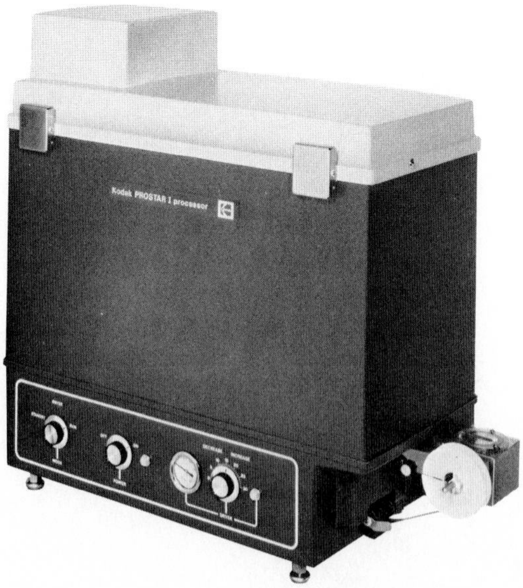

◄ *The Kodak Prostar is a small processing unit weighing about 100 pounds. It processes both 16 mm and 35 mm film, at a speed of 10 feet of film per minute.*

The Kodak Komstar is a Computer Output Microfilm device that combines imaging and processing functions for 16 mm microfilm and 105 mm microfiche. The content of microforms produced by COM can be changed and updated by changing the computer's programming. ►

ing point and commences a second row of images below the first row, and so on until the usable area of the film has been filled.

Microfiche are produced by manual methods or by automatic machines. Microfiche are also produced in quantities in the form of long rolls of film 105 mm in width by means of continuous processing machines. The latest trend in microfiche production has been the development of step-and-repeat cameras that contain a small, built-in processing unit. By pressing a few buttons, an inexperienced person can quickly produce completely processed microfiche ready for use.

Duplicators. Microfiche can be duplicated by means of a variety of different kinds of equipment, ranging from large, high-speed, high-capacity duplicators to small desk-top machines.

COM. In terms of production, the most powerful micrographics tool today is COM—Computer Output Microfilm. COM devices, of which there are now many, can convert information in the form of magnetic tape to readable images in the form of high-reduction, high-quality microtexts with astonishing speed, versatility, and economy. The content of microforms produced by COM can be rapidly changed and updated by changing the programming of the computer. In addition, COM equipment offers speed and cost advantages over computer paper printers.

User Equipment

Readers. Once a microfilm or a microfiche has been produced, the next important equipment is an optical display device, usually called a "reader," which will restore the minuscule micro-images to a readable size.

Each microform imposes different design requirements in reading devices. Readers range in size from small hand magnifiers to very large and costly console models controlled by sophisticated electronics or computer systems. Between these two extremes there are many projection devices that are manually operated.

Microform reading devices are of two basic types: internal projection devices, in which the image is displayed on a translucent screen; and external projection devices, in which the image is displayed on a white, opaque reflecting surface.

The ease of using a microform reader depends very much on the type of microform being read. In using microfiche, the user inserts a sheet of film between two sheets of glass and then positions images according to column and row on the reader screen. Roll microfilms, on the other hand, are "threaded" under and over guide rollers and between glass flats from a supply spool to a take-up spool. This threading operation resulted in the development of what are known as "cartridge" systems and readers. A cartridge containing a roll of microfilm needs only to be placed on the supply spindle of a reader. When the film is advanced, either manually or by motorized drive, it automatically threads itself to the take-up spool. With motorized readers, images can be advanced and scanned very slowly or can be either advanced or rewound at very high speeds. With the microfiche format, it is quite easy to cross-reference between, say, page 10 and page 190 by simply moving the column and row

positions. With roll microfilm, the intervening pages are passed across the reader screen.

Reader-Printers. In order to facilitate still further the transfer of information by means of micrographics, another type of reader known as the reader-printer was introduced. A reader-printer is a microform reader that has a display screen for reading, but which is also a push-button enlarger. The necessary machinery and chemicals have been compactly built into it so that the viewer of the projected screen image of a document in microform needs only to press a button to have an enlargement on paper delivered in a matter of seconds, and at small cost. This allows the user to take away a paper copy that can be perused and studied at leisure.

Data Systems

The technological world requires rapid access to enormous amounts of data that are stored in what have come to be called data banks. The data in these data banks is often very fluid and changeable. Additions and deletions are constantly occurring. The combination of the computer and micrographics, with their joint capability for rapid updating of data, rapid production, rapid duplication, and inexpensive dissemination, has done much to make the use of data banks more efficient. Today there are many microform reading devices on the market that are no longer called microform readers. Instead, they are categorized as "data display" devices.

Materials

Micrographics requires the use of films that have a very fine grain structure and very high resolving power. It has been axiomatic in photography that high resolution is accompanied by high contrast. This combination is highly suitable for recording black-and-white texts. Originals weak in contrast—for example, pencil drawings or notes—can often be considerably enhanced in readability by an increase in contrast. High-contrast films, however, because of their short tone scale, are not suitable for

With a reader-printer, it is possible not only to read microformed information directly off the screen, but also to obtain copies of that information.

recording continuous-tone illustrations such as photographs and most book illustrations. The problem of high resolution versus high contrast is now being more carefully studied.

Light-sensitive diazo dye materials are much less costly than silver, but are much too slow in their response to light to be used in cameras. They have proven to be very useful in a wide variety of duplicating processes where intense ultraviolet light could be used as the exposure source. Although diazo materials do not have as long a life expectancy as properly processed silver materials do, nonetheless they have proven to be very useful for the dissemination of duplicates of both roll and sheet microforms.

Another material that has been moving ahead in popularity as a means for producing microform duplicates is called "vesicular" film. Most diazo materials require ammonia in the image development step. Vesicular coatings require only light and heat to form an image. Both diazo and vesicular films have very high resolving power and are relatively inexpensive.

Color Microfilm

Another relatively recent development in micrographics, first introduced by Eastman Kodak Company, is color microfilm. Micrographic systems and materials were originally designed strictly for black-and-white reproduction of textual materials. Today, the use of color in innumerable publications —scientific journals, textbooks, news magazines, newspapers—has become so widespread that micrographic reproductions in color have become more than a desideratum. In some systems applications they have become a necessity. As the use of color broadened in printing, micrographics had to meet the challenge.

Micropublishing

Micropublishing is one of the most important activities in the use of micrographics today. Although at first it grew relatively slowly, it is now growing very rapidly and extending itself into many new fields. Correctly speaking, much of it should be called "micro-republishing," because the microform is made from an already existing publication in the form of print on paper. An increasing number of presses are offering their publications simultaneously in the form of "hard copy" (print on paper) and in microform.

Micropublishing has been used for the republishing, and incidentally the preservation and dissemination, of thousands upon thousands of volumes of serial publications, journals, newspapers, technical reports, rare books, and manuscripts from every part of the world. The list of micropublications is virtually endless.

Through the economy and enormous space-saving capability made possible by micropublishing, innumerable libraries have been able to vastly extend their resources.

Micrographics has become a major industry that affects our lives in many ways. The literature alone on micrographics is impressive. For readers interested in further information, the best source is the National Micrographics Association located at 8728 Colesville Road, Silver Spring, Maryland 20910.

Further Reading: Frieser, Helmut. *Photographic Information Recording.* Belmont, CA: Pitman Publishing Corp., 1975; Saffady, William. *Micrographics.* Littleton, CO: Libraries Unlimited, Inc., 1977; Spigai, Frances G. *Invisible Medium: State of the Art of Microform and a Guide to the Literature.* Washington, DC: American Society for Information Science , 1973.

Microphotography

Microphotography is the term used to describe the process of making tiny images of large objects, as in document recording. The term should not be confused with *photomicrography,* which is the process of making large images of tiny objects, usually through a microscope.

Uses of Microphotography

Today, document microphotography (*See:* MICROGRAPHICS) is very common and is widely used by banks, libraries, and businesses as a convenient method of reducing the bulk of large masses of reference material and records. Reticles for optical instruments have been produced by microphotography since the late 1930's. More recently, emphasis on microminiaturized electronic circuitry and components and high-density data storage has greatly extended the interest in, and applications of, microphotography.

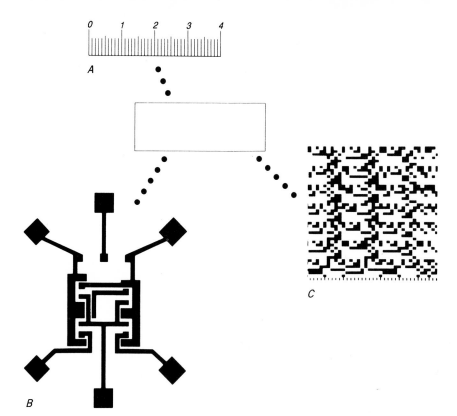

A

B

C

(A) Microphotography offers a simple way to make precision reticles for optical instruments. This reticle, shown at 150 times actual size, is typical of one type commonly used. The divisions in the original were 10 micrometres apart. (B) This microcircuit, reproduced 200 times final size, is an example of a simple integrated circuit used for microminiaturized electronics. (C) Photographic materials have the highest information-storage capacity known to man. Kodak high-resolution plates, for example, are capable of storing 1,000,000,000 bits of information per square inch. This would make it possible to store an entire 24-volume encyclopedia on a plate just 2½″ × 2½″. The example illustrated here shows a typical use of photographic "bits." The row of small, regularly spaced marks at the bottom are timing marks used for control purposes. The original image was 0.02 inch square.

In engineering or scientific applications, the original (or artwork) for microphotography is an enlarged and carefully rendered representation of the final image. A draftsman may generate this image on glass plates, plastic film, or paper. The microcopy, usually a reduction of from several times to several hundred times, is made in a camera specially designed or modified for microphotography. The optical system, consisting of a lens, a focusing mechanism, and a source of illumination, must satisfy more stringent requirements than those encountered in ordinary photography.

In microphotographic applications intended to aid in selectively etching or plating small devices, the micronegative is often used to transfer a very precise photographic image to a material coated with photoresist. (*See:* PHOTOFABRICATION; PHOTORESIST.)

While the principles of document microfilming are the same as those for the other applications of microphotography, the usual document applications do not place as stringent requirements on materials, techniques, or equipment. Also, the requirements of many applications of document microfilming are common, and automatic equipment is readily available on the market.

Techniques of Microphotography

Microphotography offers much to modern technology, particularly in the fields of microelectronics, optical instrumentation, and data storage. Shown here are enlarged reproductions of three types of microphotographs, and to help you appreciate the actual sizes involved, representations of the micro-images are also shown. All three micro-images appear as if reduced 1000 times from original artwork.
• *See also:* MICROGRAPHICS; PHOTOFABRICATION; PHOTOMICROGRAPHY; PHOTORESIST.

 Mired

The output of a continuous-spectrum light source can be described in terms of its color temperature on the Kelvin scale. Sunlight has relatively equal

MIRED VALUES OF COMMON LIGHT SOURCES

Source	Typical Color Temperature (K)	Mired Value	Decamired Value (Rounded off)
75-watt bulb	2800	357	36
100-watt bulb	2900	345	35
200-watt bulb	3000	333	33
Professional light bulbs	3200	313	31
Photolamps	3400	294	29
Clear flash	3800–4200	263–238	26–25
Sunlight	5000	200	20
Carbon arcs	5200	192	19
Daylight	5500	182	18
Blue flash	5500	182	18
Electronic flash	5500–6100	182–164	18–16
Overcast sky	6500–7500	154–133	15–13
Skylight	9000–20,000	111–50	11–5

amounts of all wavelengths. The relative spectral energy distribution is relatively even at the earth's surface, and its color temperature varies from about 3500 K to 5500 K depending on the solar altitude. Daylight (sun plus sky) has an average color temperature of about 5500 K. Incandescent lamps have color temperatures of from about 2800 K to about 3400 K. Devices such as filters that can change the wavelength composition, and thus the color temperature, of light do not possess color temperature in themselves. In order to measure and describe the effect they have on color temperature, a different unit called the mired is used. Mired is an acronym for *mi*cro-*re*ciprocal *d*egrees; it is determined as follows:

$$\text{Mired Value} = \frac{1,000,000}{\text{Color temperature (K)}}$$

Filters such as Kodak light balancing filters and Kodak Wratten photometric filters modify the effective color temperature, and, as a result, the mired value of any one light source by a definite amount. Each filter can therefore be given a "mired shift value," represented by the expression:

$$\left(\frac{1}{T_2} - \frac{1}{T_1}\right) \times 10^6$$

when T_1 represents the color temperature of the original light source, and T_2 the color temperature of the light through the filter. This value will be either positive or negative, depending on the color of the filter. Yellowish filters, which lower the color temperature and therefore increase the mired value, will have a positive mired shift value; those in the bluish series, which raise the color temperature and reduce the mired value, will have a negative mired shift value.

The section on mired values in the article COLOR TEMPERATURE explains how to use mired values to determine the filtration required for a desired change in color temperature.

A related unit, the decamired, is one-tenth of a mired, or:

$$\frac{100,000}{\text{Color temperature (K)}}$$

It is used by some filter manufacturers to express shift values.
• *See also:* COLOR TEMPERATURE; COLOR THEORY; FILTERS; LIGHT.

Mirror Lenses

The use of concave mirrors as objective lenses for telescopes was proposed as far back as 1639 by Mersenne. Believing (erroneously) that achromatic lenses were impossible, Isaac Newton constructed an early form of reflecting telescope; its major advantage is simply that a mirror is inherently free from chromatic aberration.

A later form of reflecting telescope was designed by Cassegrain; in it, a convex mirror is used as a secondary reflector to project the image formed by the main mirror through a hole in the latter, to the eyepiece or photographic plate. This mirror increases the magnification of the system in much the same way as increasing the focal length of the main mirror would increase it.

Secondary Spectrum

Although it is possible to make achromatic lenses, color correction by the combination of different types of glass is never completely perfect. Two colors can be brought to a single focus by an achromatic lens, but there is a residual error of focus for other colors, known as "secondary spectrum." This can be minimized by the choice of glasses, and sometimes by using three different types of glass, but it can never be completely eliminated.

Secondary spectrum is of little importance in lenses of short focus, which are used in most amateur cameras. Unfortunately, it increases in magnitude with the focal length of a lens, and becomes a serious problem in long telephoto lenses. For this reason, interest is again being shown in reflecting systems, and a number of them are currently available for use on cameras.

Spherical Aberration

The Newtonian and Cassegrainian reflectors both have a serious problem; if the mirror is spherical in form, there is spherical aberration in the system. To avoid this, the mirrors of most astronomical telescopes are made parabolic in shape; if the curve is properly chosen, it will almost totally correct the spherical aberration. However, spherical correction is attained in this way at the expense of an increase in astigmatism and coma in the outer parts of the field. This is of little importance in telescopes, which usually have a very narrow angle of view, but it becomes serious in wide-angle optical instruments and in photographic objectives of even moderately wide fields.

In 1932, Schmidt proposed that a telescope could be built utilizing a spherical mirror for control of coma and astigmatism, while adding a complexly curved corrector plate in the plane of the diaphragm in order to eliminate the spherical aberration. By this principle, telescopes of large aperture and wide fields of view could be built; many are now in use in observatories for sky mapping.

A similar optical system has been used, with the addition of a secondary mirror as in the Cassegrainian telescope, for use as telephoto lenses on cameras. These are very successful, but are expensive to make because of the complex shape of the corrector plate.

Other workers have since suggested that a similar result could be attained by using corrector plates having simple spherical curves with small or even

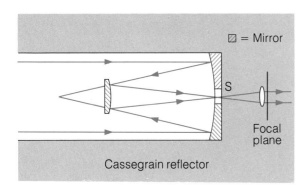

☑ = Mirror

S

Focal plane

Cassegrain reflector

(Left) In the Cassegrainian reflecting telescope, a convex mirror is used as a secondary reflector to project the image formed by the main mirror through a hole in the secondary mirror to the eyepiece or photographic plate.

(Right) The Schmidt plate telescope utilizes a spherical mirror for control of astigmatism and coma. At the same time, a complexly curved corrector plate in the plane of the diaphragm eliminates spherical aberration.

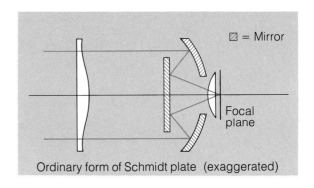

☑ = Mirror

Focal plane

Ordinary form of Schmidt plate (exaggerated)

(Right) The Maksutov system is like the Cassegrainian system except for the meniscus lens, which has zero power and is thus essentially achromatic. This type of system is used in a number of telephoto lens designs.

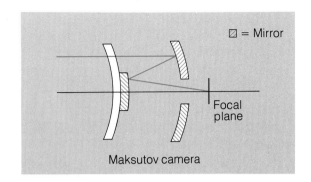

Maksutov camera

(Left) The Gabor telescope system utilizes corrector plates having simple spherical curves with small power, but with spherical aberration opposite to that of the main mirror, therefore canceling the system's spherical aberration.

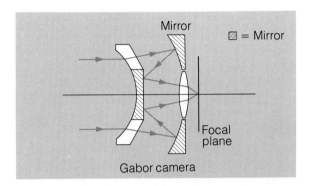

Gabor camera

zero power, but with spherical aberration opposite to that of the main mirror, thus canceling the spherical aberration of the system. Gabor designed one such system, intended for projection systems in television. In Russia, Maksutov designed a system somewhat like the Cassegrainian telescope except for the meniscus lens, which has zero power and is therefore essentially achromatic. This system is used in a number of telephoto lenses.

Reflecting Telephoto Lens

The reflecting telephoto lens, or so-called mirror lens, has the advantages of large aperture, long focus, and excellent chromatic correction. It has minor disadvantages, the main one being that a diaphragm cannot be used, and the lens must always operate at maximum aperture. Exposure must therefore be controlled by the camera shutter, by the use of neutral-density filters, or both. Another characteristic of mirror lenses is that out-of-focus specular highlights are imaged in the picture as ovular rings (doughnut-shaped areas), while normal lenses image such highlights as the round or hexagonal shape of the diaphragm.

The term "catoptric" refers to imaging systems in which only reflecting (mirror) elements are used. Virtually all mirror-type lenses for photographic use are "catadioptric"—a combination of reflecting and refracting (glass lens) elements.

It has recently been found that the overall length of catadioptric lenses can be shortened by making them virtually solid glass. One disadvantage of a long lens is that it moves the center of gravity in front of the camera, which makes steady holding difficult. The shorter, compact structure of a solid catadioptric lens makes handholding reasonably possible in spite of the long focal length. It does, however, increase the overall weight.

• *See also:* LENSES; MIRRORS; OPTICS.

Catadioptric mirror-type lenses for photographic use are a combination of reflecting and refracting elements. The overall length of this type of lens can be shortened by making them virtually solid glass, thereby making the lens more easily hand-held, inspite of the increased weight.

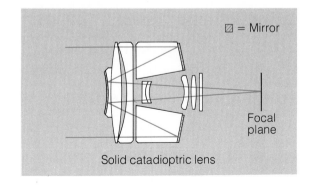

Solid catadioptric lens

Mirrors

The plane mirror is a simple and, at the same time, a very useful optical device. Theoretically, it is free from all of the usual aberrations that afflict other optical systems such as lenses, prisms, or curved mirrors.

The principle of the plane mirror is simple; as shown in the accompanying diagram, light from the object is reflected at the surface of the mirror to the observer's eye. The angle of incidence (A) is always equal to the angle of the reflection (B). The angles are measured to a line normal (perpendicular) to the mirror surface. The observer sees the reflected image as if it were behind the mirror. It appears to be as far behind the mirror as the object is in front of it, and the image appears to be exactly the same size as the object would at the same distance; a plane mirror does not magnify. This type of image is called a virtual image.

By the geometric rule of identical or congruent triangles, the distance from the observer to the image in the mirror is exactly the same as the distance from the observer to the mirror, plus the distance from the mirror to the object. That is, since

the distance C is the same as the distance D, then C plus E is equal to C plus D.

Photographing Mirror Images

To photograph an image in a mirror, the camera must be focused upon the total camera-to-subject distance, C plus E, not merely upon the distance from the camera to the mirror. When reflex or rangefinder cameras are used, focusing is done upon the reflected image, and the focusing scale of the camera lens will show the total distance E plus D.

A situation that arises quite often in practical photography is a picture showing both the subject and its reflection in a mirror. In the accompanying diagram, it is obvious that the distance to the subject (A) is considerably less than the distance from camera to reflected image (B plus C) or the actual total distance from camera to subject by way of the mirror (B plus D).

While it is easy enough to compose a picture showing both object and image, it may be very difficult to get both in focus at the same time, due to this difference in distance. In some cases, it is not necessary to have both in focus; most of the time, the actual subject is only partly shown, and may be allowed to go out of focus, while rendering the reflected image with maximum sharpness.

(Left) With a plane mirror, the angle of incidence (A) equals the angle of reflection (B). The distance from the observer to the image in the mirror (E plus D) equals the distance from the observer to the mirror plus the distance from the mirror to the object (E plus C). (Right) It is not easy to get both the object and the mirror image in focus at the same time, because the distance from camera to subject is considerably less than the distance from camera to reflected image (B plus C) or the distance from camera to subject via mirror (B plus D).

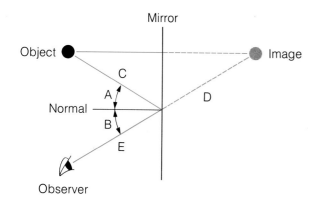

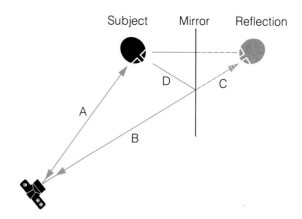

Where it is necessary to have both object and image in focus, the only solution is to focus upon some intermediate distance, and then stop the lens down far enough to secure sufficient depth of field for sharp rendition of both. The exact point of focus must be found by examination of the ground glass; it will not necessarily be exactly midway between the two distances. If a scale-focusing or rangefinder-focusing camera is used, it is best to measure with a tape distances *A* and *B* plus *D,* then focus upon a distance about one-third of the way beyond *A*. In many cases, if adequate depth of field is available, it is best to focus upon the mirror itself; this will usually produce both object and image adequately sharp, and in addition, will produce a sharp image of the mirror frame, which may also be desirable.

Using Mirrors

Since a mirror causes lateral, or left-right, reversal, it can be used to correct the image of misprinted photographs, to copy documents from the back, and to make similar corrections when desired.

A mirror placed inside a small object, in a narrow corner, or on the ceiling or floor can provide a view of details from an angle otherwise inaccessible to the camera. If the image reversal is objectionable, a second mirror can be used to make it right-reading as it reaches the lens.

A technique often used in museum displays is to mount an object such as a bowl on a glass shelf and place a mirror at an angle below it so that it is possible to see the interior and the exterior, bottom view, simultaneously. Similarly, a mirror placed behind and somewhat above the object makes it possible to see details facing away from the camera, as well as those normally visible to the lens.

Mirrors are often used in rear-projection systems to reduce the projector-screen distance. A small front-surface mirror placed at a 45° angle just below an enlarger lens will project the image at right angles. This technique is often used to get extreme enlargements when the enlarger head cannot be raised far enough above the easel or floor, and cannot be turned horizontally. If the negative is placed emulsion-side-up in the enlarger, the mirror will project a properly oriented image.

Mirrors are also useful to direct beams of light in small-object photography; there are many kinds of dental and machinist's mirrors that can be used

in this way quite easily. Enlarging mirrors of the type sold for makeup and cosmetic uses, and special-purpose reducing mirrors, will create unusual effects in reflecting larger beams of light. The intensity and harshness of light reflected by a mirror can be changed by stretching one or more layers of mesh tightly across the surface. Shadow patterns within the light beam can be created by pasting opaque shapes on the mirror surface, or by drawing with opaque crayons or similar materials.

Choosing Mirrors

When large subjects are to be photographed, a conventional mirror with the reflective coating on the back must be used; other kinds of mirrors are likely to be too expensive. The glass must be completely flat and colorless ("water white") to avoid distortion and a color tinge. The problem with a back-surface mirror is that it may cause a double image because visible reflections occur from the front surface of the glass as well as from the rear reflective surface. This problem is most likely to occur when the subject is in dark surroundings; these conditions make the glass surface a kind of mirror, just as darkness outside an ordinary window does.

Double images can be avoided by the use of a first-surface mirror, in which the reflective coating is on the forward or upper surface of the glass so that the light rays pass directly from subject to mirror surface to lens, without passing through the glass. Such mirrors are especially useful in the image-forming path of projection setups. Extreme care must be used in handling and cleaning first-surface mirrors so that the reflective coating is not scratched. A blast of compressed air and, at most, a very soft brush can be used to remove dust. Glass cleaners, polishing cloths, or lens tissue should not be used. The mirrors in single-lens reflex cameras are first-surfaced and should be treated with this kind of care.

Coating Mirrors

A plain glass surface reflects about four percent of the light that falls on it. To increase the reflectivity of the surface, a thin layer of metal is deposited on the polished glass surface.

Silver, chemically deposited on the glass, was the only metal used for years. It is still used for second-surface mirrors, in which case it is usually overcoated with a thin copper plating to retard staining, and enameled to add physical protection.

Silver reacts with sulfur fumes in the air and becomes discolored. Hence, although it was the only method known for years, it is not too satisfactory for first-surface mirrors, which cannot be protected with copper.

Aluminum, coated onto the mirror surface by evaporation in high vacuum, is the metal commonly used today. Aluminum is more stable than silver, so it keeps its reflectivity longer. In many cases, it is overcoated with a very thin transparent coating of a mineral substance such as silicon monoxide to add protection. When applied to a thickness of one-half wavelength of light, the coating can actually increase the reflectivity of the aluminum surface.

Such high-quality first-surface mirrors are used in reflex cameras, in the rangefinders in viewfinder cameras, and as imaging mirrors in telephoto lenses.
• *See also:* SPECIAL EFFECTS.

Mixing Photographic Solutions

Pre-packaged chemical mixtures for various photographic solutions offer convenience, standardized quality, and, usually, economy. However, there are a great many photographic solutions that must be compounded by mixing the individual ingredients according to a formula. This may be because there is so little demand for the solution that a manufacturer cannot economically offer it in packaged form. Or it may be that a solution or certain chemicals will not keep well when mixed and so must be prepared shortly before use. Whatever the reasons, it is not difficult to mix a solution from the formula whenever that is necessary or desirable. The primary concerns are avoiding contamination, working methodically, measuring accurately, and handling chemicals with prudence and care.

Water Supply
Impurities in water supplies are not responsible for as many troubles as is usually supposed. Although most tap water does contain some impurities, most of these have no photographic effect.

Large quantities of suspended organic matter, particles of finely divided sulfur, hydrogen sulfide, and soluble metallic sulfides are the only impurities likely to cause serious trouble with developers. Organic matter is usually precipitated on mixing the developer, but, frequently, biological growths and bacteria thrive in a developer and form a slime or scum on the walls of the tank. Certain types of these growths act on the sulfite in the developer and change it to sodium sulfide, a chemical that fogs the emulsion. Organic matter may also give trouble in the washing process, since it is likely to be coagulated by the alum introduced from the fixing bath and settle on the surfaces of the negatives or prints. This can be avoided by filtering the water, or reduced by using a rapid rate of replacement of the wash water. The addition of boric acid to an acid fixing bath, up to a maximum of 15 grams per litre (2 ounces per gallon), is also helpful.

Sulfides can be removed from a developer by developing some waste film or by adding 0.4 gram of lead acetate per litre (25 grains per gallon) of developer. The precipitated lead sulfide and excess lead will settle, and the clear liquid can then be siphoned or poured carefully off the top for use.

Extremely hard water may give a finely divided precipitate when the developer is mixed. This precipitate will usually settle out on standing, but even if it remains in suspension, it will have no photographic effect.

Certain developers that are clear when mixed may form a finely divided precipitate after they have been used. This is a normal effect and is not an indication of poor mixing or impure water.

A chemical analysis of the water supply usually reveals very little concerning its photographic usefulness. The only really useful test is to prepare the required photographic solution with the suspect water sample and actually try it; then compare these results with those obtained with the same developer or fixing bath prepared with distilled water. In most cases, both solutions will be alike in their photographic effect, even if not in appearance.

Types of Containers
Glass, hard rubber, polyethylene, enameled steel, and stainless steel are the materials most commonly used in the construction of containers for mixing, storing, and using photographic solutions.

All are used safely with any ordinary solution. The choice is determined primarily by economy, convenience, or size availability.

Not all metals are suitable. Tin, copper, and their alloys may cause serious chemical fog or rapid oxidation when used with developers. Aluminum, zinc, or galvanized iron should not be used with either developers or fixing baths.

The same consideration should be given to the materials used for mixing—paddles, rods, or stirrers. Hard plastic stirrers are readily available and inexpensive. Flexible rubber blades, wooden handles, and other absorbent materials must be avoided. After they have been used, it is almost impossible to flush them clean to insure that absorbed chemicals will not decompose and dissolve during use.

With any vessel, care should be taken to avoid inaccurate measurements of volume. It is common practice, when a bottle is used, to bring the solution to final volume by filling to the top or neck of the bottle. In many cases, however, so-called litre or quart bottles hold considerably more or less than the nominal volume. Unless they are calibrated, they will cause errors in solution strength. Calibration is simply a matter of accurately measuring out a specified quantity, pouring it into the container, and marking the level to which the container is filled.

Cleanliness

Contamination of solutions during mixing is a frequent cause of defective negatives and prints. All mixing apparatus should be cleaned thoroughly immediately after use to prevent the formation of incrustations that may dissolve when a new solution is mixed.

It is desirable to use a separate mixing vessel for each solution. If several solutions are mixed consecutively in the same vessel, they should be prepared in the order in which they are used in processing. Traces of developer in a fixing bath will have little or no effect, but small quantities of hypo in a developer may cause serious fogging or image tone changes.

Chemicals, particularly those in the form of light powder, should not be mixed in the darkroom or in places where sensitized goods are handled. Chemical dust becomes airborne and settles on bench and table tops. As a result, spots and stains may appear on prints or negatives. Also, chemical dust may settle on the surfaces of other processing solutions and cause contamination. For this reason, solution storage tanks should be equipped with dust covers.

Filtration

The quality of photographic solutions can be maintained by filtering the water used for mixing and by filtering the solution before use or, more importantly, before returning a reusable solution to its storage container. This is especially useful to remove bits of emulsion and other particles from a developer before it is replenished. Filtration is required in preparing some formulas to remove unwanted precipitates that form during mixing.

The primary function of solution filtration is to remove foreign particles and particles of undissolved chemicals. Water supply lines are the major source of foreign particles, which include rust, dirt, mineral scale, and bits of metal or other material of which the pipes and fittings are composed. In addition to the physical damage hard particles can cause to softened emulsions, metals may react with solution chemicals and affect their working properties.

In-Line Filtration. Water filters can be installed in the supply lines, as close as possible to the control valves of the mixing sink. Separate filters are required in the hot and cold water lines. They are generally composed of a disposable inner core and a permanent outer casing. The casing of the hot water supply filter must be metal to resist excessive expansion and distortion at high temperatures; the cold water filter may have a clear plastic casing to permit visual inspection of the core. Filtration is accomplished by the core, which is a spiral-wound honeycomb of fibrous cord. Water flowing into the center of the core is forced through the honeycomb, which traps particles down to microscopic size, and flows out the exit line. The core must be inspected periodically and replaced when heavily discolored, or when clogging by particles has reduced the water flow.

A similar in-line filter with a permanent nylon or glass fiber core can be used at the spout of a mixing faucet. Such filters were derived from those used in some aircraft fuel lines. The addition of a threaded or snap-on hose fitting makes it easy to attach the filter, and to remove it to avoid unnecessary clogging when filtered water is not required—for example, when washing equipment or flushing used solutions down the drain. The core can be cleaned by reversing the connection to the faucet so that water flows back from the outside to the interior of the core, flushing out trapped particles.

Household filters using cylinders of activated charcoal particles are commonly used to improve the taste of water by removing dissolved gases. They are of doubtful value for photographic purposes because the gases are not likely to have a significant effect on solutions, and because some charcoal particles tend to flow into the output, especially when the cylinder is new, necessitating further filtration for photographic safety.

De-ionizing filters of the type sold for household use in refilling steam irons and similar appliances are useful when a substitute for distilled water is required, but they do not remove particles to any significant degree and thus provide little or no physical protection for emulsions.

Funnel Filtration. Mixed solutions may be filtered conveniently by pouring them through suitable material in a funnel. The simplest expedient is a wad of cotton placed at the bottom of the funnel. Unfortunately, when the cotton is dry, it is easily dislodged by the force of solution being poured into the funnel. When wet, the cotton tends to compress at the bottom of the funnel, reducing solution flow to a bare trickle.

Filter paper is the best material to use in conjunction with a funnel. Chemically neutral paper is available from laboratory supply houses and even some pharmacies; the filters sold for home coffee makers are also suitable for most purposes. Paper towels and similar substitutes should be avoided. They are likely to be chemically impure for photographic purposes, and they may not have sufficient wet strength to resist tearing when a large quantity of solution is being filtered.

Filter papers are usually supplied as circles; they must be folded in half once each way, and then opened into a cone for use (see the accompanying illustration). The design of the funnel can have a significant effect on the efficiency and speed of filtration. Interior ribs will hold the filter paper away from the sides of the funnel so that solution can flow through the sides as well as the apex of the paper cone. Exterior ribs will hold the funnel away from the mouth of the bottle or container so that air can escape freely as the solution rises.

Laboratory supply houses also offer funnels of porous ceramic material, or with stainless steel mesh inserts. Although highly efficient, these are relatively expensive. They are difficult to clean by ordinary darkroom methods; however, it is absolutely necessary to clean them after each use, especially when changing from one solution to another. Filter paper is very inexpensive and can be discarded after a single use.

Mixing Solutions

When solutions are made up, the constituents must be dissolved in the proper sequence in order to avoid undesirable reactions and to facilitate complete mixing.

To avoid the possibility of error in mixing, most of the formulas in this Encyclopedia are arranged so that the ingredients are named in the order in which they should be dissolved, unless the directions specifically state some exception to this rule.

When solutions are made from packaged preparations, the instructions supplied with the package should be followed. With preparations supplied in powder form, the entire contents of a container should be used in making up a solution, and no attempt should be made to prepare a small quantity of solution by using only a portion of the chemicals.

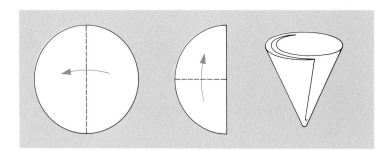

Filter paper is folded into quarters and opened into a cone for use in a funnel.

Mixing Photographic Solutions

Otherwise, because of possible segregation of the granular constituents during shipping and handling, considerable difficulty may be encountered in obtaining solutions with uniform characteristics. To compound a formula properly, work methodically.

Read the Formula Carefully. Note the ingredients and the quantities called for. If necessary, convert the measurements given to the units in which your equipment is marked (see the section Making Measurements in this article). Assemble the storage containers of the required chemicals.

Warnings and Precaution. Note carefully all warnings and precautions given in the formula instructions and included on the container labels. Double-check the ingredients with the list in the section Handling Precautions in this article. Only you can control the conditions and the methods by which you work.

Measuring Ingredients. Measure out the ingredients, as described in the following section. Use separate scoops or spoons for the dry chemicals, and separate vessels for the liquids. Keep the measured chemicals apart from one another.

Preparing the Water. Pour the water to be used to dissolve the chemicals into a suitable wide-mouth container, which will make it easy to add the ingredients and stir the solution freely. Measure out about two-thirds of the total liquid volume called for in the formula. In mixing developers, toners, and color processing solutions, it is wise to use distilled or deionized water. If these are not available, boil some water in a ceramic or tempered glass container (do not use aluminum or copper vessels) to drive off dissolved oxygen. Allow the water to cool to mixing temperature. Photographic solutions are usually prepared by dissolving the constituents in water at a specified temperature. Developers are mixed at 32 to 50 C (90 to 125 F); most packaged fixing baths are mixed at a temperature not exceeding 27 C (80 F).

If you have extremely hard water, it can be softened by adding sodium hexametaphosphate (Calgon) before proceeding. Check your local water supply department for guidance.

Mixing Procedure. Dissolve the chemicals in the water. *Follow the order given in the formula.* Some chemicals will not dissolve in the presence of others and so must be added first; other chemicals will dissolve more easily when certain ingredients have already been added. Mixing in improper order may cause unwanted compounds to form that can reduce or destroy the effectiveness of the solution.

Be sure that each dry chemical is completely dissolved or each liquid is thoroughly mixed in before adding the next ingredient. Proper agitation during mixing is important, not only to increase the rate of solution of the chemicals, but also to avoid undesirable effects. A stirring pattern or a type of agitator that will not introduce excessive air into the solution should be used. Developers are particularly prone to oxidize readily; a few minutes of violent agitation may weaken the developer noticeably and produce staining compounds. On the other hand, insufficient agitation may permit the chemicals to settle at the bottom of the mixing vessel and form a hard cake that will not dissolve readily. Lastly, add water to bring the solution to the required final volume. If you started with two-thirds of the formula volume, less than one-third will be added at the end, because the dissolved chemicals will have added to the volume being mixed.

Care should be taken to stir the solution thoroughly after the addition of the final volume of water. The concentrated solution at the bottom of the vessel is heavier than water and will tend to remain at the bottom if not thoroughly mixed. Mechanical agitation is a convenient means of promoting proper mixing. Several types of electric mixers are available, including commercial models used in preparing large batches of chemicals. They should not operate at such high speeds or at such an angle as to induce frothing or aeration of the solution.

Cooling the Solution. If the formula mixes to a *working solution,* measure out the required quantity and cool it to working temperature. An easy way to do this is to use a metal or glass container and place it in a larger vessel that has cold water running through it. Stir the solution frequently to distribute the cooler portion from the bottom and outer zones with the warmer solution in the center; take the solution temperature frequently.

If the formula has mixed to a *stock solution,* measure out the required quantity and dilute it with cooler water to bring it to (or very close to) working temperature.

Making Measurements

The metric system is by far the easiest to use, because all units of measurement are multiples of 10.

The U.S. Customary and Avoirdupois systems do not involve equal multiples. If it is necessary to convert from one system to another, use the conversion factors summarized in the accompanying table, or the more extensive tables in the article WEIGHTS AND MEASURES.

Dry Chemicals. The accuracy demanded in measuring small quantities of chemicals for photographic formulas may exceed that of the equipment found in some photographic laboratories. Therefore, if you intend to mix your own photographic chemicals from the formulas given in this Encyclopedia, you should be sure that your scale will weigh masses of up to 100 grams within an accuracy of 0.5 gram, and that you have a small graduate capable of fluid measurement accurate to 0.5 millilitre.

Where minute quantities of a dry chemical are called for, it is frequently more practical to mix a dilute stock solution of the chemical and use an appropriate quantity of that solution instead, as described under the heading Percentage Solutions in this article.

Do not put dry chemicals directly on the pans of a laboratory balance; instead, use equal-size pieces of paper (squares of filter paper, or paper toweling, for example) on each pan. This will avoid contamination and make it easy to lift off each measured quantity and set it aside. The paper on the pan that receives the weights need not be changed each time, of course. If a quantity of a single chemical must be weighed, and that quantity is too large for your balance, divide it into two or more smaller quantities. Do not do so unnecessarily, because each weighing will result in a small error, and these errors are cumulative.

Liquids. Graduates used to measure small quantities of liquids often have small cross sections (diameters) in relation to their heights. In such a container, a liquid will form a meniscus, or ∪-shape, at the surface because surface tension causes it to cling to the walls of the container. To measure accurately, hold the graduate at eye level and add liquid until the bottom of the meniscus ∪ reaches the desired calibration mark. Measuring to the height of the outer edge of the meniscus will result in less liquid than called for.

When viscous liquids such as Kodak HC-110 developer concentrate are measured, be sure to rinse out the container with water two or three times and

add it to the solution; by doing this you will make sure that all the measured chemical is used.

Percentage Solutions

Some chemicals—especially those which absorb atmospheric moisture readily—keep better in solution. In other cases, it is necessary to measure out a very small quantity of dry chemical—smaller than a balance can accurately determine. Both these problems can be overcome by preparing a percentage solution that contains a known quantity of dry chemical dissolved in it. Then, by measuring out an appropriate quantity of the percentage solution, it is possible to obtain a particular amount of the chemical.

Metric System. It is simple to make a percentage solution using metric measurement. Take as many grams of the dry chemical as the desired percentage, and dissolve them in enough water to total 100 millilitres. For example, to make an 8 percent solution, dissolve 8 grams of the chemical in enough water to make 100 millilitres (that will be less than 100 millilitres of water, because the bulk of the chemical will provide some volume). Usually it is most convenient to make a 10 percent solution (10 grams per 100 millilitres, or 100 grams per litre), because then each 10 millilitres of the percentage solution contains 1 gram of chemical.

Liquid Dilutions. When a percentage solution is to be made of a liquid, the problem is a bit different; of course, if the liquid is 100 percent in strength or substantially so, then it is merely necessary to dilute it with the required amount of water. But many liquids used in photography are already diluted. For example, Formalin is a 40 percent solution of formaldehyde. If it is to be further diluted, a special method is required to determine the quantities required to produce a final solution of a given strength. The "criss-cross" method is probably the most convenient (see the accompanying diagram).

Saturated Solutions. A saturated solution is one that contains as much of a chemical as will dissolve in the particular solvent. This varies with the chemical in question and with the solvent, as well as with the temperature of the solution. Thus, ordinary hypo (sodium thiosulfate) crystals are soluble in cold water (0 C) to nearly 800 grams per litre; in hot water (60 C), you can dissolve as much as 3000 grams in a litre. Obviously, when the latter solution is cooled to room temperature, it will be unable to hold that much chemical and most of it will crystallize out. For this and other reasons, saturated solutions are seldom if ever used in photography.

Storing Solutions

Most photographic solutions will remain in good condition for weeks or months if properly stored. The primary precautions are to prevent oxidation and to keep the temperature at 18 to 21 C (65 to 70 F) or lower. For more detailed information, see

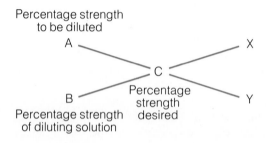

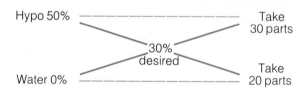

At A write the percentage strength of the solution that is to be diluted. At B write the percentage strength of the diluting solution. Use 0 for water. At C write the percentage strength desired. Subtract C from A and write the result at Y. Subtract B from C and write the result at X. Then if X parts of A are diluted with Y parts of B, the result will be a solution of C percentage. For example, if it is desired to make a 30 percent solution of hypo from a 50 percent stock solution, write 50 at A, 0 at B, and 30 at C. Subtracting 30 from 50, write 20 at Y. Subtracting 0 from 30, write 30 at X. Reading the result, if 30 parts of 50 percent hypo is diluted with 20 parts of water, the result will be a 30 percent solution of hypo. When water is being used to dilute a stock solution, this procedure can be expressed: Take (desired percent) of stock solution and (stock percent minus desired percent) parts of water.

the article STORAGE OF SENSITIZED MATERIALS AND PROCESSING SOLUTIONS.

Every container must be clearly labeled so that the contents cannot be mistaken. This is as important with mixed solutions as it is with basic chemicals. Use surgical tape or other cloth tape, not paper labels, for liquid containers, and indelible ink such as that in laundry markers. It is a good idea to put labels on container caps, too, so that a fixer-soaked top will not be put on a bottle of developer. Single letters—"D" for developer, "F" for fixer, and so forth—will do.

Handling Precautions

No concentrated liquids or dry chemicals should come in contact with the skin or eyes. Reasonable care in handling chemicals makes it easy to control contact. It is only sensible to wear plastic or rubber gloves, to work in a well-ventilated area, not to lean directly over a mixing container, and to avoid breathing fumes or chemical dust.

If serious contact with a dangerous chemical does occur, the best procedure is to flood the affected external area with water; if a chemical is ingested, do not take anything without professional advice. *In either case, contact a physician, hospital, or poison control center immediately.* The numbers for these services should be permanently posted by the telephone nearest the chemical mixing room or darkroom area.

Special attention should be paid to handling the following chemicals. This list is not exhaustive, but covers the compounds most likely to be encountered in mixing photographic formulas. *Always observe warnings and cautions printed on chemical labels and in chemical formulas.* There is no way a manufacturer, supplier, or publisher can supervise your working methods.

Acids. Always pour acid into water, or water-based solutions, not the reverse. Do not pour concentrated acid into an alkaline solution; dilute the acid first. Pour acid slowly; stir the solution continuously.

Alkalis. Dissolve strong alkalis such as sodium and potassium hydroxide separately in *cold* water. Do not use a glass container because alkalis produce great amounts of heat as they dissolve.

Acids and alkalis are corrosive; they will burn or dissolve many organic materials, including skin and flesh.

Carbolic Acid (Phenol). Poisonous and caustic.

Cyanide, Potassium; Cyanide, Sodium. Deadly poison; dangerous to handle. *Never mix with an acid,* as cyanide fumes may be released.

Ferric Oxalate. Corrosive.

Formaldehyde. Poisonous vapors in sufficient concentration.

Formalin (Formaldehyde-Water Solution). Poisonous.

Iodine. Corrosive crystals.

Mercuric Chloride; Mercuric Iodide. Deadly poison; corrosive.

Phenol. Poisonous and caustic.

Potassium Ferricyanide. Poisonous in concentration.

Potassium Hydroxide; Sodium Hydroxide. See alkalis.

Potassium Permanganate. Poisonous.

Silver Nitrate. Caustic.

Sodium Dithionite. Flammable. Keep dry; may ignite if damp.

Thiocarbamide; Thiourea. Extreme irritant.

Preventing Contact Dermatitis. Dermatitis is a broad term used to describe skin inflammation of any kind. However, the skin condition often called dermatitis by photographic workers is a skin allergy usually caused by prolonged or repeated contact with certain chemicals. This allergic response is more correctly termed "contact dermatitis."

The precautionary information on the labels of chemical containers will indicate whether any ingredients might cause a skin reaction. Practically any chemical can initiate an allergic response in a few individuals, but in photography, the chemicals most likely to cause the condition are the developing agents. Statistically, more people are affected by contact with color developing agents than by those used in black-and-white processing. In addition, individuals have varying sensitivities to a particular chemical or chemicals.

Dry chemicals can have the same effect on the skin as chemical solutions because they are dissolved, or partially dissolved, by moisture in or on the skin. The majority of people can avoid contact dermatitis by taking reasonable precautions to prevent contact with the chemicals. People who have a history of a skin disorder or allergy are more susceptible and should be particularly careful in handling chemicals. Sooner or later a careless worker is quite likely to be affected. There is an initial period during which no response to contact with the chemicals seems to occur. This period varies widely among different individuals; it may last for days, for months, or sometimes for years. During that time, it is easy for a person to decide that he or she cannot be affected by the chemicals. Then, however, the skin may develop an altered reaction that results in contact dermatitis. It is not reasonable to assume that dermatitis will not occur simply because it has not up to this point.

The condition usually starts with persistent itching and redness of the skin on the fingers, wrists, or forearms. If these signs occur, it is essential to get medical advice immediately. Since photographic workers are subject to the same skin disorders as everyone else, a physician must evaluate each case of contact dermatitis in relation to all possible causes. Without professional evaluation, there is no way to be sure whether the condition arises from poison ivy, contact with photographic chemicals, allergic reaction to a pet, or some other cause.

A person who has once had contact dermatitis can quite possibly develop it again, and may even be more sensitive to the cause than before. For this reason, it is important to take extra care of the skin when working with chemicals. There are no good protective hand creams for this purpose. Any such preparation applied to the hands may introduce fatty material into a solution and cause adverse photographic effects in the material being processed. The best protection is to observe the following safe handling precautions faithfully at all times.

Safe Handling of Photographic Chemicals

1. **Read the label** on chemical containers so that you will know what precautions to follow in handling the contents.

2. **Avoid contact with chemicals** whenever possible. Handle chemical solutions carefully to avoid splashing. Wipe up or wash away solution spills at once. Do not raise dust in handling dry chemicals. Keep the working area clean, and launder clothing frequently. Keep all protective equipment, such as goggles, rubber aprons, rubber gloves, and the like, free from chemicals.

3. **Wear rubber gloves** whenever possible. Remember that rubber gloves are effective in preventing contact with chemicals only when they are kept clean both inside and outside, and when they are chemically decontaminated to remove processing chemicals that are absorbed by the material from which the gloves are made. See the section on decontaminating rubber gloves. Disposable rubber or plastic gloves, which are used once and then discarded, can be used to avoid decontamination.

4. **In case of skin contact** with chemicals, particularly developers, wash your hands or other affected areas of skin immediately with plenty of water. Then apply a pH balanced soap, such as Phisohex or a similar acid-type product—ordinary soaps, which are alkaline, are not as effective. While this soap is still on your skin, rub your hands together. Be sure to include in this cleansing motion the skin between your fingers and any other area of skin that may have been in contact with chemicals. This action removes chemicals that may be retained by the ridged texture of the skin.

5. **Protect broken skin** because any such injury may allow chemicals to penetrate more readily than they do when skin is intact, thus the risk of getting dermatitis is increased.

6. **Protect your eyes** by wearing goggles when you handle chemicals, particularly acids and corrosive alkalis or solutions that contain these chemicals. Keep the goggles clean so that they do not bring chemicals into contact with your face.

7. **In case of eye contact** with chemicals, immediately flush your eyes with plenty of cool water for 15 minutes. Use a gentle stream of water or a specially designed eyebath for this purpose. If necessary, get help to hold your eyelids apart while washing. When your eyes are affected, always get medical attention immediately.

8. **Launder frequently,** say, twice each week, all clothing worn while handling chemicals. However, if a garment is wetted with a chemical solution—a sleeve, for example, becomes soaked—change the garment immediately.

9. **Clean up** chemical spills and splashes. Pick up spills of dry chemicals with a vacuum cleaner. Dry chemicals and the residue from dried chemical solutions can become airborne and contaminate the working area.

10. **Ventilation** in the workplace should be adequate to rapidly carry away airborne chemical dust and vapors generated by chemical solutions. Objectionable or irritating vapors need to be removed by means of exhaust hoods or other extraction devices that remove contaminants at the source. Before starting work, make sure that all ventilation systems are operating.

11. **Train newcomers** and temporary help in the proper way to handle chemicals.

12. **Empty completely** and rinse out all used chemical containers before discarding them. Such containers, as well as contaminated waste material, can be a danger to refuse collectors.

13. **Never use coffee cups,** paper cups, drinking glasses, or any other container that might be mistaken for a drinking vessel to contain or measure chemicals.

14. **Do not eat food** or drink beverages in workrooms where chemicals are mixed or used. After handling chemicals, always wash your hands before eating.

15. **Report immediately** any unusual skin condition that you suspect might be dermatitis to your physician or, if you encounter the chemicals in your work, to your supervisor or in-plant medical department.

(continued)

16. **Dispose of used chemicals safely.** The most common method of disposing of used photographic solutions is to pour them down the drain along with running water. Follow the disposal of the solutions with plenty of clean water. To avoid undesirable chemical reactions between solutions, discard them one at a time and run plenty of water into the drain after each solution is discarded.

Since dumping a large quantity of any chemical into the sewers is a potential source of water pollution, large users of processing chemicals should pay careful attention to their disposal practices. (*See:* DISPOSAL OF PHOTOGRAPHIC SOLUTIONS.)

Decontaminating Rubber Gloves. To provide effective protection against skin contact with chemicals, rubber gloves must be chemically decontaminated to remove processing chemicals that are absorbed into the material from which the gloves are made. After using the gloves for one day, they should be decontaminated by the following method:

1. Soak gloves for 30 minutes in a 1 percent solution of potassium permanganate and hot water (about 48.8 C [120 F]).
2. Rinse gloves with water.
3. Soak gloves for 30 minutes in a 5 percent solution of sodium bisulfite and water at room temperature (about 21 C [70 F]).
4. Rinse thoroughly with hot water.

The above chemical solutions should be renewed frequently.

NOTE: Examine the gloves for obvious damage, such as cracks or tears. To test for small punctures that may not be visible, fill the glove with water. Close the wrist part by holding it tightly with one hand and squeeze the glove with the other hand.

Mixing Large Quantities

Generally speaking, any formula can be expanded to make large volumes of solution simply by multiplying the amount of each ingredient by an appropriate factor. However, mixing large quantities of solutions involves some serious considerations in handling chemicals.

Ventilation is of critical importance. Suction fans must be used to carry away fumes, and they must exhaust into safe locations. Most municipal codes have severe restrictions in this matter.

Mixing personnel must wear protective clothing and breathing masks. When large quantities of dry chemicals are handled and poured, they create sig-

nificant amounts of dust that can affect personnel and contaminate surfaces and other equipment.

Containers and the racks, shelves, or tables that support them must be sufficiently strong. The floor also must be able to support the considerable weight involved. The average weight of a litre of chemical solution is 1.1 kilograms (9¼ pounds per gallon).

Chemical reactions commonly generate heat. With some alkalis, the amount of heat generated increases exponentially as the quantity of chemical is increased. Careless handling can lead to boiling and spattering of solutions, or the distortion of plastic containers to the point where they may lose strength and collapse or cause spills.

Motorized mixing devices are essential to insure uniform mixing and complete dissolving of each ingredient. However, mixers must not cause splashing or spattering, or create oxidation because of excessive turbulence.

An emergency pull-chain shower head should be located in the bulk mixing area so personnel can immediately flush chemicals from their bodies in case of accident. This is a legal requirement, covered by federal, state, and, usually, local ordinances.

• *See also:* CHEMISTRY OF PHOTOGRAPHY; DARKROOM, PROFESSIONAL; DEVELOPERS AND DEVELOPING; DISPOSAL OF PHOTOGRAPHIC SOLUTIONS; FORMULAS FOR BLACK-AND-WHITE PROCESSING; STORAGE OF SENSITIZED MATERIALS AND PROCESSING SOLUTIONS; WEIGHTS AND MEASURES.

Further Reading: Carroll, John S. *Photographic Lab Handbook.* 3rd ed. Garden City, NY: Amphoto, 1976; Eastman Kodak Co. *Small Batch Processing of* KODAK PLUS-X, TRI-X, *and 4-X Reversal Motion Picture Films,* pub. No. D-9. Rochester, NY: Eastman Kodak Co., 1974; Eaton, George T. *Photographic Chemistry.* Dobbs Ferry, NY: Morgan & Morgan, Inc., 1965; Mason, L.F. *Photographic Processing Chemistry.* (Focal Library Books) Belmont, CA: Pitman Publishing Corp., 1975; Russell, G. *Chemical Analysis in Photography.* (Focal Library Books) Belmont, CA: Pitman Publishing Corp., 1965.